SOILS FOR THE ARCHAEOLOGIST

BY THE SAME AUTHOR

Bones for the Archæologist

SOILS
FOR THE
ARCHAEOLOGIST

by

I. W. Cornwall

B.A. (*Cantab*), PH.D. (*Lond*), F.Z.S., *Lecturer: Department of Environmental Archaeology, London University Institute of Archaeology*

PHOENIX HOUSE LTD

LONDON

Printed in Great Britain in 11pt Garamond by
C. Tinling & Co., Ltd., Liverpool, London and Prescot
for Phoenix House Ltd, 38 William IV Street,
Charing Cross, W.C.2.

FIRST PUBLISHED 1958

CONTENTS

ILLUSTRATIONS

PREFACE

FOR ARCHAEOLOGISTS and others, many without much scientific background, arguments about soils would very often be incomprehensible without some detailed exposition of the facts and theories on which they are based. At the same time, it would be impossible to make this book altogether self-contained without including much that is in all the textbooks of the related sciences and has been far better expounded by their authors. Thus, while the practical details and applications of the more useful physical and chemical methods have been described, the underlying theory and standard operations of, for example, wet chemical analysis have been omitted.

Those who are interested in the more technical aspects of soil-analysis probably already know more about chemistry and microscopy than this author. For them, the book is designed as a guide to the application of their peculiar talents to the solution of archaeological and environmental problems. For archaeologists, however, most of whom are unlikely to undertake more than the very simplest practical experiments for themselves, it is meant to take the 'magic' out of soil-investigations and to show what sedimentary petrology and soil-science can do towards explaining the phenomena which many of them encounter daily on their excavations. The laboratory worker is to too many excavators a sort of witch-doctor, and, because his operations (not necessarily very complex) are mainly conducted behind a closed door (chiefly to prevent complaints from colleagues of 'smells'), they acquire an entirely false aura of mystery. While it is very flattering to the soil-worker to be regarded as a being with somewhat supernatural powers, it would help both him and the regular archaeologist to a greater understanding of the many problems that face them both if the potentialities and the limitations of his methods were better appreciated. A close collaboration between the excavator and the soil-specialist has often already advanced the knowledge of both. The future undoubtedly promises even better things from such mutual aid and understanding.

The writer has spent a large part of the last ten years learning how to extract relevant information from soils and archaeological deposits. The interest shown by past students and established archaeologists in the subject encourages him to believe that it is now worth summarizing the assembled information as far as it goes, to form at least one course of the base upon which may be raised in the future a solid structure of knowledge of value to the wider study of man.

ACKNOWLEDGMENTS

THE MATERIAL FOR A BOOK of this kind, touching, if only lightly sometimes, on many related fields of scientific and archaeological work, could never have been assembled without a great deal of help from friends and colleagues, many with special knowledge and skills. Whenever I have found my own reading and experience inadequate, I have relied heavily on those of others and have seldom been disappointed.

Foremost among them, I have to thank Professor F. E. Zeuner, of the Department of Environmental Archaeology, University of London, for my first introduction to the study of soils as part of the natural environment of early man, for skilled guidance, and for many profitable excursions and discussions during the past ten years. While my own work has chiefly been concerned with sites near home, he has made large collections of comparative material from overseas, without which my view of soils and archaeological deposits generally would necessarily have been very restricted.

Next, I thank the numerous excavators who have welcomed me at their sites, posed their problems, lent me drawn sections and photographs, provided me with much instructive material and the experience of varied deposits in the field, which alone make the samples on the laboratory bench intelligible. They are too many to enumerate. Some will find their publications referred to here by name; others will recognize details of information and conclusions to which they have led me. Still more, not specifically mentioned, deserve my gratitude for the opportunities which they have given me to gain general experience. If they find here anything new and interesting to them, their kindness has contributed to its collection. My best thanks to all.

Finally, I gratefully acknowledge my indebtedness to many scientific colleagues whose books and papers I have read and to those known to me personally whose brains I have shamelessly picked in discussion. I have learned much from them, some of which has gone into this book. I hope that they will feel, as I do, that their time was not ill spent.

Bushey Heath, Herts.
1957

Introduction

◆◆◆

UNTIL SOME THIRTY YEARS ago archaeology was almost entirely pre-occupied with the study of human artifacts, too often divorced from the context in which they occurred. This, if read as fully as knowledge at the present day permits, may often shed light on the conditions of life of ancient peoples, which their handiwork, by itself, is not able to reveal.

Evidently, the soil containing and covering the works of ancient man is an important part of that context. Cultural remains of pre-historic man (and, to a lesser extent, those of early historic peoples) are frequently found at some depth in the ground. It is obviously of importance to discover how they came to be buried and, if possible, how long the deposits covering them required for their formation. Only in the earth in which and below which artifacts are found can such questions as these have an answer.

For information about the earth the archaeologist turns first to the sciences of geology, geography and pedology (soil-science). None of these, in most cases, possesses the answers to his questions ready-made. Geology is, for the most part, concerned with much larger matters than the sequence of events towards the end of the latest and shortest chapter of an immensely long record of earth-history. Comparatively few geologists have an interest more than passing in the Pleistocene Period, of which the events, to them, rank rather as do the happenings of the nineteenth century to the prehistorian. Nevertheless, the basic principles they use to study accumulations amounting to thousands of feet in thickness and of world-wide extent still apply to Pleistocene and Recent deposits, which are developed on a much smaller scale in depth and are, in geological terms, usually of quite local distribution, laterally.

Pedology has developed chiefly as an adjuvant to agriculture. In the short time that systematic investigations into the properties and distribution of soils have been in progress, a considerable volume of knowledge has accumulated as to their nature, mode of formation and maintenance in fertility, some of which is of value to that other disturber of the uppermost layers of the Earth's crust—the archaeological excavator. The investigations of the archaeological, as opposed to the agricultural, pedologist are not confined to the soils of today. The excavator's trenches, and, even more, commercial excavations, may expose land surfaces and soils of earlier ages, now buried beneath later accumulations and become as much 'fossils' as the organic remains and human artifacts which may be associated with them.

A buried soil need not have lost entirely the recognizable properties of soil and it may still be made to yield information of the climatic conditions under which it was formed and hence to indicate something of the environment, and even the particular period of past time, in which the makers of the associated human industries lived.

The parent sources of the materials composing archaeological deposits and soils are, ultimately, the rocks exposed at the surface of the earth, either close to the site or sometimes (in the case of glacial, river-borne or wind-drifted deposits) at some considerable distance from it. To a much lesser extent they include materials imported by man, and organic matter due to his activities and to the natural growth of vegetation at or near the site, both during and since the human occupation. Apart from those materials actually brought by man, the transport and deposition of the layers must have taken place through natural agencies, operating in ancient times and, often, still today, as in the remoter geological past. The mechanism of these agencies has been worked out by geologists and many of the techniques, developed by petrologists for examining ancient sedimentary rocks, are of use also in investigating soils and archaeological deposits.

The study of soils as applied to archaeological problems falls into two parts. Excavators generally call in the soil-investigator to help in explaining the stratigraphy of their sites. 'Why is this stuff black?' 'Is this the original "turf" below my barrow-mound?' 'How was this deposit formed?' 'Is this ditch-filling natural or artificial?' Such are typical questions, and, indeed, who but a soil-man should be qualified to answer them?

The other approach, however, is of wider importance. It is the identification and study of ancient *natural* soils for the information which they may give about the environments of contemporary ancient cultures. Just as Palaeontology is the study of fossil organisms, so Palaeopedology is the study of fossil soils and a branch of Natural Science in its own right. It is one thing to be able to say to an excavator: 'That is the buried surface. You need dig no deeper, for everything covered by it is "natural".' It is even better to examine the same buried soil and to be able to tell the archaeologist that (for instance) the climate at the time that the barrow was built was somewhat warmer and drier in summer than it is today. This is a piece of information about the environment of the barrow-builders which may have a bearing on the human geography of the time far beyond the recognition of a mere base-line below which it is useless to seek archaeological remains.

The two approaches, of course, are complementary and not mutually exclusive. It would be mere snobbery to say: 'I am a pedologist. It is not my job to explain stratification to excavators'. On the other hand, excavators have an interest, often to a greater extent than they realize, in the character of the 'natural' underlying human structures or of soils intercalated among distinct artificial stages, as in the reconstructions of a mound or between additions to a rampart.

There are still a few excavators who regard the soil-investigator (among other specialists) as a sort of clairvoyant, able not only to date a site or deposit directly by chemical analysis, but even to divine what is in their minds when they send soil-samples! The most careful and complete physical and chemical examination will yield no information of use to excavator or consultant specialist unless both are clear in their minds as to what they hope to learn from the experimental results. 'Why is this stuff black?', on the other hand, is a legitimate, clear and perhaps easily-answerable question. If the blackness is due to carbon, the material is probably from a hearth or destruction-level. If due to organic matter, the sample may represent a decayed wooden structure, food refuse or a humic horizon forming part of a natural soil-profile. Should it prove to be due to a deposit of iron or manganese compounds it is likely to be a natural soil-phenomenon. Exact information as to the cause of the dark colour will enable a probably correct interpretation of the deposit or layer to be made.

Thus, the fullest exchange of ideas, both as to fact and theory, between the archaeologist and the soil-man will often lead to useful conclusions. Without it, no report on soil-samples will be of any value to either. Such close coöperation involves both sides in trying to see the point of view of the other—the soil-investigator must put on archaeological glasses and the excavator make himself something of a connoisseur of soils; history or prehistory must be married to science. Neither party need aspire to excel in the speciality of the other, but the obligation to step momentarily into the other's shoes is mutual.

Palaeopedology is a special study requiring an acquaintance with many types of present-day soils, some physical, chemical and morphological knowledge, rather extensive laboratory facilities—and experience. In particular, quantitative work is essential to a proper understanding of soil-phenomena. Nevertheless, finding the answer to the question: 'Why is this stuff black?' and to many similar qualitative questions is well within the capacity of any intelligent, but un-chemical, layman equipped with a rack of test-tubes, a gas-burner, a few simple chemical reagents and some rule-of-thumb instructions as to procedure. Much time is spent, when examining samples from most sites, over routine experiments (p. 153) such as these. Owing to pressure of demand on the available time of the few workers on archaeological deposits, excavators are kept waiting for months, sometimes even years, for answers to such queries, when they could often do the few necessary tests for themselves in an hour or two.

Even if most archaeologists have not the time or the inclination to go as far as this, every interpreter of a section in an excavation should have at least some background information about the methods and potentialities of soil-studies, if only to appreciate what soil-science, in the person of the consulting specialist, can and can not do to help him.

This book is intended to synthesize, for those archaeologists whose background is chiefly humanist, the kind of information that an archaeologist trained in certain methods used by the natural sciences can extract from the evidence provided by the deposits themselves. These methods, in conjunction with the interpretation of archaeological objects, are beginning to provide us with a more concrete picture of the environment of early man than has hitherto been available. It is important to realize, however, that the successful application of scientific methods in archaeology requires that the student should have a grounding in the facts of archaeology as well as in scientific work. It is the integration of the two approaches that is most urgently needed.

The writer is an archaeologist with some basic scientific training who has been drawn to soil-work as applicable to archaeological deposits. Why should not similar, but different, 'dual personalities' be evolved by interesting pedologists, chemists or sedimentary petrologists (for example) in the archaeological applications of their special skills? If prehistory can be married to science, why not equally well (or even better) science to prehistory? Archaeology would certainly profit by the union—and, it might well be, give something worth while in return.

Part I

ARCHAEOLOGICAL DEPOSITS

1

Earlier Stone Ages

+·+

ARCHAEOLOGICAL DEPOSITS, as much as the artifacts they contain, are documents from which information may be obtained about the way of living of the makers of the objects found and about their attitude to the environment of their time.

If they are to survive, man and his culture must be adapted to some extent to the natural environment. The lower the level of culture, the more closely is man obliged to conform to the demands of the environment, so that, in the earliest times, every detail of his existence was dictated by it. With advancing technology and the increased exploitation of natural resources which that made possible, civilization has more and more tended to control, and not be controlled by, its natural surroundings. Even today civilized communities are still from time to time reminded of their inexorable heritage, when whole districts and townships become, for a time, playthings of large natural forces from which we have not yet learned to protect ourselves.

In prehistoric, or even in early historic times, the culture of the inhabitants of these islands was thus most closely dependent upon natural environment. If any important feature of it changed, even temporarily, to man's disadvantage, he was forced either to adapt his habits to the change or to migrate in search of more favourable conditions. For instance, it is said that the great folk-movements of the Early Iron Age in Europe, which left their mark even on these far shores, were initiated by the climatic deterioration about 700 B.C. (from which we are, it seems, still suffering!) known to climatologists as the Sub-atlantic Phase, which succeeded the more continental Subboreal Phase during which the Bronze Age peoples of Europe had flourished.

Thus any information derived from deposits which enables us to reconstruct, however partially, the environments of past cultures will contribute to our understanding of the way of life of the people concerned and help us to appreciate both the favourable natural factors on which their culture was based and the unfavourable, against which it was designed to protect them.

Even were there no historical record of the destruction of Pompeii and Herculaneum, a cursory examination of the deposits covering them would suffice to indicate the nature of the disaster which overtook them. The intrinsic signs yielded by most archaeological deposits are generally less striking, less complete and less unequivocal than this, but, no less than at Pompeii, the natural as well as the cultural history of the site is written in its deposits and may sometimes be read from them.

Definitions

An archaeological deposit in the strict sense may be defined as a deposit containing any objects of man's making or evidence of disturbance by him. As the layers immediately underlying, interstratified with or covering archaeological deposits, though themselves archaeologically sterile, may contain natural evidence of value in determining the environment of the human occupation or evidence of its date, it is clear that these must also be included in our study, if all the available information is to be obtained from the site.

Many archaeological deposits, as defined above, come within that definition only because they contain the artifacts of man; for the rest the material composing them is natural, as is the manner of their formation. Deposits associated with man's dwelling-places, however, may be composed more or less of material artificial in its character, or at least artificially disposed. The 'tells' of Near-Eastern cities are an extreme example of this. That of Jericho is a mound seventy feet high, entirely composed of mud-brick and other building materials accumulated over thousands of years, as one city after another arose on the levelled debris of its predecessors. The artificiality of such deposits is recognized by the excavator when he calls the layer stratigraphically underlying the lowest level giving artifacts 'the natural'. While, for the excavator, this may seem to have little interest, for the student of soils it represents the probable parent-material of most of the deposits on the site and is therefore worthy of close study.

Since any Pleistocene deposit may contain evidence of early man, it could be maintained that the real boundary beyond which we need not pursue our inquiry is the base of the Pleistocene deposits present at the particular site. In practice the question presents no difficulty. The excavator of a Neolithic site, even if it be situated on a Pleistocene terrace-gravel, has to confine his attention to evidence relevant to the period which he is studying. Though the subsoil may abound in hand-axes and bones of contemporary animals, it is, for him, 'the natural'. For a student of the Palaeolithic period it may be the archaeological deposit of chief interest.

Similarly, in the study of soils the investigator has no difficulty in concentrating on the problems of the particular period to which the site relates.

As indicated above, deposits containing human artifacts can be subdivided into those mainly natural in character and those which are themselves chiefly artificial. Remains of the earlier human periods will be found chiefly in the first group, those of later times (Neolithic and onwards) in the second. Such subdivision is only a convenient approximation, for the lake-dwellings of Neolithic and later periods are preserved in almost entirely natural lake-deposits and it is not un-common to find even mediaeval pottery in caves.

For the student of all periods, therefore, it is important to understand in outline geological processes like river erosion, marine transgression, and the formation of fluviatile, lake and beach deposits. In addition, every archaeologist ought to have some acquaintance with processes connected with the formation of soils, such as solifluxion and soil-creep, hill-washing, mechanical displacement of soil particles by frost and chemical disintegration. It is impossible to understand the environment of early man without this equipment.

Though some of these processes will be referred to here, we cannot side-track the main theme to provide all the explanations of them which an absolute beginner might need. Such information is available in textbooks of Pleistocene geology and geomorphology (e.g. Zeuner 1945, 1952; Charlesworth, 1957.), and some knowledge of them must be assumed in any reader who is interested in Palaeolithic or Mesolithic archaeology.

The chief types of mainly natural archaeological deposits are as follows:

(1) Glacial and glaci-fluvial deposits
(2) Marine deposits
(3) River-terrace deposits
(4) Wind-blown dusts
(5) Lake and bog deposits
(6) Heath and sandhill deposits
(7) Deposits on chalk or limestone sub-soils
(8) Volcanic deposits

These will be treated in the first three chapters.

Glacial and glaci-fluvial deposits

Though widespread, these can, of their nature, not contain much of human industry which is actually contemporary. The climatic con-ditions which they represent were exceedingly inimical to human survival. Boulder-clays, the ground-moraine material of an ice-sheet, show that ice actually traversed the area where they are found. Outwash-gravels and sands may be formed at some distance, indeed, from the actual ice-edge by the reworking of morainic material by streams of melt-water, but they still connote the presence of an ice-sheet or glacier in the region and a climate unsuitable to the way of life of at least the earlier Palaeolithic peoples. Not until the Last Glaciation do men seem to have learned to make a living in such surroundings—and even then their relics are found in caves and shelters rather than on or about the sites of contemporary ice-sheets.

Thus, the archaeological contents of a boulder-clay, for instance, are certainly not in their original context. The famous Sidestrand hand-axe (Reid Moir, 1923), the earliest undeniable evidence of man in Britain, was found by Sainty embedded in the base of the Cromer Till, a boulder-clay attributable to the earliest glaciation known to have left its ground-moraine in this country. Clearly the manufacture of the implement must antedate the glaciation to which the Till is due, but this, by itself, tells us nothing of the environment of its maker, who must have lived on a now-vanished land-surface overridden by the Cromer Till ice, perhaps miles away from the place where the hand-axe was found after being incorporated in the ground-moraine.

Investigation of such a deposit would be confined to an attempt to identify the moraine with a particular glacial phase, in the hope of establishing a *terminus ante quem* date. This can be done in some cases by heavy-mineral analysis (see p. 133). Solomon (1932) did so investigate the Till and assigned it to his North Sea Glaciation (a probable correlative of one of the Alpine Mindel phases) on account of its content of Scandinavian minerals.

A similar case was the discovery (Reid Moir & Burchell, 1930) of flint flakes of a somewhat Upper Palaeolithic appearance from beneath the Hunstanton and Hessle Boulder-clays of Norfolk and Yorkshire, respectively, which are believed to be of Last Glaciation age. Here, the erratic rocks (far-travelled rocks foreign to the neighbourhood) were studied and it was concluded that the glaciation responsible for the moraines was of Scottish, not Scandinavian, origin.

Marine deposits

Pleistocene marine deposits are not very extensive in Britain. The East Anglian 'Crags' and isolated patches of marine sand and pebbles on the North Downs and Chilterns (Wooldridge, 1927) are the earliest deposits of the period, but these have not, hitherto, yielded anything which is unquestionably man's handiwork. Even the 'implements' (granting them that status for the sake of argument) from the various stone-beds underlying several stages of the Crag deposits are certainly not *in situ*, for they represent sweepings by the sea from a much older land-surface over which it had encroached.

Some few exposures of interglacial raised beaches, such as that at Slindon, Sussex (Pyddoke, 1950) and at Black Rock, Brighton (Martin, 1929), respectively attributable to the Great and Last Interglacials, have associated with them implements of early man. In the former case study of the deposits is of environmental interest, for the position of the hand-axe from Penfold's Pit, lying, unabraded, on the surface of a marine sand and covered by 'head' (a solifluction deposit), shows that its maker lived on the surface of the Interglacial beach. He presumably followed the way of life of a *strandlooper*, like the authors of the Postglacial shell-mounds of Ertebølle, in Denmark, or those of South Africa, whose local Afrikaans name has given the general term for peoples practising this kind of food-gathering economy.

The identification of a raised beach requires geological investigation

(Zeuner, 1952b) and the study of the contained fauna of erratics and heavy minerals may help in dating and correlation. In the case of Slindon, soil-studies were applied to the materials of the 'head' by Dalrymple (1955) in order to identify the source of the tumbled mass. Some temperate-soil rafts were identified, suggesting that the mature soil of the Interglacial, solifluxed with the onset of the following glaciation, was not greatly different from that of the present day, and that the climate of that time was not unlike today's.

Postglacial marine deposits are represented at Walton-on-the-Naze, Essex (Zeuner, 1952a), where a marine or estuarine clay containing foraminifera covers sites with flint implements, potsherds, potboilers etc. Besides this there were wooden hut-structures and evidence of wattle walls sited near the bank of an ancient creek. The archaeological material belongs to the period from the end of the Mesolithic (Lower Halstow culture) up to the earliest Bronze Age (B-beaker). The *Scrobicularia* Clay (named from the characteristic foraminifer) covering all this shows that there has here been a rise in the sea-level to perhaps 9 feet above Ordnance Datum since the Early Bronze Age. (See p. 207).

River terrace deposits

River-gravels resemble marine deposits in the difficulty of proving or disproving approximate contemporaneity of the implements found with the deposits. Warren (1951) pointed out what is obvious, but frequently overlooked: that we find human implements in river-*bed* deposits, while their makers certainly lived only on the *banks*. The objects may have been swept in by floods, but what is far more likely is that they lay, originally, on the surface of the floodplain, where they were left by their makers. Later the encroachment of swinging and widening meanders reworked and redistributed the floodplain deposits, incorporating the implements in those of its new bed.

Thus, practically all river-bed implements are derived, that is, not in position as left by man but drifted for at least a short distance from that position. An abraded ('rolled') palaeolith is not necessarily derived from any much older deposit than one which is unabraded (though such *may* be the case). They could easily be strictly contemporary, the difference in condition being due entirely to the distance travelled before once more coming to rest. Such drifting from the original position on the bank, and then from one situation to another in deposits of the same floodplain, may have taken place again and again. Derivation from a much older and higher terrace-level is probably much rarer. It would depend on erosion by a tributary stream or on solifluction bringing the object down on to the lower floodplain, for a river can seldom re-work its own ancient terraces once it has cut much below their level.

Animal bones found with a palaeolith, if not much rolled, are much more likely to be contemporary with its final deposition than with its

manufacture. Under suitable chemical conditions bone may be reasonably well preserved, but only the hardest and densest parts are likely
to survive even one disturbance by the river and redeposition. It is
impossible to estimate the amount of the probable difference in age
between an implement and the associated bones. If the artifact is
quite unabraded they may well be strictly contemporary, but any
important degree of abrasion makes it reasonably certain that a considerable time-difference separates them. Whether such differences
are of an order of magnitude high enough to matter, in view of the
great stretches of time embraced in a single interglacial period and the
slowness of technical evolution in Lower Palaeolithic times, is another
question.

It is not impossible, on the other hand, for an implement made and
abandoned in an interglacial period to have been washed down and
incorporated with a deposit of the succeeding glaciation, in company
with the bones of an arctic fauna. This fact may explain some of the
archaeological anomalies observed in river deposits, and the consequent confusion in dating. Nothing external to the implement can
warn us when this has happened. Even its condition may be reasonably
good and not suggest that it has been derived. Under certain circumstances, however, a patina not typical of the locality in which it is
found may reveal its true identity. Even this will happen only when
the implement has long been exposed on the surface, or buried in
such chemical circumstances (e.g. a chalky soil, which may give it a
white patina) that its appearance is obviously foreign to its immediate
context.

The gravels themselves may contain little, apart from bones, which
is capable of resolving questions of date. The example of derived pre-
Pleistocene shells in river-gravels should not, however, be forgotten.
Well-known examples of this are *Gryphaea* from the Chalk and *Pectun-
culus* from the Crags, which are not uncommon in gravels containing
outwash-material from boulder-clays deriving the fossils from these
original deposits. Study of erratics and heavy minerals may reveal the
presence of foreign materials, attributable to the outwash of an identifiable ice-sheet or to a drainage system different from that of the present
day. The Oxford gravels of the Thames contain erratics from a boulder-
clay in the Vale of Moreton which may be contemporary with
Solomon's Great Eastern Glaciation (Sandford, 1932). They must,
therefore, be later in date than the ice which brought these erratics to
the district. Gravels in the Vale of St Albans, much older than the
present River Colne and due to a stream flowing northwards, contain
Lower Greensand Chert. For this to have reached the Colne valley
from the exposures of the Greensand in Surrey, it is necessary to suppose that the present Thames valley was not in existence at that time
and that the Colne valley then carried the drainage from the north-
western part of the Weald (Wooldridge, 1938).

Apart from gravels and sands, which form the bulk of terrace deposits, floodloams and 'brickearths' can give some intrinsic information about their history. 'Brickearth' is any sediment which lends itself to the making of bricks, tiles etc., regardless of its geological nature. Somewhat sandy or silty clays, river floodloams and loesses are embraced in the term. Mechanical analysis, the determination of the particle-size composition of the material, may suggest whether they are entirely water-laid, or whether any important proportion is likely to have consisted originally of loess or other wind-transported material.

A floodloam is the deposit laid down by a mature river on the flat plain extending laterally from its channel to the valley slopes on either side (flood-plain). In times of wet weather the normal channel cannot contain the volume of water flowing down the valley, so that the floodplain is more or less inundated as well. The water outside the banks, being widely spread out, flows with a much smaller speed than the current of the channel and its speed is further checked by the friction of drowned vegetation on the banks. Much of the finer sediment which is in suspension in the main current cannot be held up when the water spreads over the banks and it is here deposited as a fine-grained loam (sand, silt and clay) of very variable mechanical composition, according to the local conditions, but generally containing approximately equal proportions of all the grades below medium sand.

Depending on their origin and derivation, floodloams may or may not be calcareous. If not too fully weathered and acid in reaction they may contain determinable shells of land or water molluscs. As with animal bones, the species present may indicate particular climatic conditions at the time of the deposition of the loam. Again, derivation comes in to complicate the picture. To quote an example given by Prof. Zeuner, the famous Levalloisian section of Baker's Hole, Ebbsfleet, Kent is covered by fresh-water deposits and a hill-wash of Last Interglacial deposits. In these was found a fragment of a shell closely resembling *Corbicula fluminalis*, nowadays extinct in the Thames, but characteristic of some interglacial deposits of the river. Careful identification in the Natural History Museum suggested that this was a fragment of a *Cyrena*, derived from the Tertiary deposits in the neighbourhood. Later, large-scale quarrying in the area revealed a subsidiary valley filled with Pleistocene sands and gravels and containing beds full of fragments of Tertiary marine molluscs, such as *Cerithium*. Since these beds occurred at a level higher than the Baker's Hole site and since the side-valley ran towards it, the inclusion of Tertiary shells in the Pleistocene deposits is now easily explained.

Similar conditions must have obtained many times during the Pleistocene, when earlier Pleistocene shells were derived and redeposited in younger formations. In such a case, derivation is difficult, if not impossible, to establish.

At or below the neck of a river estuary, where the water is at least intermittently salt, a river loam may contain Foraminifera. These are the calcareous tests of minute marine unicellular animals, mostly no larger than a pin's head. In the hands of a specialist, however, the assemblage of species found may be indicative of environmental conditions—even indicating, perhaps, limiting temperatures and salinity for the water in which they lived. Their mere presence proves that the water was salt or brackish.

Chemical alteration of loams, as at the surface of the Lower Loam at Swanscombe, may prove exposure to weathering under temperate climatic conditions. This would be an indication, as at this site, of a disconformity in the deposits—a break in sedimentation and withdrawal of the river to a lower level. In the case quoted the weathering of the loam amounts to complete decalcification of the upper portion, while the lower still retains well-preserved shells of both land and freshwater molluscs. A considerable interval of time is indicated, occupied, it is supposed, by the Clacton Channel stage of the river, before it returned to deposit the Middle Gravels on the weathered surface of the Lower Loam.

Such weathering can easily be demonstrated by comparison of the mechanical composition and chemical properties of the weathered and unweathered parts of the loam.

Wind-blown dusts

Some 'brickearths'—probably more than we yet know—prove on mechanical analysis to consist largely of particles of the silt grade (0.06—0.002 mm.). An analysis showing 70% or more of the sample lying between these limits is typical of a fresh (i.e. unweathered and unmixed) loess and is common to all wind-borne sediments. Wind is, of course, capable of transporting sand-grains, but these (coarser than 0.06 mm. up to 2 mm.) merely travel in a series of longer or shorter leaps, coming to earth as soon as the wind-force drops below a certain quite moderate figure. Dunes may thus advance a good many miles from the place of origin of the sand, but the grains do not long remain in suspension in a medium as little dense as air. Silt and clay grains, however, are light enough and have a surface large enough in proportion to their weight to remain bodily suspended while being transported for very long distances by quite moderate winds. The finest material, the clay (smaller than 0.002 mm.), will settle out only slowly, even in still air, so that it may, by turbulence, reach the upper atmosphere and be deposited grain by grain, widely dispersed and incorporated with more rapidly-forming sediments. In any case, it is thus lost as an entity, at least in terrestrial and marine shelf-deposits.

Not so the silt. This is heavy enough, in relation to its surface area, to settle fairly rapidly. The enormous and wide-spread loess deposits, occurring in the Pleistocene periglacial regions, were formed in this way, at some distance from the ice-margin, whence the prevailing wind blew. It happens that frost-splitting of rock-fragments ceases at the lower boundary of the silt-grade, 0.002 mm., so that land-surfaces under a frost-climate abound in rock-particles of the silt-grade and coarser and have little clay, save that ground out by glaciers. Vegetation near the ice-margin is scanty, so that this material is widely available for the winds to sort out those particles which they can carry off. Loess, therefore, has the property of a narrow band of particle sizes—it is an extremely well-sorted sediment.

Now, owing to the comparatively oceanic climates obtaining in Britain, even during the height of the glacial periods, true loesses (i.e. wind-sorted sediments *in situ*) do not here assume the stratigraphical and chronological importance to archaeology which they have on the Continent. The very fact that they are of comparative rarity and are generally atypical in some respects adds to their interest. The very existence of something like a loess, in view of our present-day climate, is an assurance of former environmental conditions very different indeed from those with which we are familiar.

Owing to subsequent water-sorting, many such deposits may have lost to some extent their aeolian character. Flood-loams largely composed of aeolian dust are not infrequent. They occur, for instance, at several places in the eastern and southern counties, as on younger Thames terraces near Iver, Bucks (Lacaille, 1936) and at various sites near Ipswich, Suffolk, where they have been discovered by Mr H. E. P. Spencer of Ipswich Museum. One such occurred at Bobbit's Hole (West, 1957), the curve of another from the Brett Valley, Suffolk is illustrated in Fig. 1. Over 80% of this material, which is finely laminated and evidently water-laid, falls in the silt-grade (0.06–0.002 mm.) a size-sorting which is almost certainly due to wind-action. Though it is clearly not a loess *in situ*, it probably contains a high proportion of derived loess material.

Other brickearths yielding palaeoliths occur at levels which exclude river action as the depositing agency. Some of these may well have originated as loesses, but they may have since been redeposited, weathered and mixed with local materials to such an extent as to have their loessic character obscured or even effaced. An opportunity recently occurred to re-examine the brickearths from an old and famous section at Caddington, Bedfordshire, where large collections of palaeoliths were made in the later years of the last century by W. G. Smith (1894). It had been suspected beforehand that these brickearths, now some hundreds of feet above the present watercourses, would prove to be at least in part loessic, but mere inspection before analysis showed that they were much too fine in average grain-size to show any loess character. The material is probably mainly redeposited Clay-with-Flints (a Tertiary weathering-soil on the Chalk) accumulated by rainwash and streams in an ancient basin which,

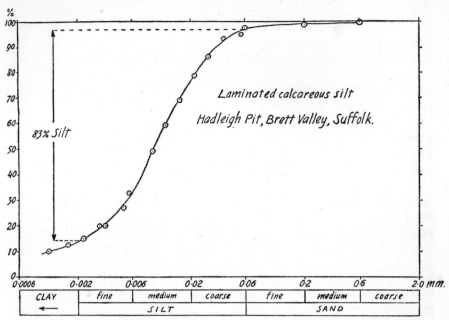

FIG 1.   Mechanical-analysis curve of a water-laid sediment showing wind-sorting.

according to Smith, contained a lake in Palaeolithic times. Nevertheless, high-level brickearths are worth examination with a possible loess origin in mind, for, unlike river floodloams, wind-borne particles are not confined to any particular level and, if other sources of material such as existed at Caddington can be excluded, it is likely that wind has had a part in their conveyance.

2

Deposits of Caves and Rock-Shelters

CAVES AND ROCK-SHELTERS are almost non-existent in the south-eastern counties of England, owing to the absence of sufficient masses of coherent rocks able to withstand, since early times, the disintegrating effect of weather. The so-called 'rock-shelters' of Oldbury Hill, in Kent, near which a flake-industry of Mousterian appearance with hand-axes has been found (Brit. Ass., 1891) may, in their time, have afforded some shelter to man. Their exposure, however, on the north side of the hill, makes it a little doubtful whether the site was suitable, in glacial times, for more than very temporary occupation. There is nothing to show that they were a reason for the location of the pre-historic material, which, indeed, lay at some distance down the slope from the present-day overhangs. The shelf of indurated sandstone which forms the scarp of the hill is evidently being weathered back fairly rapidly even in our time, so that the position of the face in Palaeolithic times must have been many yards north of this. It follows, therefore, that the contemporary terrace fronting the 'shelter' has also been weathered and washed away, or deeply buried by talus, so that the industry is almost certainly not in its original position. The site of the finds is now covered by the tennis-court of a house built since the excavations, so that it is likely that any future excavation at Oldbury, even if it succeeded in locating another group of implements, would scarcely repay, in useful information, the considerable labour involved.

In the more western and northern counties, where occur hard limestones such as the Carboniferous formations of the Mendip Hills, the Devonian of the Torquay region and the limestones of north and south Wales, Derbyshire and Yorkshire, caves, 'potholes' and fissures have attracted the attention of lead-miners, archaeologists, palaeont-ologists and the modern, generally less scientifically-minded, cave-exploring fraternity.

While most of our well-known caves have been explored and ex-ploited and a few—all too few—scientifically excavated and adequately published, there must remain numerous sites still to be discovered which were once occupied by later Palaeolithic man. Such intensity of occupation, from the end of the Last Interglacial onwards, as we meet in the Dordogne region of France cannot be expected in these less-favoured latitudes, but it is certain that not only deep caverns afforded shelter to Middle and Upper Palaeolithic man. In other words, cliff-shelters of favourable aspect (preferably facing south), where there may once have been a protective overhang, probably afforded here, as in France, at least seasonal habitations. Little search seems, as yet, to have been made for such sites.

Formation of caves and their deposits

Cave-earths are probably the least well understood deposits containing relics of man's industry, and even, possibly, his bodily remains. Caves and fissures begin, in the main, as solution-cavities, etched through long ages by water carrying in solution carbon dioxide and humic acids—the latter derived from surface vegetation. This percolates through natural joints and weaknesses in the limestone. Once they are opened, the surface drainage tends to go underground and many caves thus carry sizeable streams which, in floodtime, have considerable erosive power. Water-erosion is thus added to chemical solution as a cave-forming agency. It is known, further, that cave-formation by solution takes place with greater rapidity under pressures higher than that of the atmosphere far below the water-table owing to the increased solubility of CO_2 with pressure. Some caves so formed are now dry owing to the present-day level of the water-table having fallen below them. This also happens in solution-caves which have never been entirely drowned, when a stream finds a vertical or oblique fissure leading to a lower level and abandons its original courses and continues its work deeper down. Many cave systems thus comprise cavities on two or more levels. Those interested in caves will find a fund of information in Cullingford (1953) and Sutcliffe (1957).

Most limestones contain more or less of finely-divided non-calcareous, and therefore relatively insoluble, material. Where there are deeper channels to carry off the greater part of the water, processes of solution are still going on more slowly than before in the abandoned former watercourses. In the course of centuries, therefore, appreciable amounts of siliceous and aluminous residues are released and deposited on the cave-floors. No doubt, also, a certain amount of silt and organic matter reaches the caves through the agency of rain-water, percolating directly, if in no great volume, from the surface.

Kerekes (1951) states that in Central European caves the loamy formations, formerly thought to consist of the acid-insoluble residue of the limestone alone, are far too voluminous to have been derived solely from this source. He calculated the volume of limestone represented by the space of the cave and compared the volume of the deposits with the corresponding volume of insoluble residue calculated from analysis of the limestone. The insolubles in the limestone could not account for all. He observed that, in places where fissures opened into a cave, there was often a cone of relatively fine-grained sediment immediately below. He concluded, therefore, that a good deal of the finer material is brought into caves by percolating water. Such cones are found where the cave lies under a bare karst (a weathered and fissured surface of limestone), or where this has only a thin covering of incoherent soil-material. Where the limestone has a thicker and more coherent cover they are invariably absent. Such loams often contain minerals foreign to the limestone.

Wind, too, when the weather is dry, contributes some air-borne dust to caves with any considerable opening above ground, though, under present-day conditions of perennial vegetation-cover in Britain, this access of material is probably not important in amount. Not always have climatic conditions favoured the growth of trees, or even of a close cover of herbage. In such circumstances wind-borne dust may well have supplied, over long periods of time, enough material to make possible large accumulations of cave-earth. Kerekes notes that cave-loams are often thickest and more calcareous near the entrances of caves. In Central Europe the material is probably largely loess. Mineralogical, physical and chemical investigations could undoubtedly resolve some of the more puzzling questions about the origins of cave-earths and assign to a particular deposit the appropriate proportions in which these agencies have contributed to its formation.

The coarser constituents of particulate (clastic) cave deposits are predominantly fragments of the local limestone. Where exposed to weather, fragments are continually being detached from the rock by insolation (expansion and contraction due to temperature-changes) and frost-weathering (expansion of ice in water-filled crevices on freezing). If not removed by flowing water the pieces of limestone are incorporated in the accumulating cave-deposits. The weathering of limestone is, of course, much intensified where the climate or exposure is such that frequent changes of temperature about the freezing-point of water can take place. In our climate these conditions only obtain intermittently in winter and only affect the exposed parts of caves. During the glacial periods, however, even the interiors of deep caverns were affected by frost-weathering, where nowadays little or no accumulation of limestone rubble is taking place. A large proportion of cave-breccias (angular fragments re-cemented) owes its origin to this agency. It should be noted that consistently low winter temperatures do not produce as much frost-rubble as frequent alternations of frost and thaw. Limestone cliffs on two sides of the same valley, where one faces north and the other south, will demonstrate this. Where, in a period of frost, the north-facing side may not thaw for days, weeks, or, in harder climates than ours, even months together, whenever the sun shines the rock of the south-facing side may rise above freezing-point at least at midday. Re-freezing of water in fissures at sundown will continue the work begun overnight on this side, while no change will take place in a similar fissure which, on the north-facing side, has remained hard-frozen all day. Frost-rubble does not, therefore, demand extremely cold conditions—indeed, its formation would be slower where winters were so hard that intermittent thawing did not often break continuing frost.

Limestone rubble generally accumulates where it falls, unless the slope is so steep that it rolls and slides downhill, forming a talus-slope or scree at the angle of rest of the material. This can happen in caves where sizeable fragments of limestone enter it from above through an aven or chimney.

Another agency capable of conveying coarse limestone debris into caves is solifluction, but this is only possible when the cave-floor slopes down from an external opening. It requires, moreover, so intense a frost that the limestone underlying any mass of frozen earth and stones near the opening is deep-frozen and impermeable to water when the thaw first sets in. Otherwise, instead of flowing cave-wards in a waterlogged condition, the water in the thawing mass will gradually drain into the limestone and no movement at all will take place in the mass as a whole. The necessary conditions are seldom met with in this country, save in glacial periods.

Preservation of materials in caves

From the point of view of the archaeologist and palaeontologist the virtue of the calcareous nature of cave-earths is that, in addition to flint, chert and in general acid-insoluble materials, animal and human bones and artifacts made of bone and ivory are often well preserved. On the other hand, the alkaline reaction and porosity of the limestone ensure practically complete oxidation and disappearance of most other matter of organic origin, unless first carbonized. It has been stated that traces of fatty acids and even less stable organic compounds derived from animal tissues can survive (Stokar, 1939) but little work along these lines has been done so far. It would require the coöperation of a skilled organic chemist.

Phosphates (bone is mainly calcium phosphate) will of course survive, but it must be made clear that one source of phosphate in caves, apart from bones of larger mammals and its possible occurrence in some quantity in the limestone itself, is the presence of bats and owls, which often lodge in deserted caves and contribute their castings and droppings to the deposits. Since birds of prey subsist largely on small rodents and other birds and eject in their castings the indigestible parts of their prey, the presence of 'rodent layers' in cave-earths denotes the abandonment of the cave by man, as the birds are unlikely to have shared their quarters with even more predatory human beings. Rodent remains in the hands of a competent specialist may yield climatic information of no less chronological interest because man himself was not at the time present. Bat-dung contains the undigested chitinous remains of the numerous larger insects on which the animals principally feed. Entire elytra (wing-covers) of beetles and other determinable fragments are not uncommon and it is likely that an entomologist could supply interesting environmental evidence, given such material.

Snail-shells, also, being of a calcareous nature, are well preserved in cave-earths and may provide useful climatic data.

The work of Lais on cave-deposits

Lais (1932) assembled snails from all the distinct levels seen in the section of a cave at the Isteiner Klotz, Baden. No species found in the ancient layers was absent from the cave at the present day, but he found that, in three of his layers, the warmth-loving species, having their main distribution today in the south of Europe—and, therefore, in his region, marginal species—were entirely absent. He concluded, with some assurance, that these layers were formed in times with a climate less favourable than the present. This conclusion found support in the results of his physical and chemical investigation of the deposits. He found that the carbonate content, composed of limestone fragments fallen from the roof of the cave and 'sinter-grit', crumbs and concretions formed by dripping water falling on pre-existing deposits, increased notably in cool-moist periods as contrasted with the warm-dry. The two layers with the most warmth-loving snails also contained the least carbonate. These were associated, respectively, with Mesolithic and with Bronze-Age archaeological material and evidently represented the comparatively warm-dry Boreal and Subboreal climatic phases of the Postglacial. The finer constituents of the cave-earth at these levels, separated by mechanical analysis, were red-brown in colour, evidently blown into the cave and representing particles of the contemporary reddish soils (Terra fusca or Terra rossa, pp. 98-9) there forming.

Layers with Neolithic pottery, intervening between the above two deposits, contained far more 'sinter-grit' and no warm snails. Clearly, the cloudier and wetter Atlantic period, beginning and ending gradually, with a precipitation-maximum in the middle, as shown by the carbonate content, was responsible for these differences. The fine constituents were brown, not red, indicating ordinary brownearth weathering outside the cave. The layer following the Bronze-Age deposit, corresponding to the Subatlantic and extending up to the present, shared, in somewhat slighter degree, the features of the Atlantic deposits.

In several caves yielding Palaeolithic remains the same author (Lais, 1941, and Fig. 6, p. 131) has carried out quantitative estimations of the calcareous constituents present in the various size-grades in each layer. It was noted that frost-weathered rubble falls predominantly in a coarser grade than does chemically-weathered material with edges rounded and etched by solution-processes. The latter is certainly associated with the percolation of considerable quantities of water: therefore with a temperate climate. Frost-weathering requires only small amounts of

c

moisture and Lais suggests that, where the rock is not saturated, the water occupies only the wider fissures, which are more easily penetrated, so that, on freezing, the detached fragments tend to be large. Limestone rubble separated by solution, on the other hand, is saturated down to its finest pores. The resultant material tends to fall into the finest grades. On the evidence of such mechanical, chemical and visual analyses, plotted as separate curves for each particle-grade over the different layers, it should be comparatively simple to distinguish glacial from interglacial cave-deposits by means of samples of the deposits themselves, independently of their organic contents.

Samples taken from close to the entrance of a cave may not show climatic and chronological zoning very clearly. Even at the present day, some frost-weathering is taking place externally, so that it must have continued, if more slowly, through the Interstadials. A few yards inside the entrance is the most likely situation for any subdivision of the calcareous rubble to be found.

At the Mauern caves, in Moravia, Lais noted from inspection and after mechanical analysis that some of the loams evidently owed much of their material to loess. Interstadial weathering was denoted by less calcareous and more highly-coloured zones in the loam. The weathering indicated by the redder colour did not, of course, take place *in situ,* but the material blown or washed into the caves was similar to the loess-loam (weathering-soil on loess) then forming the surface soil in the neighbourhood.

The warm-continental Boreal period was seldom represented by considerable deposits. Neither frost nor rainfall were sufficient to form them.

We can hardly expect to find such detailed subdivision of British cave-deposits, seeing that climatic contrasts in the West are blurred by the proximity of the sea, which acts as a thermostat, preventing extremes of temperature. The work of Lais, however, is quoted in some detail to show what scientific methods applied to cave deposits are capable of showing, in favourable circumstances. It would certainly be worth while to apply similar tests here, in the hope of identifying at least the more extreme oscillations of climate in our own caves.

Lais pleads for some standard nomenclature among archaeologists to describe cave-deposits. Too often the only description given in publications is 'compact cave-earth', 'stiff clay' or 'black hearth level'. Only after physical and chemical analysis can the true description of a cave deposit be given. The term 'soil' should be rigorously excluded. No cave-deposit is a soil, in the exact meaning of the term.

Colour can be accurately described by reference to some colour-chart. That already widely used in the U.S.A. and in this country for describing soil-colours is the Munsell Soil Color Chart (see p. 119). Grading-tests will give grounds for a description such as 'silty loam', which has a definite quantitative meaning in pedology.

Stalagmite, or dripstone

It is well known that water charged with lime salts dripping from the vault of a cavern may in time form an 'icicle' of calcium carbonate called a *stalactite*. From the place immediately beneath a stalactite at which the dripping water falls on the floor of the cave may grow upwards in a similar way a formation of *stalagmite*, which may in time meet the hanging stalactite to form a veritable column. Not all per-colating water enters the cave in such a way as to result in either of these formations. Much of it may seep through the walls and, instead of dripping from a particular spot, trickle steadily down in a narrow or spreading stream forming curtains or transversely-ribbed sheets or bosses, whose form is infinitely variable and often extremely beautiful. Reaching the floor, which may be relatively impervious, the trickling water is augmented by that dripping straight from the roof and may spread out in sheets and deeper pools, from which, in time, a fairly level crust of mineral deposit may be formed. This not only coats the surface of the former deposits and that of any loose stones or objects lying on them, but may percolate for some distance into them, cement-ing them with calcium carbonate into a coherent, often very hard rock known as *cave-breccia*. All such formations of calcium carbonate (and more rarely of other minerals) formed by the percolation, drip or flow of mineralizing solutions may be grouped together under the terms *dripstone* or *flowstone*. The adoption of this term among spelaeologists is comparatively recent and in all the older literature any formation not actually pendent from the vault is called 'stalagmite'.

Floors of dripstone or simply 'stalagmites' are frequently a feature of cave-sections in Britain and all over the world.

The fact that at one time cave-earth, at another loose rock rubble, and at a third dripstone should be formed on the floor of a cave suggests that external environmental factors have changed, so that these changes in the nature of deposition are of the greatest interest to the archaeologist, who may find the implements of ancient man and other evidences of his activities among the deposits.

The factors causing and influencing the formation of dripstone in particular cases are still not fully explained, but the general principles underlying its deposition are simple. Percolating water in some quantity is the first requirement; if the local climate is arid, or arctic, so that subsoil water is perennially frozen, no dripstone will be formed. Given sufficient water, there must be a certain thickness of limestone above the cave for percolating solutions to become saturated; if not saturated, very considerable evaporation will be necessary before any salts will be thrown out of solution—indeed, too much or too rapid percolation will probably result in under-saturation and, once more, no dripstone. Finally, there must be enough ventilation of the cavern for evaporation into drier air of at least some water from the saturated solutions entering it. Without any evaporation in the cave there will be no super-saturation of the solutions to cause deposition of some of their dissolved mineral load. There is, in fact, more to it than this. The concentration of carbon dioxide gas (CO_2) in the cave atmosphere plays a part, but, without here going into the (not very difficult!) chemistry, it may be said that, in respect of CO_2 also, adequate ventilation will assist the formation of dripstone.

The intercalation of a dripstone floor in a cave-section has often been interpreted as the result of a period of cold climate. In Britain, however, or in any of the regions within the periglacial zone during the Pleistocene glaciations, a glacial period is one not only colder but *drier*, owing to the supposed diversion by the high-pressure belt over the ice-sheet of the rain-bearing westerly depressions to a more southerly course. In lower latitudes than ours, as, for example, in the Mediterranean region, a glacial phase may mean increased rainfall owing to the southerly diversion of the depressions, the wetter conditions favouring the formation in caves of dripstone, while, with us, the same phase reduced the amount of percolating water necessary to its formation.

Dripstones are, therefore, more directly due to *wetter* than to *colder* conditions.

The section of the Pin Hole cave, Derbyshire (Armstrong, 1931) shows two rubble-layers and a dripstone floor, with cave-earths between the rubbles and between the upper rubble and the dripstone. The distinct boulder-layers are evidently the products of two periods of intense frost-weathering—glacial phases, whatever the datings assigned to them. The dripstone also seems to connote a cold period, but, if this is correct, why is there not a third layer of angular limestone instead of stalagmite?

A possible explanation is that the third cold period was less intense so that the glacial anticyclone was insufficiently developed to divert the westerly depressions. If this were the case, we should expect to find lesser dripstone formations at the onset and weakening of each major glacial phase, when similar conditions probably prevailed, but of these there is no evidence.

The explanation is likely to be found in local conditions. Zeuner (1952b) has pointed out that, by the time of the dripstone formation, the deposits in the cave had mounted to such an extent as partially to block the entrance. This would interfere with excessive ventilation and prevent frost-weathering and favour the retention of such moisture as there was to lay down the dripstone floor.

In view of the 'sinter-grit' observed by Lais at the Isteiner Klotz (see above, p. 33) it is not clear exactly what determined this form of calcareous deposit while Pin Hole has a stalagmite. The deposits are not, of course, contemporary, but while percolating water remains unfrozen some difference in conditions, other than temperature, must have been at work in the two cases.

Lais thinks that an incoherent calcareous grit is formed when water saturated with lime salts is quickly evaporated in well-ventilated situations with a temperature not too low. If percolating solutions are unsaturated, even rapid evaporation will cause the salts to be deposited rather slowly—as dense dripstone. Low temperatures down to the freezing-point will have the same result, by depressing the vapour-pressure. Certainly, dense crystalline dripstones are being formed at the present day only in the nearly-saturated atmospheres of deep, wet caverns, where their deposition must be extremely slow.

Evidently we still do not know everything about dripstone form-ations—or, for that matter, about other cave-deposits. Scientific methods applied in this field will doubtless add considerably to our knowledge of the environments of the remoter periods of prehistory.

3

Lake, Heath, Limestone and Volcanic Deposits

✦✦

Lake deposits and peat-bogs

THESE TWO TYPES of deposits of archaeological interest are treated together, because they are genetically connected in many cases and tend to grade into each other.

The eventual fate of every lake, if not prematurely drained, is to be gradually filled up with sediments until the water becomes shallow enough to enable plants of the reed (*Phragmites*) association to take root in its bed. In our latitudes it then passes progressively through the stages of swamp, marsh and bog. Later it may support brushwood and low trees and, finally, it may dry out to become firm land carrying forest.

As relatively ephemeral features, many lakes which doubtless existed in Palaeolithic and Mesolithic times are no more. In North-West Europe they are essentially a feature of recently-glaciated regions, being formed by the damming of valleys by morainic material or through the grinding out of depressions in the bedrock under the sole of the glacier. On the retreat of the ice these basins filled with meltwaters and in highland regions today their overflows, fed by modern streams, are still cutting away at the barriers which retain them. Their fate hangs in the balance between the rate of this erosion and of silting, but falling water-level and eventual filling of their basins will surely combine to obliterate them in the end.

The marl of an interglacial lake at Lehringen, near Verden-an-der-Aller, Hanover, now worked as raw material for bricks and tiles, yielded in 1942 the skeleton of an *Elephas antiquus* (the extinct, straight-tusked forest elephant) of the Last Interglacial, associated with Levallois flakes (Adam, 1951). The most interesting archaeological feature of the find was a wooden spear, of yew, with a fire-hardened point. Evidently the animal was killed by Palaeolithic men and the circumstance has given us a vivid glimpse of the hunting methods of these people, hitherto only surmised.

The long-famous Clacton wooden spear-fragment—also, curiously enough, of yew wood—probably of the Penultimate (Mindel-Riss) Interglacial and associated with Clactonian flakes, is the only parallel from this country (Warren, 1923). The site is an ancient channel of the Thames, then flowing northwards across Buckinghamshire, past Watford and Ware towards the Blackwater estuary in Essex (Wooldridge, 1938), and, beyond this, north-eastwards across the North-Sea plain.

Another well-known example of a fossil lake yielding Palaeolithic remains is the Hoxne site in East Anglia (Reid Moir, 1927; West 1955). Acheulean implements of a stage comparable with that of Clacton and Barnfield Pit, Swanscombe, belong to the Great Interglacial, on the evidence of the pollen from the sediments, worked out by West.

Since British lakes of today are themselves chiefly Postglacial features, only remains of later date than the Palaeolithic can be expected to occur in their deposits. The Star Carr site (Clarke, 1954) of Early Boreal date (Mesolithic) was on the banks of an early postglacial lake, now already past the bog stage of degradation and under the plough (see below, p. 209). Not only Mesolithic, but Neolithic, Bronze-Age and Iron-Age settlers favoured lake-side dwellings. Their reasons for the preference were, no doubt, economic rather than aesthetic, though, man being what he is, it is likely that he took pleasure then, as now, in still waters.

The lake provided him with water, timber on its banks for buildings and boats, reeds for thatch and for arrow-shafts—and even, perhaps, pipes for making music. Fish could be speared, netted or hooked in both shallows and deeps; waterfowl and wild game frequented the banks, and man's own flocks and herds were amply catered for.

In the more ancient lakes, now mostly become bog and fen, are found the dwelling-sites of Mesolithic peoples. Whether they lived at the lakeside all the year round is doubtful. Their way of life probably demanded frequent changes of station, following the migrations of geese and salmon and the movements of the larger game. In any case, the structures they built have an impermanent appearance.

The later lake-dwellings were certainly permanent settlements. In this country we have nothing to compare with the Swiss pile-villages, but the Neolithic settlement of Ehenside Tarn (Darbishire, 1873; Fair, 1932) and the Iron-Age lake-village of Glastonbury (Bulleid & Gray, 1911–17) show that here also we may hope occasionally to find pre-historic remains in such circumstances.

Apart from mineral sediments brought in by rivers and streams, lakes contain characteristic deposits of organic origin. Where lime is plentiful it may be precipitated from the water by aquatic plants such as some of the pond-weeds (*Potamogeton* etc.). Crusts of calcium carbonate form in contact with them (in the case of *Chara* as an internal skeleton) and eventually fall to the bottom of the lake and are mixed with the shells of freshwater molluscs and the finer clay sediments to form marls, which are often very pure and pale in colour. Portner (1951) has, further, shown that local and seasonal variations in CO_2-concentration in lime-bearing lake-waters control a purely chemical precipitation of calcium carbonate. He calculates that, in the case of Lake Neuchâtel, the precipitated amount is as much as one-quarter to one-third of the quantity received in solution from its affluents.

Another typically lacustrine deposit is gel-mud (*dy*—Swedish) an amorphous deposit often formed by the chemical precipitation of organic (humic) solutions, perhaps in the presence of calcium-salts. In view of the scarcity of knowledge about the nature of humus and the properties of its solutions, the chemistry of the formation of gel-muds is not fully understood. Unicellular algae such as diatoms and microscopic animal plankton (drifting organisms) also contribute to gel-muds in proportions controlled by the particular conditions. In lakes where little detrital matter is being deposited, whether mineral sediment or macroscopic plant-remains, siliceous diatom frustules may compose the greater part of the deposits. This mass of microscopic plant-skeletons is sometimes so pure that 'diatomite', as the mineralogists call it, may be pure white. Late glacial and Postglacial lakes in the more northern parts of these islands represent favourable environments for such deposits at the present day. They are sometimes associated with remains of prehistoric lake-side settlements.

Bacterial action is probably largely responsible for the formation of bog-ironstone, mainly limonite (hydroxide) and siderite (carbonate), in the shallows of peaty lakes. Not only may the minerals occur in such situations with traces of human occupation, but in the Early Iron Age and early historic times they were important and easily accessible sources of iron-ore.

In acid waters, where the catchment-area of the lake is deficient in bases, organic deposits take the form of only partially decomposed plant-remains (*gyttja*—Swedish). Especially in deep waters, where oxygen may be deficient, whether sufficient bases are present or not, complete decomposition is not attained either. Here the supply of remains of macroscopic plants is comparatively small, so that diatoms and animal plankton form the bulk of the material, which may develop hydrogen sulphide and methane through incomplete oxidation of proteins and carbohydrates and have an offensive smell (*faulschlamm*— German; *sapropel*—Swedish).

In the shallows and close to the shores, though oxidation may take place with ease, the supply of plant-remains is so massive that it tends to outpace decay. Once there is some accumulation of leaves, stems etc., the roots of living plants tend to hold it together and to prevent disturbance by wave-action, so that further deposits locally exhaust the oxygen and favour the preservation of what lies below the immediate surface. Different types of plants contribute to this peat as the shores are approached.

In water of medium depth (2 m. or so), only the totally-immersed plants grow. As it shallows to less than 1.5 m., water-lilies (*Nuphar*), reeds (*Phragmites*), horsetails (*Equisetum*) and the like, with permanently-submerged roots but aerial stems and leaves, take their place. The marshy banks, which are not continually waterlogged, form a habitat for sedges (*Cyperaceae*) and rushes (*Juncaceae*), plants of marshy places. All these and their associated species contribute characteristic remains, so that a botanist examining a lake-peat can easily estimate the depth of water and conditions represented by a given horizon in the section.

In deposits such as these, much evidence of human occupation is preserved which would otherwise have perished. Wood, bark, leaves, exines of pollen and spores of fungi, vegetable food-refuse, fibres, cordage, textiles, and grain may be found. Some animal proteins, such as keratin and chitin, the materials of hoof and horn and of arthropod (insect, crustacean) exoskeletons respectively, are resistant to these conditions, so that leather, rawhide, wool, hair, horn and objects made from them, insect remains (e.g. beetle wing-cases) and even bone and antler may be preserved. The last two may be more or less decalcified but their form will be preserved by the organic, and less soluble inorganic, constituents remaining.

In deep, cold lakes human and animal bodies may be converted into masses of a waxy substance called *adipocere* (fat-wax), which replace the more complicated compounds, fats and proteins, of which they were originally composed and roughly preserve their external form, at least in the more fatty regions. The face, extremities, and the thinner parts of the limbs are generally reduced to the bones (Wasmund, 1935). Salt water does not interfere with this process. Similar conditions obtain in waterlogged soils, and in cemeteries where the bodies lie permanently below the water-table they are frequently found on exhumation to have been converted into adipocere.

An outstanding case of preservation of a body is the well-known Iron-Age man of Tollund Bog, Jutland, discovered in 1950 (Glob, 1951). In this case the facial features, down to the very stubble on his chin, were preserved, the leather cap and belt and the leather thongs with which he had been ritually strangled. Even the stomach contents were sufficiently intact for barley, linseed and other plants, both cultivated and wild, to be found, giving most valuable and unique information on the food of prehistoric man.

That such preservation can continue for periods much longer than that which has elapsed since the Iron Age is shown by the woolly rhinoceros carcase of Starunia, Poland (Zeuner, 1934), in which the hide and hair were preserved, as were the remains of the associated insects and some of the fat, converted into adipocere. This is assigned to a Last Glaciation date, so that, one day, some fortunate find in the bed of a fossil lake, still waterlogged, may reveal the actual body, not only the bones, of Palaeolithic man, with all his otherwise perishable equipment, almost completely unknown to us today, though it must have once existed.

Heath and sand-hill deposits

It is now well known that the Mesolithic inhabitants of western Europe were confined in their distribution by the spread of forests in early Postglacial times to those areas where, for one reason or another, the timber was not too dense. Coastlines and coastal dunes afforded a suitable environment for those of them who depended on the sea and the beach for their food-gathering.

Inland, it is soil and topography which together determine whether the natural forest shall be dense or sparse, and it is largely in areas of poor, acid soil and on the more exposed uplands that their remains are found.

The Lower Greensand and other almost exclusively siliceous bed-rocks, as, for instance, the Millstone Grit of the Pennines, are already poor in bases. By weathering in our climate they change into porous sandy soils and become very acid. In these conditions they support only scattered woodlands, mainly birch and pine, with gorse, heather, bracken and other typical moorland species. If to this be added an exposed, well-drained position, almost desert conditions will obtain in a dry period of weather or climate. Archaeological sites in such situations are plentiful in this country. For the Mesolithic period, the Surrey commons and the Greensand hills of the Weald, the Breckland in Cambridgeshire and Suffolk are well known for their concentrations of sites.

This environment seems to have been favoured occasionally in later periods, though for different reasons. Bronze-Age barrow-builders chose not only Surrey Greensand but the New Forest and Bournemouth Plateau-Gravels, for example. It is possible that the ease with which barrows can be erected on sandy soil determined the location of these, but their monuments are widespread on other sub-soils also, as, for instance, on the Chalk. What seems to have been sought was, primarily, a commanding position, open to view from a distance, whilst friability of the soil entered the picture, if at all, only as a secondary consideration.

Finds of any period made in acid, permeable soils (e.g. podsols—pp. 108-12) are conspicuous by their poverty. Unlike a lake or bog site (which may be equally acid) these soils are porous and abundantly aer-ated. Practically nothing is preserved save flint and other acid-resisting rocks and such organic remains as have been carbonized by fire. Even wood and plant-remains do not persist unless they happen to lie in the B-horizon of the podsol, where there is already an excess of humic matter and a partial blockage of the drainage owing to pan-formation. Bone disappears without trace and, with no bases to fix the phosphoric acid as an insoluble, even chemical tests often fail to detect its former presence. The use of fire may be shown only by sooty stones, reddened earth and the presence of charcoal, all traces of ash having been leached out. Even turf structures, such as the core of a barrow built out of sods, may be hard to recognize as such owing to the persistent oxidation and leaching, whereby originally humic matter tends to become degraded by the general bleaching of the podsol.

Since these sandy areas, which are often exposed, carry such a comparatively sparse vegetation, they have often been somewhat ex-posed to wind erosion, among other denuding agencies.

Sandy heaths normally have a fairly continuous cover of coarse vegetation under present-day climatic conditions, save where recent traffic or heath-fires have destroyed it, but in this case (or even when an unusually dry summer has killed the grasses) strong winds can effect considerable erosion in a short time. Such erosion generally takes the form of 'blowouts', steep-sided shallow depressions where the wind has been able to undermine the comparatively tenacious, if thin, humic layer at the surface and to work on the incoherent bleached layer of the profile. This must have happened even more extensively in the probably somewhat drier Boreal and Subboreal periods, in the former of which the Mesolithic cultures of western Europe flourished while the Bronze Age seems to have been contemporary with the other. As a consequence of this we seldom find Mesolithic industries or Bronze-Age material in an original stratified position, but almost always on the surface or near to it—sometimes, indeed, laid bare by wind-erosion.

The Mesolithic site at Abinger Manor, Surrey (Leakey, 1951) was only preserved under the plough-soil to the extent that the pit-dwelling was cut to some depth into the solid Greensand. Its discovery was due to the finding of numerous unstratified flints in the ploughed field. The work of the farmer was, here, only supplementing the natural processes of erosion which, sooner or later, would have exposed the material. Unless enclosed in the body of a mound or deliberately buried in the soil, as with hoards and urnfields, nearly all our Bronze-Age material is unstratified. Some chance discoveries, in unusual topographical circumstances, may yet give us stratified deposits in which the examination of the soil may lead to useful conclusions as to the environment of the time.

In such circumstances as have been described, little or nothing but the flint implements and, as at Abinger, pits and perhaps post-holes, will be preserved. If we hope materially to increase our knowledge of these periods, their people and their equipment, regard must be had to the soil conditions and such sites be chosen for excavation as through waterlogging, for example, may have preserved some organic remains. The same consideration applies to funeral monuments. Those on chalk or loam soils are more likely to add to our knowledge than those on sandy sites, though acid conditions preserve pollen-grains in the soil which are valuable indications of environment (Dimbleby, 1955).

Deposits on chalk and limestone subsoils

As in the case of inland hunter-fisher settlers the preference for sandy soils was economic, so for Neolithic and, to some extent also, for Bronze-Age peoples the preference for light calcareous soils was conditioned by their way of life.

Childe has shown that, on the Continent, their westward routes of advance followed the loess-belts, because this type of soil afforded comparatively open country, requiring the minimum of clearing for their agricultural operations as well as providing pasture for their beasts.

In England, loess is very local, but the Chalk Downs and other lime-stone areas afforded a correspondingly open environment for the early farmers, though one less fertile.

The Chalk, today, scarcely gives a true picture of its natural vegeta-tion. Centuries of occupation and use by man and his domestic animals —especially sheep and goats—have altered its character. Norman-imported rabbits have also taken their toll. These three grazers have this in common: that their tastes in diet are entirely catholic, so that no green thing comes amiss. Their influence on the Downland vegetation has been to make it difficult, or, if they are present in sufficient numbers, impossible, for trees to propagate themselves where not fenced.

The typical natural trees of the Chalk country are beech, hawthorn and yew. This is not to say that oak, ash and others do not occur. Now the beech forms so dense a canopy of foliage in summer that the mast which falls from it has but small chance of growing to maturity unless carried to a little distance from the parent. This office is performed by birds and rodents, especially squirrels and others which hoard winter supplies. A suitable site for a beech-seedling is at the edge of the wood, where, if left to itself, it will soon outgrow grass and herbs and obtain its proper share of light and air. So, in their own ways, do the other species also. The haws of the thorn, for example, are eaten by birds and the seeds are dispersed in their droppings.

Sheep, goats and rabbits feed chiefly on grass, which, when numerous, they keep mown down to a close sward. In so doing, they equally nibble off the tender shoots of any tree-seedlings which they may find. When grass is scarce, as in drought or snow, they will bark saplings and devour such of the twigs as they can reach. If often enough repeated, both these forms of attack are fatal to the young trees.

It is therefore clear that we must visualize the prehistoric Chalk country as more thickly wooded than today, though never covered with dense forest, owing to the porosity of chalk soils, their lack of moisture in dry weather and the exposure of the trees to the pruning and drying effect of wind on the heights. Thus there are, and were, areas, especially near the summits, where the soil-climate is rather that of steppe than of forest, producing a correspondingly poorer flora.

Indications as to climate in the Neolithic period of these Islands, perhaps two thousand years B.C., suggest one rather milder and more oceanic than at present. In these circumstances the Chalk would offer not only somewhat open parkland, but also well-drained dwelling-sites and practicable routes across country. By the Bronze Age, perhaps 1400 B.C., a more continental type of climate had intervened. We know exceedingly little about the domestic arrangements of Bronze-Age people in this country, but if the climatic inference that rainfall was less than it is today is valid, it seems likely that all limestone country was appreciably more arid than it is nowadays. The fact that Bronze-Age people sited their funeral monuments on the Chalk and high limestone hills (among other kinds of soil) is no proof that they lived there. No primitive community lives farther than it need from water and the fact that numerous round barrows are sited on gravel in river valleys (as at Cassington, Oxfordshire, for example) suggests that here the drier soils were but thinly forested and probably afforded pasture for animals not far from water. A guess drawn from these considerations would be that it is in the valleys (on the lighter, better-drained soils such as gravel), not on the hills, that we must seek Bronze-Age settlements. It has, of course, been suggested that the reason why we do not find permanent Bronze-Age dwellings is because they never existed. It is known that our Bronze-Agers were herdsmen and it is implied that they followed their flocks and herds, as do present-day nomads, living only temporarily here and there in tents. However that may be, it is certain that they did not build permanent houses on the Chalk.

The wetter Iron-Age climate, combined with evident consider-ations of defence, was a possible reason for a more intense reoccupation of the Chalk in that period, though the evidence from hill-fort excava-tions does not suggest that they were occupied as dwelling-sites for any length of time. Nevertheless, finds of the type of the Early Iron-Age farmstead at Little Woodbury (Bersu, 1940) throws a good deal of light on the economics of hill-farming of the time.

Whatever the soil or climate, hill-top sites are constantly subject to denudation. All material loosened by weather or by man's operations tends to wash or blow away downhill. In the case of prehistoric hill-sites, therefore, it is unlikely that a complete stratigraphical record will be preserved *in situ* unless the section happens to lie in a natural depression or in an artificial feature, such as a ditch or a pit cut into the subsoil. Prehistoric and later ploughing, besides the work of earth-worms, has been responsible for much widespread mixing of the upper 6 inches of soil and weathering and rainwash have often completed the work of levelling eminences, filling depressions and carrying away much that once may have lain there. Heavier and bulkier objects, such as quernstones, may remain in the place where they were once used, but not *in situ* in contemporary deposits, for these will long since have been removed by natural agencies.

An extreme case of this was to be seen at an Iron-Age site on the summit of a rounded limestone hill at Dainton, S. Devon (Willis & Rogers, 1951). The section was seldom more than a few inches deep, consisting of a thin turf, perhaps two inches of red-brown soil and the unaltered bedrock. In these circumstances any examination of the soil was clearly valueless. What was left merely represented the balance between present-day soil-formation and the contemporary processes of denudation. There was nothing to show that any of the soil was more than a few years old. Some collapsed dry-stone structures, perhaps hut-foundations, yielded a few finds, the preservation of which was eloquent of these conditions. Potsherds were small and their edges were eroded both by weather and by having long lain loose on the surface, under the feet of the human and animal traffic on the site. Animal and human bones, though in actual contact with the limestone, were marked and deeply etched by rootlets, having been only just below the turf ever since they were left there. The edges of ancient fractures (and, like the pottery, the bones were much comminuted) were so worn that even manifest joins could only be made to fit with great difficulty.

The soil formed on chalk or limestone is the chemical antithesis of that on sandy sites—base-rich, silica-poor, generally rather shallow and with a marked crumb-structure, tending to heaviness and stickiness where deep or where remains of Tertiary weathering-soils (e.g. 'Clay-with-flints') have survived. It varies enormously according to the lie of the land—thin and dry where eroded on slopes, thick and silty in the bottoms where it is constantly being added to by material conveyed from above. In neither case is the profile likely to be mature. Since it has frequently been under the plough from the earliest times, an undis-turbed soil is hardly ever seen even in the more level places, where one might expect to find a more typical profile. The natural climax-soil is a brownearth, in our climate, but the transitional type known as rendsina is more commonly found where unweathered chalk is at no great distance below the surface.

Volcanic deposits

While in Britain we have no evidence of local volcanic activity in human times, elsewhere important masses of deposits have been formed, covering and intercalated with archaeological remains. Pompeii and Herculaneum of course spring first to mind, but eruptions no less spectacular, if unwitnessed by literate peoples, have taken place both before and since Roman times, of which the deposits form part of sections interesting to archaeologists.

Volcanic action is accompanied by the emission of enormous volumes of gases and vapours from the vent, as well as the more permanent and obvious lava-flows. Indeed, it is the subterranean pressure of these, building up through the ages, which gives rise to the catastrophic explosions whose influence is more widespread than that of any lava-stream. When such a sudden release of pent-up pressures takes place, large volumes of molten rock are blown out of the crater, solidifying as they fly, and, according to their size, come to rest nearer or further from the volcano. The larger masses are called volcanic bombs, those of pebble-size lapilli and the finest particles ash or dust.

Now, should a stream of lava cover a site of human occupation, little indeed will be left that is recognizable to the archaeologist. Not only will the incandescent heat of it destroy much of the evidence, but the mechanical thrust and weight of its advance will level and crush structures, so that little will remain in position to testify to its former arrangement. Moreover, lava, when cold, forms hard and often very solid rock, which would have to be quarried away to expose anything lying beneath it. Only through such quarrying operations would the existence of archaeological remains come to be known.

Lapilli and ash, on the other hand, being already solidified by the time they reach the ground, remain as fairly loose sediments and present no serious difficulty to the excavator. The ash, in particular, being of fine grade and having perhaps been blown to a considerable height by an explosion, may continue air-borne for some time and be transported by winds for hundreds of miles before coming to earth as a recognizable deposit of mineral dust.

Such a layer of volcanic ash in an archaeological section may provide an important datum for correlation and dating of more than merely local validity.

An example known to the writer at first hand was a slightly grey layer in the Younger Loess III, no more than 1 cm. thick, seen in the famous loess section at Wallertheim, Rheinhessen, Germany (Zeuner, 1953). This showed uniformly in every part of the site and was thought from its appearance not to be due to weathering and soil-formation, though this was the first interpretation of Schmidtgen and Wagner, its discoverers. Tests showed the dark colour to be due to dark mineral particles, not to organic matter. The heavy minerals of a small sample were therefore separated by bromoform (p. 134) and a specimen of the concentrate was sent to Dr Frechen in Bonn, who was able to identify the assemblage with that of a late volcanic outburst well known in the Eifel district, many miles away. Similar dust of volcanic origin from the Eifel vents, of Late Glacial and Early Postglacial dates occur in geological and archaeological sections over a large area of South and Central Germany, where they form horizons, often datable by pollen analysis, both where they are found and at the craters whence they came. There must be many similar cases in regions of prehistoric and recent volcanic activity.

4

Neolithic and Later Periods

✦✦

WITH THE IMPROVEMENT of human control of the environment the deposits at archaeological sites yield progressively less natural evidence of environment and more of man's own activities.

On Neolithic and later sites the prehistorian begins to be mainly concerned with artificial structures in and on the soil, not so much with the soil itself and its natural contents, though these may, on occasion, be made to tell something which he will be grateful to learn.

Causewayed camps, megalithic tombs and monuments, round barrows, urnfields, hut-circles, farmsteads, hill-forts and stone-built 'castles'—all have their problems for the student of soils, but mainly problems different from those which the deposits of the earlier Stone Ages posed. The same sorts of problems are carried forward from prehistoric into historic times, with the added complications introduced by Roman roads, villas, towns, forts and cemeteries and the tombs and settlements of Angles, Jutes, Saxon and Danes—even to mediaeval sites.

With climate, fauna and flora not far removed from those of our own times, the fossil evidence for environment decreases in importance. Snails from a supposed Roman cellar cannot be expected to differ materially from the modern assemblage to be found living in a similar situation, but the conchologist may nevertheless be able to determine from excavated shells the micro-environment which proves the structure to have been dark and damp, thereby supporting its interpretation as a cellar.

As to soil-samples, the form of the questions asked by the excavator is likely to be more specific: 'Is this black layer due to burning, or does it represent organic matter?'; 'Why is this layer in a pit-filling greenish? Is it waste from copper-smelting?'; 'What was this organic matter? Could it have been tan-bark or leather?'; 'Please identify this substance'; 'Was there ever a body in this barrow?'

All too frequently, in the present state of our knowledge, the answers to such specific queries have to be inconclusive. For example, we know too little about what happens to various kinds of organic matter when they decay in the ground to characterize wastes from leather-manufacture unless some structure indicative of bark or leather is preserved or actual identifiable tannins remain. The chemical degradation-products of such things behave very like those of almost any other kind of organic matter, as, for example, natural humus in the soil.

Sometimes it can be said that investigation has ruled out one or more possibilities without confirming any other; occasionally, experimental results justify a firm answer 'Yes' or 'No', or a definite identification of the substance in question, but it is often necessary to confess that we cannot offer any definitive opinion on the phenomena observed in the field or in the laboratory.

In any soil-inquiry it is necessary to know all the relevant circumstances. If possible the investigator should have seen the deposits in the field, noted their present-day surroundings, studied modern soil-conditions and have taken his own samples from the actual sections. Failing this (and with the best will in the world the soil-man cannot visit every excavation from which he may receive samples) detailed drawings of sections to an approximate scale are indispensable and photographs in addition are an advantage. The exact position of every sample submitted should be shown on the drawn section. Samples from a natural soil-profile near the site should always accompany those from the site itself. In interpreting a barrow-section, for example, a knowledge of the undisturbed natural soil will prevent the ascription to human interference of some widespread natural phenomenon—a mistake which can very easily happen when the investigator has not seen the site himself.

From the Neolithic to the Iron-Age, in Western Europe at least, we are not often faced with the multiplicity of constructions, reconstructions, changes of plan in successive periods and deliberate levelling-off of earlier structures which are met with in later buildings. The Near Eastern city-sites, often continuously occupied from the earliest settlements up to historic times, are, of course, a different matter.

In our region, the plough has frequently only spared such structures and deposits as lay beyond its reach. If the soil is not deep, the disturbed zone may extend down to the very surface of the 'natural', leaving only ditches, pits and post-holes, which were cut more or less deeply into it, still containing archaeological deposits *in situ*. If we are more fortunate there may still remain at least a thin layer of undisturbed occupation deposit.

Pits and ditches cutting into the natural subsoil may sometimes have been filled and levelled deliberately in ancient times. Often, however, they were left open and the filling we find today has taken place chiefly by the working of natural agencies, assisted in many cases by the dumping of domestic and industrial rubbish by later inhabitants. The distinction between natural and artificial fillings is not always easy to make, for even natural fillings may contain artifacts which happened to be lying on the surface nearby.

It is worth while to consider in a little detail the natural process of filling of such artificial holes and depressions.

Natural filling of pits, ditches, etc.

As with all natural processes hitherto noticed, the material and mode of access of the filling will depend on local conditions at the time—on

D

soil, topography, climate, flora and, to a generally rather slighter extent, on fauna. On a settled site, the continued activities of man in the immediate vicinity will, from time to time, be superimposed on those of nature, giving the often extremely complicated stratification which may be observed in (say) the filling of the ditch of a hill-fort. To simplify matters a purely natural filling will first be considered.

In accordance with the larger processes of denudation and deposition, resulting, in the course of geological time-spans, in peneplanation of a whole countryside, even small eminences will tend to be degraded and every small depression become a site of accumulation. Nature abhors not only a literal vacuum, but any hollow place into which material can fall, or be swept, to fill and level it. Any relatively steep-sided hole dug by man is a direct violation of natural equilibrium and Nature, in her own methodical inexorable fashion, will at once set about eliminating it.

A question at once faces us. What did ancient man do with the excavated material? In the case of a barrow-ditch or the fosse of a ramparted earthwork the answer is obvious: he evidently piled it up as a mound over the burial or as a comparatively steep bank, even, perhaps, with its slope continuous with that of the ditch.

Almost before the constructors' backs were turned, a trickle of earth, drying out on the bank, might find its place at the bottom of the ditch. However well the bank was faced with turf or revetted with stone or timber, the first heavy rain would cause not trickles but muddy torrents to wash away all loose particles into the ditch, forming what the excavator calls the 'rapid silt'. This is, for all practical purposes, contemporary with the digging of the ditch. Once some seasons have passed and (in our climate) a close cover of vegetation has rooted in the newly turned earth, denudation of the bank and silting of the ditch slows down, so that even the first few inches after the rapid silt may have taken ten times as long to form. Indeed so slow may it become that vegetation will succeed in colonizing the sides and bottoms of the ditch at an early stage and a natural soil-profile begin to form on the silt.

If it be supposed that the excavated material was not wanted for any purpose by the diggers, but that the hole was intended as a pit, perhaps for the storage of grain, it would be left where it was, not far from the lip of the hole. In that position—and human nature being what it is, the pile of earth would seldom be taken away, or even scattered—it would readily be washed back, at least in part, into the hole. With autumn, a drift of leaves and other vegetable rubbish would find its way in. Frost, next, would play a part, loosening the walls and undermining the turf, so that the following spring drought and wind would bring the edges tumbling in (fig. 3, p. 58). A few years of this in not very coherent sandy soil would make a steep-sided ditch into a comparatively wide, shallow depression, in which grasses and herbs would take root and flourish, with an unaccustomed depth beneath them of fairly

loose, moist, humic soil. Solid Chalk or stone would degrade more
slowly and a heavy, loamy soil perhaps more slowly still. Once grassed
over, the further obliteration of the depression would, in any case, be
greatly retarded. Rainwash in heavy storms would, perhaps, be the most
potent factor, but soil-creep after frost and thaw and wind-blown dust
and rubbish would account for part of the filling.

Burrowing animals materially assist in the degrading of banks and
the filling of ditches. Loose soil thrown out of a burrow is ready to be
washed away, unlike that which is grass-covered and held together by
rootlets. Banks and ditch walls honeycombed by rats, rabbits and moles
are weakened and the larger diggers, such as foxes and badgers, can
move considerable volumes of earth. All loose material finds its way
sooner or later into the deepest depression nearby—the ditch or pit.

Though the work of mammals in disturbing the soil is evident, if
localized, it is generally only a minor factor in the denudation of a site.
The burrowers which are most often present in numbers, and to which
the largest influence on soil-formation and erosion is due, are the
earthworms.

Work of earthworms

The classic work on the subject is by the great Charles Darwin (1881),
who was long interested in the action of worms and who supplemented
his observations by experiment. Some of his more pertinent conclusions are summarized here, but the reader is strongly advised to refer
to the original work, which is full of matter of importance to archaeologists.

Darwin concluded that, in many parts of England, more than 10 tons
(dry weight) of earth per acre is annually brought to the surface as
worm-castings. If evenly distributed over the area, this would amount
to a layer 0.22 ins. thick.

Worms are present in the greatest numbers in rich, moderately basic
soil, where they can most easily obtain matter, vegetable or animal, for
their nourishment. Only in peaty and sandy soils poor in bases do most
species of worms seem unable to flourish. While the soil is moist they
are most active near the surface, but in times of frost and drought their
burrows penetrate to a depth of 6 feet and more. In compact soil they
burrow by swallowing the earth in front of them and in the absence
of cavities underground, which they quickly fill, they are obliged to
come to the surface to evacuate their castings. Thus, deeper unweathered materials are constantly being brought to the surface in small
quantities, while the humic layer near the surface, which affords worms
the greater part of their food, is completely passed and re-passed
through their bodies every few years. The characteristic crumbs, of
which many base-rich soils mainly consist (as do rendsinas, for example)
are composed almost exclusively of broken worm-castings. Conversely,
the clarity of the zonation of acid soils, such as the podsol group, is

largely due to the absence of most species of earthworms and to the lack of disturbance which their activity inevitably brings.

One effect of the bringing by worms of their castings to the surface is to sink into the soil, and eventually bury, any body lying on it which is too large to be swallowed by them. This sinking is assisted by the collapse, below, of old worm-tunnels and the falling in of the subsoil which has been penetrated by them. The resultant rate of sinking of stones and other bodies is commensurate with the surface accumulation and may amount to 0.2 ins annually.

This phenomenon is of the greatest interest to archaeologists. Evidently the rate of sinking decreases with depth, in accordance with the decreasing frequency of penetration by worms below the actual humic layer, in which they normally feed, but it explains how loose objects lying on the surface sink, in a few years, below the turf and eventually become buried to a depth of a foot or two.

An example of this was visible to the writer in Regent's Park, immediately outside the laboratory window. About 1952, the authorities of the Park lifted a small area of turf near the ruins of a glazed conservatory and carried it away. Immediately below the grass-roots was exposed an area thickly covered with splinters of broken glass, evidently the product of bomb-blast on the conservatory. Only seven years had passed since the last possible date in 1945 when the damage could have occurred (but in fact it was known to have happened two or three years before that). The turves removed were about 1½ ins. thick, so that within ten years or so the glass scattered on the surface had sunk to that depth—entirely through the activity of worms. The workmen left the patch bare and its re-turfing has been entirely unassisted by man. At the time of writing (1956) the patch is indistinguishable from any other adjacent part of the park and the wartime 'destruction-layer' (as the excavator would call it) is once more out of sight. Family parties picnic there on summer afternoons unaware of the layer of broken glass on which they are sitting, so obligingly and tidily buried by the assiduous earthworms!

Darwin's observations of worms, and those of his sons, extended to actual archaeological sites, so that some of their conclusions touch the excavator and the student of soils most nearly.

It was shown that, once worms are able to penetrate ancient structures (e.g. the cement of walls or the concrete backing of a tessellated pavement), even these are involved in the undermining and sinking to which loose objects, and even heavy standing or recumbent stones, are subject. A level pavement tends to sink like a saucer in the middle, but is supported at the edges, where it is anchored to walls with deeper foundations. Save where very deeply founded, walls themselves are undermined and the masonry riddled with worm-burrows. Any cavities left by the builders are filled with the acid castings and these, in time, help to disintegrate the lime mortar.

The mixing by worms of fine material in the upper six feet or so of soil evidently causes some blurring of the stratification on an archaeological site, but will not ever affect the relative sequence of objects, such as coins or sherds, too large to be swallowed by them. Since, with increasing depth below the surface, the frequency of undermining by worms and the consequent eventual sinking of objects grows less, objects higher in the section will tend to overhaul those below them in the 'sinking-race'. The logical conclusion of the process would be to assemble all particles above a certain minimum size in a single layer at such a level that worms no longer *ever* undermined them! So slow does their further downward progress become after the first few inches, however, that the periods of time elapsed since they were first abandoned by man have not been nearly sufficient for the process to approach completion. Thus the stratification of objects left at different periods on the surface may be slightly *compressed*: it can never be *inverted* or *obliterated* by worms. Excavators may therefore take courage. The earthworms have not yet succeeded in undermining the main prop on which they rest their interpretation of stratification on archaeological sites—the *succession*!

The reality of this sinking of larger particles in the soil when earthworms are present in numbers may be seen in any section which has not been disturbed by the plough. It is particularly well exhibited in sections of soils of the rendsina type on Chalk, for the larger white-coated flints and chalk fragments in the section show up very well against the dark grey-brown humic portion. (Fig. 2).

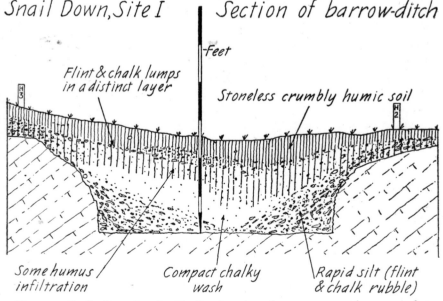

FIG 2.   A ditch-section in Chalk, showing the upper stoneless zone due to earthworm activity.

In a freshly-made barrow-mound, for example, flints and Chalk rubble are mixed at random through the whole mass. As the mound becomes turfed over and a soil begins to form, those larger particles near the surface begin to sink and a quite stoneless layer of worm-castings begins to appear just under the turf. Given time enough (a few centuries), this stoneless layer will grow to several inches in thickness and there will be some concentration of the white larger particles at the summit of the rubbly part of the section, while below it the distribution of stones will remain as random as when the mound was first built.

Should the mound be added to at a later date, fresh rubbly material will be heaped over the stoneless upper layer of this soil, its random stoniness in sharp visible contrast with the buried soil. Eventually a second soil will form on the freshly-added material, which, if more than a few inches thick, will not for many centuries involve the now buried former surface in any changes. Its characteristic stonelessness will make it stand out clearly in the section as a buried soil-surface, a quality not possibly to be interpreted as artificial, unless we conclude that the barrow-builders had put all the earth casing the first mound through a fine riddle!

For one who interests himself in the chemical and microscopic characters of soils from archaeological sites, the mixing by worms of the upper part of the profile does represent a real danger of falling into errors. Suppose the question to be whether a particular layer is of natural or artificial origin: it is doubtful whether it may justifiably be resolved by the presence or absence in it of charcoal, plaster, crumbs of brick or other artificial material—*of microscopic proportions*. These *could* have been swallowed and transported by worms, so that the presence of only a few, and very small, artificial grains must be judged with caution and with regard to the contents of adjacent levels. Any large amount of foreign material, or a single particle too large to be swallowed by worms, would indicate a probably artificial origin. The uncertainty even of this conclusion is due to the possibility of derivation of foreign particles through natural agencies other than worms, e.g. larger burrowers.

Silting of sites backed by a slope

Thus far a level site has been envisaged. Where there is any significant gradient of the surface, transport by rain-wash will, of course, follow the steepest slope. Darwin's measurements showed that, on a grassy slope inclined 9° 26′ to the horizontal (just over 1 in 6), 1.84 ozs. of fine soil, largely derived from worm-castings, would annually cross a horizontal line 1 yd. long by the agencies of rainwash and wind. Over the long periods of time considered by the prehistorian, and even more those concerning the geologist, the movement of such a bulk of soil represents very considerable denudation of surface eminences and levelling of depressions.

Natural silting of archaeological sites at the foot of a slope may be very rapid. The well-known Roman villa at Lullingstone (Meates, 1955) is situated a little above the flood-plain of the River Darent, where it cuts through the North Downs to enter the Thames valley. The site is close to the foot of a slope of Chalk covered with flinty 'hill-wash'. The present gradient of the slope is, by rough measurement, close to 1 in 4 (about 15°). While the villa was occupied, up to the end of the fourth century A.D. and for a time afterwards, silting was fairly slow. However, from the time of Edward II (1307-27), shown by coins in the mediaeval deposits, up to the present day, some 5 feet or more of stony hillwash have accumulated above the hillward part of the site, thinning out rapidly towards the river. The thickness of deposit covering the far end of the fourth-century mosaic pavement was no more than 18 inches. Probably the foot of the steep slope stood some yards further back in Roman times and the occupants may have maintained some sort of a retaining wall or bank to prevent the advance of slope deposits on to the site. It took perhaps a thousand years for the first 2 feet of debris to cover the Roman structures, but with the advance of the active slope, built out by talus, the rate of deposit was nearly quadrupled from the fourteenth century onwards. The deposit was almost entirely natural.

This is an extreme case of accumulation, as was that of Dainton (see p. 45) for denudation. Both serve to show the necessity for taking position and gradient into account in judging archaeological deposits.

Rainwash on a slope may be the most evident and persistent transporting agency in our moist climate, but it was not alone responsible for the Lullingstone accumulation. A heavy thunderstorm in the summer of 1956 caused a sudden flood to pour down the hill-side, filling the excavators' trenches to the brim within a very few minutes. When it abated the diggers ceased to tear their hair and lament the cataclysm and went to inspect the damage. To their relief things were not as bad as had been feared. The worst feature was the presence of some 2 feet of pure, stoneless clayey silt in all the deeper parts of the excavation, which, when somewhat dried out, shrank and cracked and was removed without great difficulty though with considerable labour. The event, however, was most instructive.

Even in a notably wet summer a torrential downpour followed by a veritable cataract of water pouring down the hill on to the site produced a layer of deposit, of imposing thickness indeed, but *not containing a single pebble*, save where the concentrated waterfall had poured down a vertical face in one corner. Clearly, the large flint cobbles in the stony 'wash' covering the site were not transported by rainwash, however torrential. Some other agency had to be invoked. That agency could only be solifluction, the result of frost and thaw.

The influence of even comparatively rare hard frosts on erosion and deposition is sudden and often very great. Railway and road-cuttings, both in Chalk and London Clay, were much damaged by the exceptional cold in the first three months of the year 1947. In the former this was due to the fall of considerable masses of frost-weathered chalk, producing a veritable coombe rock; in the latter it took the form of miniature land-slides when the thaw began to loosen the upper part of the surface while deeper layers were still frozen.

Now, the last twenty-five years have provided perhaps five memorably cold winters, when something little short of 1947's events could have happened. Discounting minor climatic variations, which have, perhaps, affected the issue equally to either side of the average, one may count twenty cold winters in a century, 200 in a millennium. Each event lasts, probably, only a few weeks at the most, but the whole adds up, if 1947 is a fair example, to a notable total of weathering and soil-displacement from this cause. It is fairly certain, therefore, that the access of much of the coarser material, of the size of coarse gravel and cobbles, covering archaeological sites and filling hollows, is due to frost and thaw rather than to rain.

Ditch and pit-fillings of mainly natural origin often contain a fair proportion of coarser, gravelly material. If even heavy rain is incapable of transporting pebbles on any scale, save locally where a downpour gives rise to a temporary surface stream of some volume and velocity, it must follow that the coarse material in these fillings is probably also chiefly the product of solifluction and soil-creep due to frost and thaw. If, however, there is no important slope in the ground, the source of the materials must be quite local, generally the lips and edges of the pit or ditch itself.

This leads to another consideration of some importance in the interpretation of ditch-profiles. If the coarse materials come mainly from the lip of the ditch by loosening and tumble, the profile of the ditch, as originally cut, must be different from that found by the excavator, for a ditch with sides originally vertical will in the end come to present a somewhat open V-shaped profile (Fig. 3, p. 58). This is nearly always the form found by the archaeologist, who should nevertheless give some consideration to its having once had vertical sides. If the filling should contain much coarse material which could not easily have come from elsewhere, there is a high degree of probability that we are not seeing, today, the profile originally cut.

Wind-borne ditch-fillings

In Britain at the present day wind plays but a small part in accumulating sediments, at least inland. In sandy areas there may be some deflation in dry summers, but, for the most part, important accumulations elsewhere do not result even from this local wind-erosion.

Steep-sided depressions and ditches of archaeological sites on sandy heaths may have received some proportion of their fillings from this source, but elsewhere, since the Subatlantic climate set in in Early Iron

Age times, the prevailing moisture and tenacity of the soil and its cover of vegetation have prevented this.

It was, however, noted at Cassington, near Oxford, in 1946, that the ring-ditch of an Early Bronze-Age barrow was filled with a practically stoneless, unstratified reddish-brown loam. In view of the fact that the 'natural', below some 8 inches of stony brown loam (plough-soil), was a fine yellow gravel, the stonelessness of the ditch-filling was truly remarkable and perhaps points to wind as the depositing agency. This, in its turn, suggests that the climate, at the time when the ditch was open, was somewhat warmer and drier, at any rate in summer, than it is today, without which one can hardly conceive of wind-borne sediment being plentiful enough to fill even a shallow ditch so completely. Such conditions would correspond to those postulated by the climatologists for the Subboreal phase (a climate of more continental type than that of today), which appears to have prevailed during at least part of the Bronze Age in Britain.

Unless man interferes, the natural processes of erosion of eminences and filling of depressions will go on at a rate decreasing according to an exponential curve, in accordance with the decrease of the gradients which activate the transporting agencies. In the case of funerary monuments, where there is no sign of occupation, they were apparently left to the forces of nature once they had been erected. Later interference is generally confined to the intrusion of secondary burials in the mound or its environs, already ancient and vaguely hallowed, by succeeding generations living nearby. Occasionally there is evidence of reconstruction and addition to a mound at a later time, but this is not so frequently the case here as has been found in the Netherlands (Modderman, 1954). On habitation-sites and defensive works, however, the hand of man is constantly seen at work, aiding or counteracting that of nature. This is seen in the reconstruction of ramparts, deliberate filling of former ditches which had outlived their usefulness or did not conform with the new plan, and in the rebuilding of domestic structures in different periods, often to quite different plans.

Artificial fillings

It seems that pits were dug to contain grain and other stores and, when they eventually became too foul for this purpose, rubbish and ashes were dumped into them, together with more or less natural soil-material, either from the digging of the pit itself or from some other opened nearby to replace it at the time when the first was abandoned.

A common feature of rubbish pits of all ages, cut in sand, gravel or loam of a ferruginous nature, is a zone of some discoloration of the 'natural' enclosing the pit-filling proper. In the case of a pit on the site of the Anglo-Saxon town of Hamwih (Southampton) the natural soil was a gravel of a bright yellow-brown colour, but a zone some inches thick immediately contiguous to the pit-filling was coloured a pale

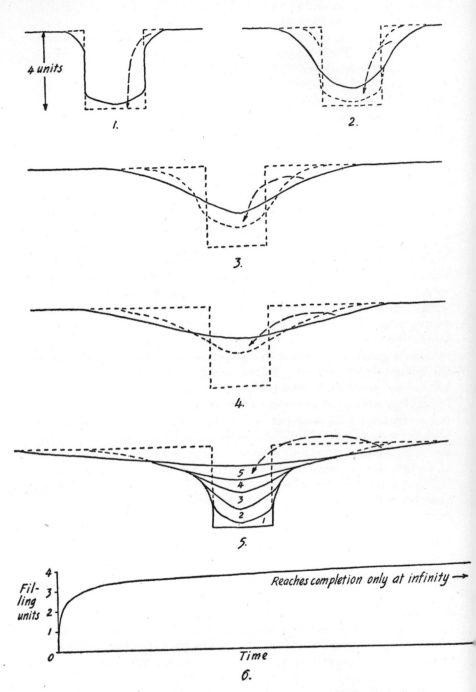

FIG 3. Theoretical process of filling of a vertical-sided ditch.

Explanation of Figure 3

The drawings suggest five arbitrary stages in the filling of a vertical-sided ditch, 4 units in depth and 3 wide, dug in a horizontal ground-surface, the spoil having been removed to such a distance that it takes no part in the re-filling during the span of time covered by the experiment.

(1) The lips of the ditch weather and crumble. Their falling-in probably takes place in a single season, forming the 'rapid silt'.

(2) Several years, perhaps a decade, have now passed. The filling continues to be supplied mainly by the steeper parts of the retreating lip, so that even the wall, just above the 'rapid silt' has receded a little, before being buried and protected from further degradation by the growing filling.

(3) At this stage perhaps a century has elapsed. The ditch is already nearly half filled and further material is now being derived from a distance between 3 and 4 units of length from the original lip on both sides. Vegetation grows at the bottom and a soil is forming at the summit of the filling.

(4) The ditch is represented only by a wide, shallow depression when (say) a millennium has passed, slowly drawing the material for its filling from an ever-increasing distance.

(5) This is the stage at which the archaeologist cuts a section today. Several millennia (but less than ten) have elapsed since it was dug and evidently it still has a long natural future, if undisturbed, as a diminishing depression.

The ditch section which we see describes an exponential curve of filling against time (see (6)). Evidently, in theory, the depression will be obliterated and the level surface be exactly restored only after an infinite time-lapse. Even after some $3\frac{1}{2}$ millennia, most undisturbed Early Bronze-Age ditches are still clearly perceptible to the eye at the surface.

The proximity of a mound or bank of spoil would complicate matters and, once involved, would eventually increase the rate of filling again, by increasing the activating gradient for rain-wash and soil-creep. Ploughing of the surface would also accelerate levelling, as would any notable access of wind-borne material from some distance. The case is thus over-simplified, and it is doubtful whether the theory which it illustrates has any practical application for dating purposes, enticing though it is as an idea!

It is not suggested that all prehistoric ditches once had vertical sides, though some may have. In that case we should not expect to find them so now.

The Snail Down, Site I, ditch section (Fig. 2, p. 53) very well shows the profile of one which may have belonged to this class.

greenish grey. The filling itself was dark grey-brown and contained a great deal of organic matter. The change in colour of the ferruginous 'natural' was attributable to the reduction of the iron salts from the ferric to the ferrous condition by the decomposing rubbish, in the absence of a sufficient supply of air for full oxidation of the organic matter. Under these conditions, it may also have been due to the formation of metallic (chiefly iron) sulphides by hydrogen sulphide released by the processes of anaerobic decay. There was no doubt that this dark zone formed part of the pit-wall *in situ* and it was continuous in texture with the unchanged yellow-brown subsoil.

Fillings of defensive ditches are, on the whole, natural, but from time to time, when their defensive function seemed to lose importance in peaceful periods, they became partly filled and grassed over. Rubbish and material dug from elsewhere was dumped in them and, to judge from the occurrence of hearths in the sections of their fillings, people even lived in them sometimes. With a renewed threat of attack by some enemy, the ditch might again be hastily cleared and deepened, perhaps incompletely or not cut to the same profile as before, so that a portion of the original filling was left standing. Thus, the stratification of such a ditch may be of considerable complexity, the natural sediments being interspersed with hearths and dumped rubbish—ashes, food-waste, bones, broken pottery or industrial wastes like iron slag—with immature soils forming in periods of neglect or abandonment. In all this, the examination of samples will identify the materials and possibly elucidate the nature and manner of formation of particular layers—differentiating, for example, an incipient soil, representing a period of neglect, from a dark layer due to included charcoal, iron or manganese, which may signify an actual domestic occupation.

If a pit or ditch is artificially filled in a single operation, there will be some later consolidation and sinking of the filling. Visible streaks or layers of different materials, even if originally horizontal, will tend to sag in the middle and form festoons. The sagging may further involve subsequently-formed deposits, whether natural or artificial, covering the pit. Even walls and structures of later date may be affected. This is a sure sign of a deliberate filling. Natural fillings slowly consolidate as they are formed.

Post-holes

Post holes are a constant feature of sites where there were houses or other timber constructions, such as gates or palisades. Sometimes the posts were withdrawn when their usefulness in these structures declined, when the holes were usually filled with any convenient rubbish to hand, or even with clean, freshly dug material. On other occasions, the post rotted in position. If soil-conditions are not too unfavourable to its preservation, a concentration of humus in the filling is some evidence that the post has so rotted. This is exceedingly difficult to prove, however. Organic matter might be due not only to a rotted post but to adventitious organic matter in the material used to fill a hole from which the post had first been pulled. To answer such a question with any confidence, we need to know far more about the constitution of soil-humus and to learn, if possible, to distinguish this from the degradation-products of wood and of other organic substances possibly intruded with an artificial filling.

Carbonization of wood
and other mainly carbohydrate materials

An important point must be made here. Excavators sometimes submit a sample labelled: 'Filling of post-hole with remains of carbonized wood'. Examination in such cases hardly ever shows the presence of any significant amount of free carbon.

It appears to be widely supposed that wood and other vegetable matter, such as fibres and food-grains, can be carbonized by the mere processes of time and decay. Humified remains of wood may be almost black, but such rotted and amorphous material will give a deep brown or black extract to boiling caustic soda, showing the presence of much uncarbonized alkali-soluble organic matter. Carbon (i.e. charcoal) will not give this test if clean. Charcoal, especially when finely divided, will adsorb humic matter from percolating solutions which it will yield again to soda, but the amount generally found from this source is but a fraction of that to be obtained by soda from even a tiny fragment of humified wood. Carbon is produced, within the span of human times, only by heating to a fairly high temperature, as by fire, or by the action of concentrated sulphuric acid—*not* present in nature or available to prehistoric man! How coal is formed is another matter. It is the visualization of coal as the end-product of originally humic matter which probably gave rise to the misconception. Some hundreds of millions of years, great pressure from overlying strata and possibly sub-crustal heat have played a part in the carbonization of coal, of which the bituminous varieties are not even today completely carbonized.

Helbaek (1953) supports this view as far as concerns prehistoric grains and plant-remains.

A large mass of rapidly-fermenting vegetation, as in a compost-heap, may heat up sufficiently to carbonize the centre of the pile, but this cannot apply to posts or any poorly-insulated organic body where the heat of decomposition can readily be lost as it is evolved.

Of course, the base of a post forming part of a wooden structure destroyed by fire might well be charred in the hole and so be preserved, but such cases are comparatively uncommon. Another possibility is that the builders deliberately charred the buried parts of their posts to stave off decay. It is an ancient practice, but to the writer's knowledge there is no evidence of this known from British prehistoric sites.

In waterlogged places the actual wood of posts and piles has a good chance of preservation, but in drier situations, and especially in calcareous soil, wood is likely to lose all trace of structure and be reduced, if anything at all survive, to an amorphous substance of crumbly consistency indistinguishable, in the present state of our information, from soil-humus. A beautiful instance of the contrast in preservation of charred and uncharred wood in calcareous surroundings was observed by Nicholas Thomas at Snail Down, Wilts. In one of the round barrows excavated was found what appeared to be a hollow tube of charcoal. This proved to have been a timber of some size which had only been partly consumed by fire before being buried under the chalk mound. Decay of the uncarbonized heart of the log, assisted by feeding worms, had removed all trace of wood, while its charred exterior preserved its original form and dimensions.

5

Building and Industrial Materials

✦✦✦✦✦✦✦✦✦✦✦✦✦✦✦✦✦✦✦✦✦✦✦✦✦✦✦✦✦✦✦✦✦✦✦✦✦✦✦

WHERE AVAILABLE, wood was the most important building material from the earliest times. Its felling and working with stone implements was a matter of great labour in the earlier periods. Consequently, only the framework of prehistoric buildings would be made of considerable timbers, while something less expensive in terms of time and labour would serve for the walls—wattle hurdling, thatch or clay-daub—supported and reinforced with smaller stakes and uprights which had no part in the support of the main structure. Roofs would, almost certainly, be thatched with reeds, straw or heather, or be covered with bark or hides.

Unfortunately, a great deal of this description is necessarily conjectural, or based on modern primitive analogy. Seldom indeed is anything but the bare ground-plan preserved, as indicated by post-holes, from which something may be deduced of the upper part of the original structure, as in the case of the Iron-Age farmstead buildings at Little Woodbury, Wilts. (Bersu, 1940).

In our climate, unprotected wooden structures above ground, once exposed to weather, rot away without trace in a few years. Only in bogs, as, for example, at Glastonbury Lake-Village (Bulleid and Gray, 1911-17), do we find much detail to support our theoretical picture, but it is not impossible, in the case where a building has been burnt, that carbonized remains of some of its perishable parts should be preserved. We assume, for example, that roofs of prehistoric buildings were thatched, though there does not seem to be, in this country, much direct evidence to support the assumption. Carbonized thatch, or even its impression in clay, afterwards fired to hardness, might be expected to survive with luck. One sample of this kind was indeed submitted during the war to the Dept. of Environmental Archaeology of the London Institute of Archaeology (as it then was) but it was unfortunately lost through enemy action.

Wattle-and-daub is better authenticated. Though the hurdling itself is seldom preserved—waterlogged sites provide the only examples—its impression in clay daub is found, especially where the building has been fired and the daub has been baked so as almost to resemble pottery. Since the daub is composed largely of the materials of the local soil or subsoil, there is seldom anything to distinguish it from the rest of the archaeological deposits unless it retains some structural impression, of timbers or hurdles. In a case where clay has been dug,

even at only a very short distance from the actual site, it might be possible to identify fragments of daub, if it differs mineralogically or in
state of weathering from the bulk of the deposits.

As with daub on a foundation of hurdles and stakes, so with pisé
(adobe) construction, tamped down between two temporary shutters
of timber or hurdle. The technique, requiring considerable quantities
of relatively cohesive material, was only employed where such material
was readily available close by—i.e. in clayey or heavy loamy country.
It is not known, therefore, in the prehistoric period since, as has been
made clear, the heavier soils were too thickly forested for occupation
by farmers equipped only with primitive agricultural implements.
When ox-drawn iron ploughs first made possible the occupation of
the heavy lands in Roman times, the timbered house with pisé walls
was developed and survives to the present day. A wall so constructed
may differ in no particular from the local soil, save where it abutted on
the main timbers of the building and so preserved their form and
texture.

In districts where the local rock was adapted to it, structures were,
from the earliest times, raised in dry masonry. One need only refer to
the retaining walls and kerbs of barrows and cairns, the bulk of the
mound consisting of loose earth or stone rubble. In later times, we have
round huts, like those of Grims Pound, Dartmoor, revetments for hill-
fort ramparts and veritable strongholds like the 'castles' of Chun and
Chysauster, Cornwall, or the brochs of the Scottish Highlands and
Islands. The stones, being invariably local, are indistinguishable from
the country rock save in their artificial disposition. In some cases, where
fire was used, the oxidative changes undergone by heated stones may
indicate domestic or industrial use. Very occasionally 'foreign' stones
require identification and determination of their possible provenance,
when no natural agency can be credited with their transport. This is,
in any case, a task for a petrologist and does not come within the scope
of soil-investigations.

Roman civilization brought to England the techniques of construction in laid masonry, concrete, plaster, *opus signinum* and other
pavings at least partly of imported or artificial materials. The manufacture of bricks and roofing- and flue-tiles replaced natural materials
and introduced new comfort in living. These concern the student of
soils less than the specialist in building materials, to whom reference
should be made for an opinion on matters of technique. It is likely,
however, that fragments, or even considerable masses, of these substances may occur in soil-samples, so that the investigator ought to be
conversant with their appearance and properties and be able to recognize them as artifacts. Just as with undressed stone used in human
constructions, so with building stones, tesserae, ornamental and paving
slabs and so on: only the petrologist and building specialist can be
expected to identify their material with confidence, though it would

not be amiss for a soil-man engaged with samples from a Roman site to be acquainted with at least some favoured industrial and ornamental stones, such as the grey vesicular Niedermendig Lava imported for querns or the Purbeck 'Marble' (a shelly limestone) used for facing and paving. These two, in particular, were brought from some distance to many sites—the lava from the Eifel region of the Rhineland, the 'marble' from the Isle of Purbeck on the Dorset coast. Whenever possible, however, the Roman builder naturally used local materials, where suitable for his purpose. The white tesserae of the Lullingstone, Kent, pavement (Meates, 1955), forming perhaps two thirds of the whole number used, were made from Chalk Rock, a widespread hard layer from the base of the Upper Chalk, doubtless exposed not far from that villa.

While wood, stone, bone and other plant and animal materials not so easily identified had served man for all his equipment up to the Neolithic stage, the coming of bronze and, even more, of iron, widened his industrial and economic horizon.

It has been shown by Childe that bronze was, in prehistoric times, a rare and expensive metal, available only to the prosperous, and that only comparatively few favoured areas in Europe yielded copper and tin ores for its manufacture. Consequently, only very occasionally can soil-samples be expected to yield evidence of bronze metallurgy and founding. One example came from the Anglo-Saxon town of Thetford, Norfolk, where a sample was found to be completely impregnated with salts of copper, whose presence had preserved quantities of small natural objects—hazel-nut shells, fish-bones—which had elsewhere perished in that porous sandy soil. No significant form could be elicited from this mass, possibly caused by decay of some metallic object, but more probably some sort of waste from bronze-working. Another sample from Thetford was clearly slag from bronze-smelting, so that it is known that the industry was carried on there.

Unlike the raw materials of bronze, iron-ore occurs in workable quantities very much more commonly, so that, though the metal is more difficult to smelt, once the technique became known its manufacture and use quickly became widespread, even for industrial and agricultural implements.

Thus, while the presence in a sample of copper compounds is certainly in most places a proof of artificiality, even if only of the corrosion of some object of the metal, iron is almost ubiquitous in nature—hardly any soil-sample is free from it—and its mere presence tells us nothing. In order to discern the existence of iron objects or an iron-working industry their form or particular attributes (such as the heat-glazed surfaces of fragments of slag) must be sought. Even a heavy local concentration of iron-salts may be quite natural, as witness the iron-pan formed in the podsol-type of soil. Even on Chalk, of which the mass is relatively free from iron, a concentration of iron-rust in a

E

prehistoric context is not necessarily artificial for the Chalk contains here and there nodules of pyrites (iron sulphide) which, on exposure, may decay and yield a quantity of ferric oxide.

Of industrial materials, pottery is, of course, one of the most important, because it is practically indestructible if reasonably well fired and is found on every site of pottery-using peoples whatever the soil-conditions and however poverty-stricken the rest of the finds. Apart from form and finish, the features which most interest the archaeologist, the composition of the ware and the mineralogical state of its constituents, may afford information about the provenance of the clay and the techniques of its preparation, working and firing. Such an inquiry is for the specialist in ceramics and for the mineralogist.

Glass, again, is a subject for specialist study, but fragments of it occurring in soils should be identifiable, as by a hardness-test and by its isotropic character under the crossed nicols of a petrological microscope.

A curious phenomenon was observed in one case of a piece of Roman window-glass submitted. A pattern on its surface was at first thought to be artificial, but proved by experiment to be natural etching-out, by weathering, of minute superficial cracks, formed when the pane was originally broken. This had the appearance of fine herringbone engraving, but was faithfully reproduced when a piece of modern glass, superficially cracked by bomb-blast, was boiled for some days in concentrated caustic soda, to simulate the solvent effects of soil and weather over the centuries.

Among other industrial remains, Anglo-Saxon Thetford yielded a lump of dark glass 'metal', which had solidified in a crucible and retained its form. It was labelled 'Dark, pitch-like substance' but its weight showed at once that it could not be pitch, jet or any organic substance, though it had a conchoidal fracture like these where it had been battered. The hardness, incombustibility and smoky green translucence of a thin edge showed it to be glass. It was therefore passed on to a specialist for examination. The surface of the object was somewhat decayed and showed a dull patina, so that its true nature was not obvious without seeing a fresh fracture and testing a chip detached from it.

Other decorative materials, such as amber, jet or shale may be found in soil-samples. Once one is conversant with their appearance they are easily recognized and any doubt may be allayed by simple chemical tests.

In many of early man's industrial processes, such as metallurgy, glassmaking or pottery-manufacture, the use of fire plays its essential part. Since wood was the almost universal fuel, industrial sites must invariably have given rise to masses of wood-ash. Generally all that remains of this to be recognized by the excavator is unconsumed charcoal, but if the accumulation is large enough and especially where the natural soil is calcareous some of the recognizable constituents of wood-ash should survive. In only one case known to the writer, however, has a sample labelled 'ash' by an excavator proved really to be wood-ash. This was, again, from Thetford. Generally, unburnt charcoal, fire-cracked stones and the characteristic reddening by oxidation and de-hydration of clay or other sediment with a considerable iron-content are the only reliable indications of fire.

The reason for this becomes clear when the chemical nature of wood-ashes is investigated. In the case of the Thetford samples, from massive grey calcareous layers found in many sections all over the site, the re-semblance to ashes was so striking that there appeared to be little doubt about the correctness of the excavator's interpretation of them. However, no reference-book available to the writer gave any indication of the nature of wood-ash, so a rough analysis of some fresh fire-ashes from a wood-burning hearth was carried out. The great bulk of the material proved to be calcium carbonate, with considerable calcium sulphate, magnesium and iron salts and the soluble carbonates of sodium and potassium, which could not be expected to survive on an archaeological site open to the weather. Now, all these, even the calcium sulphate, are somewhat soluble in distilled (e.g. rain-) water, even more so in weakly acid solutions. Unless, therefore, the soil is itself calcareous, or the ashes present in such volumes that there has not been time for their complete solution (the Thetford situation), little or nothing will remain stably in the soil save charcoal, which is chemi-cally almost indestructible at ordinary temperatures.

With this information, examination of all the Thetford samples gave analyses strictly comparable with the modern ash, save that the alkali carbonates, which are very soluble, had been leached out almost com-pletely. It nevertheless appears that calcium sulphate is the only con-stituent present in more than small traces which one would not expect to find in soils under our climate. With the caution that sulphate from plaster may be present on later (e.g. Roman) sites, this seems to be the most hopeful way of identifying ash where other, natural, sources of sulphates can be excluded. It will not do for climates, such as that of Jericho, for example, where, under almost desert conditions, gypsum (calcium sulphate) accumulates in the soil.

The cracked and shattered flints known as 'potboilers' are familiar to archaeologists. They were heated in the fire and thrown, red-hot, into vessels which would not stand direct heating in order to boil water or other contents of the pots. The characteristic 'crackled' surface is due to sudden superficial contraction on immersion in cold water. Flints or other siliceous stones heated to a high temperature in contact with wood-ash, which, as we have seen, contains potash and lime, are some-times found bearing a fine glaze. These are generally not 'crackled', having cooled gradually as the fire died down.

The glaze is a true glass, due to fusion of the surface at a bright red heat in combination with the alkali and the lime. No doubt, the observation of some such accidental glazing was the foundation of the idea of deliberate application of a glaze to pottery. Crushed flint or fine sand, mixed with wood-ash in some kind of organic excipient or clay-slip would yield an application fusible to a glaze on firing at a temperature considerably below that necessary for the biscuit-firing of the pot. Any iron present in the minerals—almost certain to be there—would give an elegant bottle-green colour to the glaze.

Preservation of organic matter in archaeological deposits

Under certain conditions, not always easily defined, original organic substances or breakdown-products of them can survive for very long periods in the soil.

Some instances of such remarkable preservation have been quoted in preceding sections, but it will be useful here to summarize the known facts and to point out directions in which further research might yield valuable results.

A rather special case is presented by the wooden objects and leather garments preserved from the Bronze Age in the copper-mining sites of Upper Austria (Pittioni, 1951). These owe their survival to the inability of organisms of decay to live in the presence of certain concentrations of copper salts, a well-known property used by horticulturists when they spray their fruit-trees against fungi with 'Bordeaux Mixture', a suspension of copper and calcium hydroxides in water. In such cases, the actual objects and substances have been preserved sufficiently well for their recognition by archaeologists and their nature is not in doubt.

Even when the actual substance of the object has not persisted, there will be little doubt possible as to its original nature when it has been preserved as a natural cast or mould. This is generally due to the deposition of some other substance in or round it while it still retained sufficient shape to leave an impression. Such are the leaf-impressions in travertine or lake-clays, the natural internal cast of the braincase in the first-discovered *Australopithecus* skull, grain-impressions in pottery and textile-weaves preserved in the corrosion-products of iron or bronze objects, with the surface of which the original material was in contact as it decayed.

An outstanding case, not alas, saved from destruction before it could be properly treated, was reported in connection with the discovery of the skull and bones of the Rhodesian Man, at Broken Hill Mine (Elliot Smith, 1927). Not only the bones were in reasonably good condition, impregnated with preservative metallic salts, but a mould of the entire body, in the flesh, was formed round it by the matrix of the cave-filling before decay.

The preservation of vegetable substances in peat-bogs and other waterlogged situations is, by now, common knowledge, though the chemistry involved has never been fully expounded, but it is less well known that even animal remains, apart from the bones, can, in certain circumstances, survive.

Some fairly general principles can be laid down to explain the observed phenomena.

With free access of moisture and oxygen, most organic matter quite quickly undergoes chemical and bacterial decomposition, which result in the breakdown of its complex constituents (proteins, fats, etc.) into simple substances such as water, carbon dioxide, nitrogen and mineral salts. If either oxygen or water is excluded, the processes of decay slow down and may, eventually, come to a halt. In poorly aerated surroundings animal substances like leather can survive almost unchanged, to all appearances, fats may be converted into adipocere and, in the absence of oxygen, decay be unable to proceed any further. Ammonia and hydrogen sulphide are typical products.

The other condition, lack of moisture, is seen in the wonderful state of preservation of archaeological objects of wood, fabrics and food-stuffs in the extremely dry rock-tombs of Egypt, or even in desert sands. Here the decaying organisms cannot live without water.

An unusual intermediate set of conditions was apparently shown by the Bronze-Age tombs at Jericho (Zeuner, 1955), which are not by any means completely dry. Nevertheless, wooden furniture, textiles, joints of meat left as offerings and even the shrivelled brains still in the skulls of the dead, had been preserved to some extent through the millennia. The reason here seems to lie in gaseous emanations from the limestone rock in which the tombs were cut—carbon dioxide and methane seeping in from depth through fissures and replacing the air which would have permitted full decay. Even the insects attacking the wood had perished —wood-worms and termites—and had been preserved.

In our less favourable conditions, it is clear that whereas alkaline surroundings favour the preservation of bone, it is above all in acid waterlogged conditions that horn, hide, leather, hair and wool may survive. Beyond this we are no longer on sure ground, but the known evidence suggests that, in special cases, much more than this can be preserved.

The Siberian frozen mammoths present a fairly simple case of perennial refrigeration in frozen ground which has never thawed since the carcases became buried, thousands of years ago, but the case of the woolly rhinoceros of Starunia (Zeuner, 1934) is more complicated. The surroundings were acid and peaty, for the beast's hide and even the hair, though loosened from it, were preserved, as were the remains of grasshoppers and other insects living at the same time as the rhinoceros. Salt water seems to have played the part of a preservative while the presence of mineral oil helped in the exclusion of air.

There are, further, some tantalizing indications that, even when all the original organic substance appears to have perished, some traces of degradation-products may yet remain accessible to chemical analysis, with the possibility, by refined microanalytical techniques, of characterizing the original substances. Phosphate, derived both from bone and from organic phosphorus-containing compounds in the soft parts of animal bodies, is a well-known valuable indicator of the original presence of animal matter. It is, of course, present also in plants, but in far smaller concentrations.

Animal fats, for example, seem to survive in traces (Stokar, 1939) not indeed in their original form as glycerides, but in part, only, as higher fatty acids, which are practically insoluble in water. Von Stokar was able to extract small traces, of the order of 0.01%, from samples of Palaeolithic deposits. The quantity was too small for identification of the exact substances involved, but their general nature was recognizable.

Encouraged by this account, the writer tried by the same method to detect fatty acids in the dense organic filling of a Roman rubbish-pit. The residue, on evaporation of a large volume of extract from the sample, was a mere smear of greasiness at the bottom of the glass vessel, so small as scarcely to be weighed on a chemical balance—less than 1/10th of a milligram.

Discussing this result with a bacteriologist friend, he pointed out that such a minute trace was not necessarily original to the pit-filling. Many microscopic soil-organisms include appreciable amounts of fat in their cell-contents. Wherever organic matter decays, such organisms are active, so that a slight fatty extract may be expected from most soils of high organic content, deriving from their living microflora and -fauna.

Von Stokar further suggests that not only fats but also sterols (higher fatty alcohols) may survive. Why this should be so is not clear for sterols are notably unstable and readily oxidized. Nevertheless, could they be identified, the presence of cholesterol would prove the original presence of animal matter and phytosterol of vegetable substances, these being characteristic of the two Kingdoms of living things.

Even nitrates (products of the oxidation of proteins) do in fact survive on occasion; against expectation, on account of their great solubility in water. Once more, caution must be observed, for traces of nitrates are present in all aerated fertile soils as humus end-products and owing to the activity, in combination with the roots of leguminous plants, of living bacteria which are capable of 'fixing' atmospheric nitrogen. In a cave-deposit, such as that studied by von Stokar, however, this could not have been its immediate source.

It is clear, therefore, that we still do not know enough about the fate, under different conditions, of organic matter in archaeological deposits and in soils. In view of the only minute amounts often recoverable and the advanced techniques required for their treatment and characterization, further progress seems likely to be forthcoming only through the help of skilled organic chemists and to be beyond the resources of an ordinary soil-laboratory and the archaeological student of soils.

The problems are far from insoluble. Indeed, to a branch of science which nowadays synthesizes dyes, drugs and complex biochemicals as a matter of course, the chemistry of humus and the degradation-products of decaying animal matter should be comparatively simple. It only appears to be that nobody equipped with the necessary knowledge and skill has yet given much attention to these problems. Agricultural soil-science has mainly treated 'humus' as if it were a quite simple entity. Instead, we all know it to be a mixture of a number of different substances—perhaps a considerable number of fairly complex substances—but the literature on the subject is scanty and it is evident that not much serious work has yet been devoted to this problem, which for soil-science with an archaeological orientation is fundamental.

Part II

WEATHERING AND SOILS

6

Weathering and Soil-Formation

✦✦✦

THE STUDY OF THE PROCESSES of soil-formation is the province of the pedologist.

The subject is of interest and importance to archaeologists mainly for two reasons. The first is that an acquaintance with natural soil-phen-omena makes easier the recognition of disturbance of the soil-régime by man's activities and prevents mistaken attribution to human interference of what may be a perfectly natural phenomenon. Secondly, the soils at an archaeological site, having been formed under the environmental conditions prevailing at and since the time of the occupation, may be able to show significant differences between the ancient and the modern environments at that place. Eventually, when we know more about the effects of the different factors involved in the formation of a soil and have learned not only to isolate them for study and to evaluate them quantitatively, it may be possible, however roughly at first, to indicate how long an interval of time is represented by the soil-phenomena observed and thus to attempt at least relative estimates of the periods in which human events took place.

Zeuner (1948) has defined soils as follows: 'Soils are the products of decomposition of the land-surface under the influence of weather and vegetation'. Thus, stones, sand, silt and clay do not, in themselves, constitute soil, until some period of time has passed and weather has been able to produce in the mineral raw materials some perceptible degree of alteration. In this respect the definitions of soil current in Europe differ from those used by American geologists, for whom fresh comminuted bedrock constitutes a soil at the point of outset of its progress towards maturity—at age 00.00 hours, as it were! To argue about such definitions is valueless. It is as if one were to maintain that the genesis of a human individual took place at the instant of fertilization of the ovum against the view that individuality really only begins at birth. As with the human germ-plasm, so with soils: there is in fact no *new* material, but a continuity with the remote past. The bedrock of today is often the weathered sediment of a past age—soil-material even by the first definition. Even if freshly regurgitated by recent volcanic action and but now crystallized, who is to say that it is not the re-melted remains of some still older rock quietly deposited in the bed of an Archaean ocean? Both beginning and end are really far out of sight. We can easily agree as to the approximate nearby point at which our interest in the passing procession begins.

A soil, then, is formed from the immediate bedrock by physical comminution, chemical alteration and by the addition of organic substances, mainly from the vegetation. In the earliest stages this may consist, not of higher plants, but of algae, mosses and lichens which prepare the way for them.

Almost everywhere soils form a continuous mantle of varying thickness over the parent rocks, save where the surface is too steep or too exposed to retain the products of weathering, or where deposition of still-unweathered material is actively proceeding.

The character of any soil, therefore, depends on the interaction of a number of factors: the parent material, the climatic conditions, the slope and exposure of the particular situation, the character of the vegetation and the animal organisms colonizing it and the time available for its growth towards maturity.

The factors of soil-formation are not themselves simple and only the last—and most elusive!—is accurately expressible by a single quantity. Not only do these factors act upon the soil: the soil reacts and to some extent controls the very factors. One has only to think of the influence of a lime-soil, for example, on the sort of plants that occupy that environment and, through the plants, on the species of insects, among other living creatures, that most flourish there. Climate, again, expressible as a function of temperature and humidity, depends, to a large extent, in its effect on soils, on the seasonal range and distribution of temperature and humidity. The two sides of the same valley, with different exposures in relation to sun and prevailing wind, will have slightly different micro-climates and therefore differences of soil, flora and fauna.

With so many variables, even where they can be quantitatively expressed, the difficulty lies in assigning to any one factor its individual weight in the total soil-effect observed. The problems are, therefore, seen to be exceedingly complex and hitherto only a beginning has been made in their investigation. The application of the methods and results of pedology to the archaeological field is still in its infancy.

Weathering

The processes of physical weathering have already been referred to in connection with the formation of natural archaeological deposits.

When a fresh surface of rock is exposed to sun and wind, frost and thaw and the other physical agencies of denudation, it becomes somewhat broken and comminuted and, if enough time is allowed, it may be reduced by them from boulders and cobbles, through the gravel and sand grades down to fine silt and clay. Such sediments do not constitute soil, by the European definition, but only potential parent material.

When to physical comminution is added organic matter and chemical alteration of the minerals present, soil-formation proper begins. The two processes, of course, go on side by side from the moment when the rock is first exposed, chemical etching assisting comminution and physical agencies opening cracks for the admission of living organisms and chemically active solutions.

The two most potent chemical actions involved in weathering are acid solution and oxidation. The former must generally be effective before the latter can take place. At least, little chemical change can take place in the absence of moisture and the presence of even very little moisture implies the probability of some solution-processes getting to work. By far the most abundant rock-forming minerals are silica (e.g. quartz) and its numerous salts, the silicates, such as felspars and micas, the remaining constituents of a granite, for example. Few of these are more than very slightly soluble in pure water at the temperatures experienced in Nature over most of the Earth's surface, though, under tropical conditions, even silica dissolves appreciably, forming colloidal sols which have the property of 'peptizing' (dispersing as sub-microscopic particles) some other constituents, notably ferric hydroxide. Nevertheless, many rocks contain also smaller amounts of non-silicates (carbonates, oxides, sulphides etc.) and some, like limestones, may be almost entirely non-siliceous. Such rocks may be relatively (though still only rather slightly) soluble in water alone.

Rainwater, however, is not chemically pure. It normally contains atmospheric gases in solution at the moment of its fall, in particular oxygen and carbon dioxide, as well as traces of nitric acid, formed under the influence of lightning-discharges. Whereas pure water can attack rock-forming minerals only slowly, even when rendered only slightly acid by its dissolved gases its solvent powers are much increased, so that, from felspars, for example, potassium, sodium and calcium salts are gradually released. These bases become available to plants in the soil and any not so taken up tend to be lost to the water-table and to be carried away in the drainage. What is left of most rocks consists overwhelmingly of silica, the more resistant silicates (such as white mica and clay-minerals containing more or less alumina), iron oxides and small amounts of other substances ('heavy' minerals) which are almost unweatherable in our climatic conditions.

In addition to these purely inorganic chemical changes, the flora, comprising both microscopic and higher plants, contributes solutions of acids to the developing soil, both in the exudations of living roots (chiefly CO_2), whereby the plants decompose minerals to release the materials they need for growth, and in percolating water which has taken into solution (generally as a colloidal sol) acid bodies (humic acids), principally derived from the breakdown of dead plant-tissues. In partnership with the carbonic and nitric acids, both from the atmosphere and from the oxidative decay of plant remains in the soil, the humic acids combine with any available bases to form organic complexes. If present in excess sufficient to increase the general acidity beyond a certain critical point, the humic acids may cause the greater part of the available bases eventually to be washed out of the soil and be lost in the drainage. The degree of such acidification depends in some measure on the nature of the vegetation-cover. Under deep-rooted forest, for example, many basic minerals valuable as plant-food may be restored to the surface of the soil in the litter which carpets the forest-floor.

These comminuting, oxidizing and dissolving agencies, with the addition of organic matter, cause changes of structure, chemical composition and colour in the upper part of the soil, which give it its characteristic appearance in the field and difference from that of the unaltered mineral substratum, and which enable even an untrained eye to recognize it as a weathering-soil.

The valuable part played by plants in the genesis and development of soils is now clear. The organic matter in the soil is mainly derived from their decayed aerial parts and roots, but animals living on and in the soil make important contributions to its substance and to the breakdown of the plant-remains, by their activity in feeding and excreting while they are alive and by rendering the stores of animal matter in their bodies to the soil when they die. A dead ox, for example, would represent an unusually large local concentration of animal and mineral substances in the process of being dissipated and returned to circulation by innumerable scavengers and micro-organisms. The importance of such a single large animal, however, is completely overshadowed by the enormous numbers of small to microscopic creatures which daily live and die in unnoticed millions, yielding each its speck of nutriment to the soil and to the searching roots which penetrate it in every direction.

Humus

Soil organic matter, vegetable and animal, is known as 'humus'. In its final form it is an amorphous dark brown-coloured colloidal substance, coating the mineral grains, avid of moisture, which it greatly assists the soil to retain in dry conditions. It shrinks greatly when dry, swelling again when wetted, so that it helps to maintain an open soil-texture, at one time causing the shrinking and cracking of denser masses into crumbs, at another cementing loose mineral grains together. It thus maintains channels of access for the penetration of air and moisture and the ventilation of carbon dioxide which are necessary for the activity of the soil-fauna and the chemical changes which are all the while going on in the spaces between the mineral particles.

Humus also enters into loose chemical combinations with clay-minerals ('clay-humus complex') and with bases such as calcium compounds present in the mineral fabric ('calcium humates'). While some valuable work has been done on the properties and function in maintaining fertility of these compounds, we know all too little about their chemical nature, so that these names, like that of humus itself, are often mere cloaks for our ignorance. It is an ancient scientific error to suppose that something, once named, is fully comprehended. The very use of the word 'complex' indicates that there is something not yet understood! Quite apart from its obvious complexity, there are clear indications that there are different kinds of humus, of which the composition and properties vary according to the type of vegetation from which it is derived (Dimbleby, 1955).

The conversion of raw plant-remains into humus is a process partly chemical but very largely biological—the work of the soil micro-fauna and -flora. Dead leaves, twigs and branches form the food, not only of worms, insect-larvae, woodlice, millipedes, mites and other animals which, if small, are generally easily seen with the naked eye. Microscopic creatures, vegetable as well as animal, including fungi and bacteria—a whole host of living things—gnaw and burrow, crumble and rot, enmesh in their tenuous mats of mycelium and devour the cast-off remains of the higher plants. Each converts what it eats into something simpler and, while it lives, leaves a trail of excreta as nourishment for some still lower organism. The worms not only attack the dead litter directly, they swallow and grind down much mineral matter in their deeper journeys and this they bring up to add to the compost with their own excreted wastes intimately mixed with it. Before long all plant-structure has been obliterated, the recognizable tissues reduced to a formless, dark-coloured, slimy paste interspersed with the minerals. This is mull-humus. Some soils consist of little but incompletely-decayed plant-remains. Others have but traces. Wherever there is vegetation and soil-life there is humus—and, without vegetation and soil life there can be no soil.

Humus-forms

Kubiena (1953) distinguishes no fewer than seventeen different structural forms of humus, based on their microscopical appearances and origins. Some of these, the main subaqueous forms: dy, gyttja and sapropel have already been referred to in discussing lake-deposits (pp. 38-41). Others are not found in our oceanic western European conditions and still more are confined to special environments, such as those of semi-desert and high mountains, which are not generally suitable for human occupation, and so do not usually occur in an archaeological context.

The main terrestrial humus-forms concerning us are, therefore, but four in number, though there exist some transitional forms between them to which Kubiena accords specific status.

Raw humus. This is synonymous with the *mør* (Danish, = mouldering) of Müller (1879). It consists of but little-decomposed plant-remains, matted together and sharply defined from the mineral soil underneath, with which there is little mixing. Its rate of formation often exceeds that of its decay, so that it may form considerable peaty accumulations. It requires a moist and rather cool temperate climate and occurs on base-poor, sandy soils which are deficient in clay minerals, of acid reaction and is itself very acid. The vegetation is generally of the pine-heath plant-association—pine, heather, whortleberry etc.—which is very fibrous in nature. The soil-fauna is poor, both in species and in number of individuals and the acidity does not favour bacterial activity, so that the rate of decay is slow. Worms, especially, are notably scarce, the usual cast-forming species of less acid surroundings being entirely absent. The plant-remains, in consequence, are little decayed, uncomminuted and retain their recognizable microscopic structures. Animal excreta are also not numerous. Percolating water extracts from raw humus peat-coloured humic acids in the colloidal state (humic-acid sols) so that drainage from such a humus-layer is acid and usually causes the development of a bleached horizon by dissolving out even iron compounds from the underlying mineral soil.

Moder (German, cognate with the Danish word *mør*, but *not* what Müller described as mør, which was raw humus). The plant-remains are largely broken down by the work of numerous soil animals, bacteria and fungi. The excreta of the fauna are an important constituent of this form of humus, as are loose mineral grains introduced by worms. Though crumbled and eroded, the plant-residues still retain recogniz-able structures, are imperfectly humified and have a characteristic 'mouldy' smell. The texture is loose and crumbly and the material does not bind when compressed.

Moder generally occurs under deciduous forest, on silicate soils poor in lime. It is, however, less base-deficient than raw humus and con-sequently less strongly acid. The better degree of humification is mainly due to the action of worms, in whose intestines the plant-fragments are digested, kneaded and mixed with fine mineral soil, facilitating the formation of clay-humus complexes, but these are never plentiful enough to affect the loose, unconsolidated texture.

A variety of moder, '*rendsina-moder*', is formed on immature cal-careous soils (see rendsina, p. 92) and consists largely of the droppings of mites (*Oribatidae*) which are able to withstand the periods of drought experienced in situations where such soils are developed. With greater maturity and depth of soil, rendsina-moder contains also the droppings of larger animals, including worms. The grey-black lime-humus aggregates or crumbs contain excess of calcium carbonate in distinct grains and appear to be largely true salts of the humic acids with lime (calcium humates), which are relatively insoluble in water.

Mull (= mould, the *muld* (pron. mūl, in Danish) of Müller, 1879). This is the humus-form of high base-status, complete humification of plant-remains, of even distribution through the upper part of the soil, with maximum adsorption of the humus on the mineral grains and aggregates, which forms the ideal agricultural 'tilth' so much sought by farmers and gardeners. Its best deve'opment requires a mineral basis neither too light (coarse-grained) nor too heavy (fine-grained), with sufficient but not too much moisture, a warm, dryish soil-climate providing good aeration and a readily-decomposable plant-cover. It is well seen in soils on loess (especially the chernozem—p. 95—) which are among the finest agricultural soils in the world.

Recognizable plant-remains or animal excreta retaining a distinct form are scarcely to be found. The dark, grey or brown amorphous humus is intimately mixed with the clay-fraction and can no longer be separated mechanically. The typical crumb-structure is due to aggregates chiefly of broken worm-castings, consisting, chemically, of humus-complexes with clay, ferric hydroxide and colloidal silica. Mull-soils have a typical earthy or clayey smell, distinct from that of incompletely-humified moder (leaf-mould).

The soil-profile

A vertical section through a soil, from the surface with its vegetation down to unaltered bedrock, is termed its *profile*.

The profile may be more or less clearly subdivided into zones, not due to successive changes in deposition, as in the strata of a geological section, but formed *in situ* from the parent rock by processes of weathering which have caused the translocation in the profile of certain soil-constituents, resulting in local enrichment or impoverishment in respect of these substances. Such zones, normally extending horizontally, are called *soil-horizons*.

Soil-profiles are subdivided into three main kinds of horizons, designated by the first three letters of the alphabet:

A-horizons, characterized by the presence of humus and by the washing out by percolating moisture of certain soluble components—*eluvial horizons*.

B-horizons, zones into which some materials washed out of an A-horizon are conveyed and re-deposited—*illuvial horizons*.

C-horizons, the chemically-unaltered parent rocks.

With the advance of our knowledge of soils and the description of numerous varieties of the main types, finer subdivision of profiles has become necessary. Subsidiary levels in the main horizons are denoted by subscript figures, as 'B$_2$-horizon', 'A$_1$-horizon'.

Transitional layers, where the boundaries between main horizons are not clearly defined, are called, for example, A/B or B/C horizons.

An horizon which is not manifestly an illuvial horizon, but which occupies the position of one and is due to deep weathering and oxidation is called a (B)-horizon (pronounced 'B-bracket').

Additional letters are used for special cases to designate layers of particular character: 'G-horizon' (G for 'gley'), an intermittently waterlogged part of the profile showing alternating oxidation- and reduction-phenomena; 'Ca-horizon', 'Fe-horizon', for those enriched with calcium or ferric compounds, respectively.

F

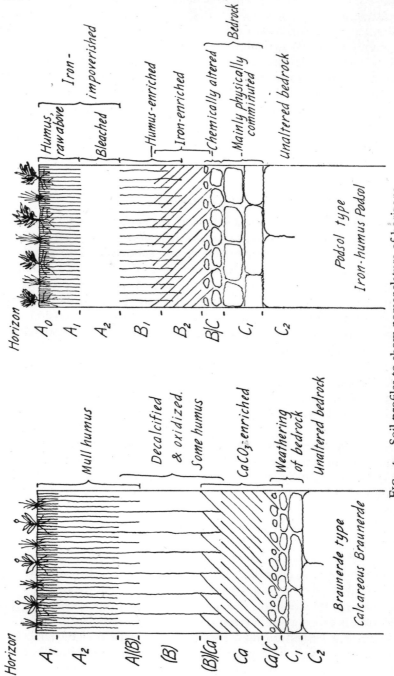

FIG. 4.   Soil-profiles to show nomenclature of horizons.

A D-horizon does not properly form part of the soil, being located below the C-horizon, or unchanged parent-rock, but it may affect the soil from below by affording a specially easy channel for the lateral passage of groundwater, either for flooding or drainage.

No one soil will exhibit all, or even most, of these subsidiary features. The two commonest types of profile in our climate are illustrated in Fig. 4.

Grouping of soils according to profile-types

In his *Soils of Europe* (1953), Kubiena recognizes five distinct types of profile:

(1) (A)C-soils, with humus development not yet to be distinguished by the naked eye, but bearing sparse vegetation and faunal life close to the very surface. This includes the very youthful stages of temperate soils and those which, in desert, high-alpine or arctic environments are arrested in development owing to lack of moisture or constant low temperatures, both of which hinder the progress of chemical weathering.

(2) AC-soils, having clear humus-horizons but no B-horizons, (e.g. ranker, rendsina, pp. 90, 92).

(3) A(B)C-soils, having visible B-horizons which are chemically weathered but are not true illuvial-horizons (e.g. brownearths and redearths, pp. 103, 99).

(4) ABC-soils, with true eluvial and illuvial horizons (e.g. podsols and bleached brown- and red-loams, pp. 108, 101).

(5) B/ABC-soils, having crusts irreversibly precipitated at the surface owing to capillary rise of dissolved or peptized constituents and intense hot-season evaporation (e.g. lateritic and salt-soils, mainly of tropical and semi-desert environments).

Soil-maturity. Climax and non-climax soils

Absolute conceptions of soil-maturity will be discussed at a later stage, when considering the influence of the time-factor in soil-formation. It is, however, necessary to introduce here some ideas of relative maturity, for these have a bearing on classification, which is the subject of Chapters 7, 8 and 9.

A soil which has only just begun to form, by weathering of a newly-exposed surface of rock (in the geological sense, sediments included) will obviously not show more than a slight development of horizons. For example, some humus must first be accumulated, of which the presence will be detectable (i.e. an A-horizon) long before percolation through it from the surface can produce any perceptible change in the parent material underneath (C-horizon). Thus, an AC-profile will be observed as the first stage in the development of a soil which, if given time, would develop a well-marked B-horizon in the conditions prevailing. Such an AC-soil is evidently relatively *immature*—it will eventually develop a more complex profile and become a typical *climax-soil* of that particular environment. Any changes thereafter (increasing maturity) will be of degree, not of kind.

Maturity is, thus, a matter of relation to the environment, not of any intrinsic character of the soil. Exactly the same slightly developed A-horizon lying directly upon the C-horizon may constitute a mature profile in other conditions, as, for example, in a colder and drier climate, the parent rock being the same in both cases. The second case is, then, one of arrested development—still what we call a *raw* soil (though mature), but now a *climax raw soil*, not merely a preliminary stage in the development of a more complex profile.

Non-climax soils are very interesting, nevertheless, because they show us youthful stages in the development of the climax profile and help our understanding of the way in which such profiles are formed.

Nomenclature of soils

Under the rules first formulated by Kubiena (1953), the name of a soil-type is a substantive and may be in any language—e.g. Chernozem (Russian = black earth), Rotlehm (German = red loam).

The name is purely a name, a label, regardless of its meaning. This may be a full, accurate and exclusive description, but more usually is not—e.g. there are numerous black soils, but only a particular sort of black soil is properly called a chernozem. Chernozems are not all black.

The type-name is designed to be recognized internationally, without translation.

Sub-types are distinguished by an additional adjective, in the mother-tongue of the writer—e.g. 'degraded chernozem'.

Varieties may have a further adjective—e.g. eutrophic, Central European braunerde (brownearth).

The *principle of priority* is generally to be observed (as in biological nomenclature), the valid name being the earliest applied in the literature with an adequate (i.e. unambiguous) description of the soil-type concerned, provided that it complies with the above rules. The principle will not be invoked to displace a name, generally accepted for some decades in usage, in favour of one which is unknown or unfamiliar, though strictly more valid owing to priority.

7

Classification of Soils (i)

✦✦✦✦✦✦✦✦✦✦✦✦✦✦✦✦✦✦✦✦✦✦✦✦✦✦✦✦✦✦✦✦✦✦✦✦✦✦✦

A GROUPING OF soils according to the horizons exhibited in their profiles has already been quoted. This arrangement, though it establishes the chief macroscopic character by which such groups may be recognized at sight, results in placing together in one group soils from very different environments and of different parentage and developmental history.

It is clear that, for the study of soils in an archaeological context, a classification by the formative environment is more advantageous.

That of Kubiena (1953) has much to recommend it, though for the present purpose it is of unnecessarily wide geographical scope and deals with soils of environments not often associated with archaeological remains. *The Soils of Europe* is a guide-book, aiming at completeness, within the limitations of our present knowledge, in describing the soils of one Continent. It is the author's aim to reduce soil-systematics to something like the agreed order to be found in the case of the biological sciences. He therefore erects a Natural System, based on the *soil-type* (corresponding with a biological species) with higher and lower categories as required.

The primary *Divisions* are three in number and environmental in character:

      A Subaqueous soils
      B Semi-terrestrial (flooding and groundwater) soils
      C Terrestrial soils.

Division A does not greatly concern us, save in the special case of lake-deposits, of which the general characteristics have already been described in Part I, under that head (pp. 38-41). This also applies to most of the groups in Division B, which are more or less waterlogged and do not offer a suitable environment for human habitations. The exception is the group of *Gley-soils*, partly, or seasonally, waterlogged but with a terrestrial flora, fauna and humus-form.

Division C is divided into Classes, as follows:

Class
CA   Terrestrial raw-soils: *a*. Climax raw-soils (arctic and hot deserts), *b*. Non-climax raw-soils. (Immature forms of the temperate regions.) Type: Syrosem.
CB   Ranker-like soils. Type: Ranker.
CC   Rendsina-like soils. Types: Eurendsina, Pararendsina.
CD   Steppe soils. Types: Serozem, Burozem, Kastanozem, Chernozem, Parachernozem, Paraserozem.

CE   Terrae calxis (Limestone-soils). Type: Terra; Sub-Types: Terra fusca, Terra rossa.
CF   Plastosols (Heavy silicate-soils). Types: Braunlehm, Rotlehm.
CG   Latosols (Lateritic soils). Type: Roterde
CH   Brownearths. Type: Braunerde.
CI   Pseudogley class. Type: Pseudogley.
CJ   Podsol class. Types: Semi-podsol, Podsol.

In order to link these more closely with the environmental conditions to which their particular properties are due, they may be arranged two-dimensionally in the form of a table, under the general characters of their parent rocks and of the various climates likely to be experienced. This arrangement also has the virtue that related members, between which there may be transitions, are brought close together and the main factors influencing their differences may be clearly seen (Fig. 5).

In this table, the extreme cold-arid and hot-arid climates, and the soils, immature owing to moisture-deficiency, developed under those conditions, are omitted, as not occurring in Western European conditions. Some of the cold-arid types must, indeed, have been formed here during the Pleistocene glaciations, but would probably have left no trace, in view of the more active chemical weathering of succeeding interglacials and the Postglacial period, which would evidently have altered them into more temperate forms. Non-climax raw soils of the temperate zone are included.

The sub-tropical soils, however, must be mentioned, because, though they cannot at the present day be formed in our region (or even, as far as we know, in any more genial interval of the Pleistocene) they are characterized by intense chemical weathering and often irreversible chemical changes, so that their remains, generally dating from Tertiary times, are found forming the parent material of present-day soils, whether in situ or as transported and derived sediments. Owing to the permanent transformations undergone by some of them, their tropical characters may be to some extent represented in the modern soils developed from their materials and cause serious difficulties unless their true nature is recognized. Such soils are called relict-soils, in contradistinction to fossil or buried soils, which lie today where they were formed, more or less cut off from present-day soil-forming processes by overlying deposits, whether natural or man-made.

Gley or Meadow-soils. This group (Kubiena recognizes three varieties) is classified by him in Division B, the semi-terrestrial soils. They are soils, more or less waterlogged, at least seasonally, of river flood-plains and alluvial flats, generally developed on floodloams, which are mainly fine in grade, though some are fairly sandy.

The profile normally comprises an A-horizon with moder or mull

Parent rock / Climate	Silica	Acid silicates	Basic silicates	Limestones
Cool-temperate (moist at all seasons)	Podsol	Ranker *or Pararendsina* — Braunerde: podsolic / oligotrophic	mesotrophic / eutrophic	Rendsina — calcareous / Terra fusca
Warm-temperate (dry summer) Mediterranean		Ranker *or Pararendsina* — Meridional Braunerde		Rendsina, Brown Rendsina, Terra fusca, Terra rossa
Sub-tropical humid		Rotlehm / Bleached Rotlehm		Rendsina, Terrafusca, Lateritic Terrarossa
Tropical (dry & wet seasons)		Roterde		
Humid-tropical (all seasons)		Braunlehm		
Continental Steppe (semi-arid)	*drier* Xeroranker *→ wetter*	Paraserosem / Parachernosem	Xeropararendsina, Burosem, Kastanosem	Serosem, Xerorendsina, Rendsina
		Chernosem		

FIG 5. Soils tabulated according to parent material and climatic factors of formation

humus lying directly upon the G (gley)-horizon which is waterlogged. Where there is a seasonal fall in the water-table, at least the upper part of this may at times be reasonably well aerated and more or less brown in colour, when it is called a (B) ('B-bracket')-horizon.

The AG profile of a simple gley-soil thus becomes A(B)G.

Waterlogging, due to the proximity below the surface of ground-water, produces characteristic features. In fine-grained materials the groundwater may be almost static. Lateral movement or drainage can take place only relatively slowly through the pore-spaces of the subsoil. The gradient, which might assist drainage, is negligible in the situations where gley-soils develop. Any percolation from the A-horizon containing humic solutions will rapidly absorb oxygen from its surroundings, taking it up, not only from solution in the water, but by reducing (de-oxygenating) iron minerals like limonite (ferric oxide, $2Fe_2O_3 . 3H_2O$) to the ferrous state, FeO.

Now, ferric compounds are red, brown or yellow in colour, depending on the amount of combined water, while the ferrous are green, bluish or black. The reduction of iron minerals, therefore, will give to the waterlogged part of the profile a pale grey, through bluish or greenish tones, to inky black colour, depending on their concentration.

If the groundwater level should fall, even only seasonally, the upper part of the gley-horizon will slowly drain and again become accessible to atmospheric oxygen, especially along cracks due to drying and shrinkage, root-holes, worm-burrows or other percolation-channels, so that the iron compounds in and near the walls of such channels will once more be oxidized, giving rusty red, yellow or brown patches, veins and mottlings in the grey or blue groundmass when seen in section. Permanent freedom from waterlogging would enable the upper part of the profile, below the humus layer, to become entirely browned, and it is this part which is called the (B)-horizon. Such a soil approaches the condition of a Braunerde (pp. 103-6).

The mottling is colourful and often striking and is generally a sign of gleying (but see Pseudogley, p. 106).

River floodloams often lie upon beds of gravel and sand. While the floodloam is fairly impervious and gleyed, the underlying beds, though also waterlogged, are more porous and admit relatively rapid lateral exchange of water with the river. Further, the gravel is generally practically free from organic matter, so that the water in it is not immediately de-oxygenated, as percolation from the surface would be. Thus, where oxygenated surface-water, as in the channel of the river, is able to seep laterally into the gravels underlying the floodplain, it may come in contact with the *lower* boundary of the overlying floodloam and oxidize its iron compounds to the ferric state, even when the upper part of the same loam is gleyed.

The gravel thus plays the part of a D-horizon—not properly being part of the soil, but influencing it by providing relatively rapid adjustment to variations in the level of the water-table and even giving an appearance of weathering to the G-horizon from below.

Transitions from gley to true terrestrial soils

A gley soil may be of any chemical composition, but is invariably of rather fine grade—otherwise the passage in quantity of oxygenated surface-water would prevent gleying. Where the floodloam which is its parent material is calcareous—a not uncommon circumstance when lime-bearing strata crop out in a river's course—even permanent lowering of the water-table, giving rise to oxidation and browning of a (B)-horizon, is unlikely to lead, save very slowly, to its complete decalcification, because of its relative impermeability and the obstruction of subsoil drainage. Subaerial weathering, given time, will eventually penetrate to some depth, aided by the percolation of water bearing humic acids in solution from the A_1-horizon. This stage is that of a Braunerde. On a non-calcareous and more sandy loam the percolation may reach such a volume and degree of acidity that even some iron-compounds are dissolved, beginning the formation of an A_2 (eluvial, iron-impoverished, even somewhat bleached) horizon. The dissolved iron passes down the profile until it reaches a level of higher base-status, where it may be precipitated from solution as an iron 'pan', cementing the surrounding deposits into a ferruginous sandstone or a conglomerate. This is a true B (illuvial, iron-enriched, darkened) horizon, designated as a B_{Fe}-horizon. The stage is that of a podsolic Braunerde (p. 108) or even of a Podsol (pp. 108-12).

Water-table hardpans

Though we have now reached a point of soil-formation at which the waterlogged gley-soil with which we began has ceased to exist, having given place to some truly terrestrial soil-type, this is the proper place to refer to a phenomenon which is concerned with the presence of groundwater at no great depth below the profile.

On silica or acid-silicate sediments, naturally poor in bases, with sufficient rainfall, a cool climate and a vegetation-cover giving rise to plentiful acid humus, a soil of the podsol type will form, in which iron-compounds will move downward with the percolation towards the water-table. In their passage, these solutions may not, in such sediments, encounter any layer with sufficient bases to neutralize their acidity and provoke the precipitation of their iron. When, however, they meet and are diluted by the groundwater, which may be in reaction close to neutrality (pH 7.0), the reaction of the resultant mixture, though still acid (below pH 7.0) will be above the critical acidity (pH 5.6) at which ferric hydroxide can be retained in solution, so that the iron will be precipitated as limonite, $2Fe_2O_3.3H_2O$. This appears to be the main mechanism—though perhaps over-simplified—of the formation of groundwater hardpans. Under these conditions, the hardpan formation may take place at considerable depth from the surface. An instance observed by the writer was at 10 feet or more (Ashbee, 1956; Cornwall, 1953), and far below any other evidence of weathering or soil-profile formation, i.e. deep in the C-horizon of the soil. In such a case, the ferruginous layer can hardly be called a B-horizon, even though its iron-enrichment is directly due to the soil-forming processes at the summit of the profile.

Class C A Terrestrial raw-soils

Type: Syrosem (Russian = raw-soil). A non-climax soil of the temperate zone, without any humus-horizon visible to the naked eye, though colonized superficially by plants and with a small number of animal organisms. The profile is (A)C, the A-horizon being rudimentary.

Physical weathering greatly exceeds chemical alteration and may extend some distance into the C-horizon. Thus, on hard rocks, a C_1-horizon may be distinguished as a somewhat loosened and comminuted layer above the unchanged parent-rock (C_2).

Soils of this type are generally fairly coarse in grade and deficient in particles of the clay-grade (< 0.002 mm.), unless these are already present in a parent sediment. Seen in thin section, the (A)-horizon shows scattered plant-fragments, undecomposed but showing attack by mites, etc. Boiling soda will yield a weakly-coloured extract from such fragments.

Kubiena details three varieties, depending on the character of the parent rock—Silicate-, Carbonate- (limestone) and Loess-syrosems— but there are no differences very significant in our context.

From the archaeological point of view, it is important to realize that a buried immature soil, in which no A-horizon can yet be seen, nevertheless may be detected by chemical and microscopical examination. Its very immaturity will suggest that no long period elapsed before the ground-surface which it represents became covered with deposits by natural or human agency, but the fact that any evidence at all of soil-formation can be discerned proves that it was for a time a surface undisturbed and bearing at least some vegetation. This does not happen overnight. Even so young a soil requires a season, or a few seasons, for its development. Its presence, therefore, guarantees a pause in construction or sedimentation for at least so long. Such a pause may be archaeologically significant.

Class C B Ranker-like soils

Type: Ranker (German = mountain-slope soil). This is a type of AC soil, sometimes, in its particular environment, immature, though more advanced in development than a Syrosem, from which it is distinguished by the possession of a macroscopically-clear humus-horizon.

In its type-locality and environment (steep mountain slopes of southern central Europe) it is a climax-soil, further development being arrested by constant denudation and renewed exposure of the C-horizon. Confined to silicate-rocks, it is poor in lime. Limestones yield Rendsina-type immature soils (p. 92).

Kubiena lists ten varieties and sub-varieties, many of which are confined to high mountains, where they form climax-soils. The following, among those described, are of interest in our context:

Proto-ranker. A youthful stage with an incoherent moder-humus A-horizon and little-weathered rock-fragments on an unweathered C-horizon of hard rock. It occurs mainly in woods and on mountain slopes in moist, cool-temperature regions.

Dystrophic Ranker (nutrient-poor, contrasted with *eutrophic*, nutrient-rich, soils). A shallow, acid raw-soil, with moist raw-humus or coarse, felted, little-decomposed moder A-horizon, formed under coniferous woods, mainly on hard, acid rocks (granite, sandstone or crystalline schist). There is an undergrowth of mosses, lichens and perhaps bilberry (*Vaccinium myrtillus*). It occurs also on heaths with ling (*Calluna*) and bell-heather (*Erica*). Acidity checks soil-life and favours incomplete decomposition of plant-residues, so that it forms an early stage in podsol (p. 108) development. Further stages in this development are dystrophic Grey Ranker, Podsol-ranker and full Podsol.

Mull-Ranker. An AC soil of dry forest and steppe, on non-calcareous but base-rich silicate-rocks (clay-schist or basic igneous rocks). It is nearly neutral in reaction, never strongly acid, with a loamy texture and mull-humus. The drier climate and neutral reaction favour decomposition and the parent rocks provide the clay-minerals necessary for humus-complexes.

Grey Ranker. An AC_1-soil with a physically-weathered grey C_1-horizon covering a hard, weather-resistant siliceous C_2-horizon. It is formed on sands and sandstones, mica-schists etc., low in iron. The humus-form is mull-like moder or, in drier climates, mull.

Podsol-Ranker. A dystrophic grey ranker with some eluviation and bleaching of the C_1 (A_2/C_1-horizon), but no true B-horizon. There may be ferruginous staining deep in fissures of the parent rock, due to percolation of iron-bearing eluvial solutions. The A_0 consists of raw humus, with an A_1 of coarse moder. It occurs on heaths, under ling and bell-heather etc., *Empetrum* (crowberry) or coniferous forest. In texture it is loose and sandy, being low in colloids. It is the immediate forerunner of the true Podsol.

Brown Ranker. In moist climates, a soil with more intense chemical weathering and release of clay-minerals and ferric hydroxides is formed, with an incipient (B)-horizon. It is non-climax and transitional to Braunerde (p. 103). In drier regions (desert-steppe) a brown *Xeroranker*, similar to *Paraserosem* (p. 97), occurs. It is humus-deficient and non-calcareous. The humus-form is generally mull in both cases.

Class C C Rendsina-like soils

Type: Rendsina (*Eurendsina*, in contrast with the second Type in this Class, Pararendsina—see below). The term is a Polish name for this type of soil.

A Rendsina is a generally shallow AC-soil formed on limestone or calcareous sediments. It is black to grey in colour owing to the formation, between the humus and the excess calcium carbonate of the bedrock, of water-insoluble calcium humates, of a greyish, never brownish, tinge. There is often a horizon of calcium carbonate enrichment (Ca-horizon) between the A- and C-horizons, which develops with some degree of maturity. The humus-form is generally mull, but sometimes moder. The excess calcium carbonate is continuously mobilized by leaching where moisture is sufficient, rising by capillarity when developed in arid or seasonally-dry climates.

In the humid belt, the Rendsina is generally not a climax-soil, for when it becomes deep enough for leaching to decalcify the upper part of the A-horizon, chemical weathering, checked before by the base-excess, enables the release of clay-minerals and iron hydroxides, with browning and transition to Braunerde or Terra fusca (p. 98).

Nine varieties are recognized by Kubiena, of which the following are the most important:

Proto-rendsina. An immature form, of which the A-horizon consists of plant-remains eroded by soil-animals, their carbonate-rich excreta and unweathered rock-fragments. It is loose in texture. There is no Ca-horizon. Plant-cover is often discontinuous. Owing to the porosity of the limestone the soil is often subject to drought in summer and the soil-life consists largely of drought-resistant forms such as mites. It is also found under forest in central and northern Europe.

Mull-like Rendsina. This is a more or less mature form, often occurring under mixed or coniferous forest. The A-horizon is rich in undecomposed plant-remains above (A_0-horizon) with incoherent sandy moder below (A_1-horizon), incompletely decomposed and with the characteristic moder smell. It is formed on pure limestones and calcareous silicates poor in clay, which accounts for the absence of the mull-form. It may be summer-dry. There is nevertheless a rich soil-fauna and the difference from true Mull-Rendsina may only be seen microscopically. There is a Ca-horizon above the C_1, the physically-loosened layer of parent-rock fragments.

Mull Rendsina. This is rich in clay-minerals and gives an earthy, not moder smell. It is coherent, forming crumb-like aggregates (mostly worm-casts), which are plastic when wet. It occurs locally under deciduous forest or meadow on marly (calcareous clay) rocks. It is porous and well aerated, water-retentive owing to the presence of mull-clay complexes. There is intense chemical weathering, incipient de-calcification above in the grey-black A-horizons and an often deep Ca-horizon overlying the C_1. Humification of plant residues is complete and there are no recognizable structures preserved, when viewed in thin section, as in moder.

Brown Rendsina. There is more intense decalcification above and inter-mediate browning, immediately below the humus layer. The A-horizon is still *grey*, but there is an incipient (B)-horizon and a strongly-developed Ca-horizon above the C_1. When clay-rich there is transition to Terra fusca (p. 98). Development is not widespread but, as with Mull Rendsina, localized in places where slope and exposure favour its particular conditions of formation. It is generally found in more level shelves on mountain slopes under forest or meadow. The soil-life is active, but inferior to that of Mull-Rendsina.

Xerorendsina (Dry-rendsina). The colour is pale grey, owing to restricted plant-cover and less humus-formation. The soil is scarcely leached at all and large excess of calcium carbonate and/or sulphate (gypsum) is present. In Europe, it is found chiefly on steppes and in karst areas of the south, where, owing to the free drainage and dry summer the soil is deficient in moisture. There is a Ca-horizon, due to such percolation as gets through in the moister seasons.

Type: Pararendsina (contrasted with *Eurendsina*). This type of Rend-sina-like soil is formed, not on limestones but on calcium-carbonate-rich basic igneous rocks, calcareous sandstones or shales, with abundant siliceous material in addition to the calcium carbonate. There is an ACaC profile. The soil is frequently non-climax, changing with greater maturity and decalcification to Ranker, Braunerde or even Podsol. It is short-lived owing to the limited calcium carbonate reserves. The presence of black or grey calcium humates while an excess of carbonate persists shows its relationship to the Eurendsina.

8

Classification of Soils (ii)

✦✦

Class C D Steppe soils

THE SOIL-TYPES included in this Class are of importance in western Europe only because, during some periods of colder and more continental climate of the past, the steppe-zone extended a great deal further to the south and west in Europe, so that soils of the steppe class may occur in a buried and fossil state in regions where they could not form today, owing to the moister and less extreme climatic conditions now prevailing.

They are in general AC soils, formed chiefly on little-coherent sediments of high calcium carbonate content (especially loess) and occur on plains or country of low relief with a summer-dry climate and often extremely cold winters. The presence of excess calcareous material and the summer drought are necessary conditions for their formation, because any deficiency of calcium carbonate or more summer moisture would promote decalcification of more than the upper part of the profile only, intense chemical weathering and their development of a (B)-horizon and the general characteristics of a Braunerde.

On siliceous parent-materials, or on those in which calcium carbonate is lacking or present only in small amount, ranker-like soils are developed (Parachernosem, Paraserosem, p. 97).

Type: Serosem (pron. 'sieroziom'. Russian= grey earth). A climax AC soil of semi-desert, on loess, marl or other calcareous sediments with a constantly alkaline reaction. The plant-cover and soil-life are scanty, so that there is only a shallow, poor humus-horizon, little different in appearance from the subsoil. Only slight leaching can take place, but a somewhat cemented Ca-horizon is commonly formed. Physical weathering is more important than chemical under these conditions. The humus is mull-like calcareous moder, owing to the comparative inactivity of chemical weathering and fauna.

Two varieties, characterized by the presence of water-soluble salts (sodium chloride etc.) derived from groundwater, are found in association with Common Serosem in steppe-depressions at the present day. These would not preserve their features in the fossil state under a surface-climate with more precipitation.

Type: Burosem (brown desert-steppe soil). An AC soil of slightly moister environment than the Serosem. The brown colour shows

better chemical weathering, which is associated with some decalcification of the A-horizon, with lower pH, and more intense formation
of a Ca-horizon. Mull-humus is characteristic. As with the Serosem,
salty varieties are sometimes found.

Type: Kastanosem (pron. 'Kashtannoziom'. Russian = chestnut
earth). A steppe AC soil transitional between the Burosem and Chernozem zones, where it is found as a climax type on calcareous sediments.
The humus-horizon is often 50 cms deep, the A_1 greyish, the A_2 red-
brown, with a marked Ca-horizon. It is found in the same summer-dry,
semi-arid climate as the two foregoing types, but is better weathered
owing to greater moisture. The colour of the A_2-horizon is due to
ferric oxide, of which the redder shade proclaims its partial dehydration
in the hot, dry summer. The mineral fabric, if iron-bearing, is probably equally red in the Chernosem, but is, here, masked by the accumulated humus.

The plant-cover of the Kastanosem is a closed association mainly of
grasses, with fewer xerophytic plants of the *Artemisia* type which
characterize the more arid Serosem and Burosem soils. Mull humus is
the rule and forms an important accumulation. This is due to the more
varied fauna, especially earthworms. As before, saline varieties are not
uncommon in poorly-drained depressions.

Kastanosems are farmed, but without irrigation are severely subject
to drought in any season in which the rainfall is short of the average.

Type: Chernosem (pron. 'Tchernoziom'. Russian = black earth).
This is the most highly-developed member of the A/C steppe soils on
loess or other calcareous sediment. The vegetation in nature consists
of grasses, but the soil is cultivated especially for wheat, to which its
deep humus-horizon and ready availability of nutrients are particularly adapted. It occurs in regions of continental climate with snow-
cover in winter, a moist spring and a hot, dry summer.

The A-horizons attain a depth of 1 metre or more and are of a black
or dark grey colour. There is a marked Ca-horizon which divides them
from the unweathered C-horizon. In moister areas, the Ca-horizon is
thick; thinner where precipitation and leaching are less. Still moister
conditions lead to incipient decalcification and development via Degraded Chernosem to Braunerde.

Sub-type: Common Chernosem. The A_1-horizon is normally very black
when moist, with a good crumb-structure which is due to earthworms
and mull-humus. In mature chernosems, it is not calcareous, the
calcium forming insoluble humates with the plentiful organic matter.
The A_2 is slightly greyer, with an efflorescence of the small excess of
calcium carbonate in the form of exceedingly fine needle-like crystals
and long filaments, resembling the mycelium of a fungus (pseudo-

mycelium). Calcium carbonate in this form is recognized as a distinct mineral, Lublinite. The crumbs of soil in the pseudo-mycelium layer are not themselves calcareous. A transitional horizon (A/Ca) is paler grey with plentiful calcium carbonate in nodules and crusts. The different horizons merge into one another and are not clear-cut.

A characteristic feature of Chernosems is what are called in Russian *krotowinas*—burrows of steppe rodents (e.g. suslik, *Spermophilus*) which have been filled again with soil. If the filling comes from a different horizon from that in which the burrow was made, it may be of a different colour, a contrasting shade of black, white or grey, and be clearly visible in section.

As in the other steppe soils, chemical weathering of mineral particles is checked by the alkaline reaction and excess calcium carbonate. The soil is normally frozen to some depth throughout the winter and snow-covered, bringing all chemical and biological processes to a standstill. With the first melting of the snow, percolation and drainage are impeded by the still-frozen deeper layers. A luxuriant crop of annual grasses springs up, associated with a plentiful and active soil-fauna. As the profile gradually dries out in summer, the grasses ripen and quickly parch brown. Calcium carbonate is leached out of the A-horizons by percolating water rich in CO_2 derived from the soil-life. On drying, $CaCO_3$ is precipitated. Any soil-water moving up the profile in summer by capillarity is deficient in CO_2 and cannot redissolve the calcium carbonate. It will, however, carry up with it any soluble bases (sodium and potassium salts) which have been washed down by spring percolation, so that humus and soluble bases tend to accumulate in the A-horizons while calcium and magnesium carbonates are leached out.

The chernosem is the soil of the finest wheat-lands of Europe—S. Russia, Bulgaria, Hungary, Austria and Czecho-Slovakia. It betokens a pronounced continentality of climate with precipitation only just adequate. It is found as a fossil soil well to the west of its present-day extension, proving a more continental climate to have existed in these areas in the past.

Sub-type: Degraded Chernosem. To the west and north of the zone of Common Chernosems, where the summer climate is moister and the winter not so severe, so that intermittent thawing of snow and resumption of chemical and biological activity in the soil is possible, decalcification and chemical weathering are more pronounced.

Below a black, mull-humus A-horizon, never so deep as in the Common Chernosem, is generally developed a thin (c. 10 cms.) browned horizon, due to formation of ferric hydroxide, a (B)-horizon. So far, the profile is completely decalcified. There follows a Ca-horizon, of which the degree of development depends on the calcareous content of the parent rock. If there is any deficiency of humus, the browning may be seen to extend up into the A-horizons also.

The soil represents a transition from Chernosem to Braunerde, but it is found as a climax-soil in a limited belt separating the wide zones in which these two types are exclusively developed.

Type: Parachernosem. Where, in the Chernosem-zone, the available soil parent material is predominantly siliceous and deficient in calcium carbonate, a deep, black, humic soil with an AC profile is formed, having mull-humus and a rich soil-fauna, scarcely inferior to the Chernosem proper. Ca- and pseudo-mycelium layers are, of course, lacking. Some browning may appear if the parent rock is rich in already-weathered iron, or if its unoxidized minerals are readily weatherable. This only becomes distinct where humus is somewhat deficient, being otherwise masked by the black mull. Despite the absence of lime salts, the low moisture prevents very intense chemical weathering, so that the browning is often not seen.

The distinction of Para-Chernosem from true Chernosem lies in the absence of $CaCO_3$ and the consequent differences in profile (notably, that there is no Ca-horizon), flora and fauna. The deep humus layers and less intense browning distinguish it from a Braunerde. The absence of any features of waterlogging or gleying prevent any confusion with a semi-terrestrial AC soil, which it may superficially resemble.

Type: Paraserosem. This is the type of soil, parallel with Serosem, formed on acid parent rocks without calcium carbonate and, therefore, without any Ca-horizon. It is seldom found as a climax-soil even in semi-desert, save on parent rocks which weather only with difficulty. It is, in other cases, transitional to Braunerde of the meridional sub-type (p. 106), with browning due to the release of ferric hydroxides. Even in conditions of low moisture, high summer temperatures can bring about a fairly high degree of chemical weathering when the reaction is acid, where, in the presence of the excess calcium carbonate of the true Serosem, a stable situation is attained far short of this.

Class C E Terrae calxis
(Limestone soils of climates with humid seasons)

Type: Terra. The soils under this head are fully mature, generally completely decalcified and in consistency earthy (rough, with coarsely cemented aggregates, unplastic even when wet) to loamy or clayey (dense, fine-grained, plastic when wet, drying out hard).

Two sub-types are described by Kubiena, grading into one another, and are distinguished by the state of their iron-compounds.

The designation 'terra' derives from the Italian popular names 'terra rossa', 'terra gialla', etc., applied to the strikingly red and yellow coloured soils found on limestones in the Mediterranean region. The former of these has priority over any other name to describe the red

G

sub-type. On this analogy, Kubiena has coined the name 'Terra fusca' (Italian = Dusky earth) for the brown or yellow forms, retaining 'Terra gialla' only for the local Mediterranean sub-variety to which it was originally applied.

Sub-type: Terra fusca (Limestone Braunlehm).

Variety: Typical Terra fusca. This is a loamy soil, poor in humus, completely decalcified and containing hydrated iron oxides mainly in the form of limonite ($2Fe_2O_3 . 3H_2O$) and hence with colours ranging from bright ochre through yellow-browns to bright red-browns, depending on the degree of hydration of the minerals and the absence of other colouring matters.

There is a thin A_2-horizon of a greyer tone at the summit of the mineral soil, with mull-humus, on which lies a sharply-defined moder layer (A_1), the whole occupying no more than a cm. or two. Between this and the solid limestone, and often filling deep fissures in the latter, is the dense, plastic, more or less highly-coloured (B)-horizon, with little save quartz, clay-minerals and ferric hydroxide. Occasionally, on very pure limestones, even quartz is rare and the (B)-horizon consists exclusively of iron-stained clay-minerals.

Such material is stiff, swollen and almost impervious to percolation when wet, concrete-hard when dry, permeated with shrinkage-cracks and breaking into angular fragments.

With incident light, under the microscope, the surface-texture is waxy in appearance and this is due, according to Kubiena, to the presence of colloidal silicic acid which peptizes the iron and clay-minerals. This may be seen in the thin section by transmitted light, when the peptized hydrated ferric hydroxide permeating the mass appears of a bright, somewhat orange-yellow colour (Kubiena says 'egg-yellow') forming streaks and structures which are birefringent under the crossed nicols of the petrological microscope, owing to flow-orientation of the sub-microscopic colloid particles in cracks and conducting channels. There are in the section some rounded, sharply-defined, almost opaque limonite concretions and others, generally smaller, of manganese oxide (manganite). The former appear dark brown and the latter dead black by reflected light.

These visual characteristics clearly show the close relationship of Terra fusca to Braunlehm (pp. 100-1).

Typical Terra fusca is found on limestones in central and southern Europe and even in south-west England. It requires not only plentiful moisture, but a summer climate somewhat warmer than our average (which normally tends to form a Braunerde type of climax-soil), for silica appears not to hydrate and peptize at the soil-temperatures normally prevailing in these Islands. In many cases where it is found in the cooler Temperate Zone, Terra fusca is, therefore, probably a relict-soil, having been formed at some time in the past when a more meridional, or at least more continental type of climate, with warmer summers, obtained.

Terra fusca is a necessary preliminary stage in the formation of Terra rossa, produced by a still hotter and drier summer climate.

Kubiena distinguishes a bleached variety of Terra fusca from Lower Austria, in which the parent material is sandy and more pervious than the usually rather clayey acid-insolubles in limestones. In this case the iron colloids are eluviated to form a bleached A_2-horizon. He insists that this differs from eluviation by humic sols, as in a podsol, owing to an over-all poverty in humus, which is, in any case, complexed with the clay-minerals as mull. He also describes an earthy variety, formed in dry 'maquis' scrublands in the Mediterranean region.

Sub-type: Terra rossa (Italian = red earth). This is a soil developed on very pure limestones which form elevated, well-drained karst-lands in the Adriatic countries (Istria, Dalmatia), where rain falls only in winter and the summer is exceedingly hot and dry. The brilliant cinnabar- or brick-red colour is due to loss of water of hydration by the iron compounds in the very high soil-temperatures experienced in the dry season. Only pure, permeable limestones, not those which are marly (with clay) afford the necessary degree of summer drought. The insoluble residue of the limestone provides all the minerals of the soil, which is completely decalcified.

The soil has a low humus-content with a thin (5-10 cms) greyer or browner A-horizon, while the (B)-horizon is of a clean, brilliant red, lying directly on the pure white C-horizon. Iron is present in large quantities as minerals (goethite, $FeO.OH$ and haematite, Fe_2O_3) of low hydration, which do not again take up water on wetting to form the yellow limonite, from which they doubtless originally derived.

Variety: Siallitic Terra rossa (Sial = Si(lica) + Al(umina)). A loamy, plastic Terra rossa, rich in clay-minerals and colloidal silicic acid, with peptized ferric hydroxide. As in Terra fusca, the ground-mass, seen in thin section, is of a bright yellow colour, but, unlike Terra fusca, there are also dehydrated and flocculated iron precipitates, some rounded and oval, some angular. These are opaque (black) in thin section, deep red in incident light.

On drying out and heating in summer the mobile ground-mass, peptized during the preceding wet season, is irreversibly precipitated and dehydrated. Some silicic acid, the peptizing agent, is lost to the drainage by eluviation, so that iron-enrichment of the soil is the general rule. However, under certain conditions not fully understood, iron may also be removed by pure eluviation, not by the action of humus, leaving only clean mineral grains in the A_2-horizon (Terra bianca. Italian = 'white earth').

In Europe, Terra rossa is probably mainly a relict formation, perhaps from Tertiary times, the dehydrated iron minerals, once formed, being extremely stable. It may still be forming on the high karsts in the Adriatic region, but it is frequently found as colluvial soil (rain-washed and transported) in the valleys, with Terra fusca on the slopes and Rendsina still higher, in limestone mountains. Certainly in the cooler and moister conditions of central and western Europe at the present day it is relict or fossil.

Variety: Allitic Terra rossa (Limestone Roterde). (Allite is a mineral deposit rich in alumina, poor in silica.) Roterde (German = red earth) is a tropical soil-type of hot climates with alternating dry and wet seasons. At the high temperatures prevailing in the tropics, silica dissolves, or is leached out as a colloidal silicic-acid sol, so that a soil on a parent rock originally rich in silica may be desilicified and leave practically nothing but alumina (Al_2O_3) and ferric oxide (Fe_2O_3), dehydrated to the mineral form haematite by the heat of the dry season. The mineral residue, consisting of iron-stained alumina, is called laterite, and is very red. Alumina, pale in colour and so relatively free from iron, is Bauxite, a valuable ore of aluminium metallurgy.

In Europe, this variety of Terra Rossa is certainly a relict. Desilicification on this scale is not possible save in a wet season which is also hot. Kubiena has recognized it in Istria and Croatia.

The soil is loose and crumbly, not plastic when wet. The iron is precipitated and dehydrated. The absence of silica, whether crystalline or colloidal, means that the thin section remains predominantly dark under crossed nicols, both precipitates and the haematite concretions being isotropic and opaque under these conditions. Mobile iron, as in Terra fusca and Siallitic Terra rossa, is absent, the peptizing silicic-acid sols having been leached out in the wet season and the iron-minerals dehydrated in the dry. In ordinary light the section shows the bright red precipitate crumbs interspersed with opaque concretions, which, however, are also red by reflected light.

Class C F Plastosols

These are the soils formed on silicate rocks which correspond to the Terra fusca or Terra rossa of limestone parent material. Like the former, they represent the residues of intense chemical weathering under sub-tropical and tropical conditions and have the bright yellow, red-brown or red colours of fully-oxidized iron-minerals in different states of hydration, little modified by humus-colour, for, like the limestone-soils, these are very poor in humus also. In Europe they are widespread as fossil or relict soils, their formation being due, generally, to Tertiary, or even geologically still older, periods of tropical climate. They are preserved from these remote times because of their great stability and resistance to further change, having already suffered extreme chemical alteration in the course of their early history.

Type: Braunlehm (German = brown loam)

Sub-type: Common Braunlehm. Formed on silicate rocks, the soil is deficient in humus, though what there is is in the form of mull, and the A-horizon is very shallow. The (B)-horizon is relatively deep, lying direct on the C. The colour is that of hydrated ferric oxide—ochreous, brown, orange or reddish-brown. It is completely decalcified and rich in silica, both crystalline and colloidal, slightly acid in reaction, base-poor and has a dense plastic consistency when wet, shrinking and fissuring when dry and breaking into hard, coherent, angular masses. If much sand is present, the texture may be more open and admit some percolation, to which the soil, continuously wetted in its formative environment, is normally very resistant. Such conducting channels as do exist are lined and choked with peptized ferric hydroxide, showing birefringent flow-structures in thin sections of the (B)-horizon. The whole dense ground-mass of clay-minerals is permeated and stained with these colloids. Apart from quartz-grains and rounded dark concretions of a chocolate-brown colour, there are no distinct bodies and no unweathered minerals in the fissured fabric.

Braunlehm is properly the soil of a perennially humid-tropical environment, in which it never dries out and so is never raised to a temperature high enough for the iron-compounds to be dehydrated and reddened. There are, of course, transition-stages to the Rotlehm condition, so that orange and reddish colours are also to be seen. Owing to its density and resistance to percolation when moist, the colloids and silica are not washed out. Moisture is thus the key to its preservation, and it has often survived from past geological ages even in our cool-moist climate.

Sub-type: Bleached Braunlehm. Braunlehms are not invariably impermeable, once taken from their original environment. If dried at some time, the material of their (B)-horizons may have been broken up and transported and to some extent mixed with other debris before being redeposited. When such colluvial material is re-colonized by plants and earth-worms, percolation-channels are opened up and some eluviation of the mobile colloids may give rise to a distinctly bleached A_2-horizon and a corresponding true B-horizon of mineral-enrichment. The unchanged part of the often deep accumulation of colluvial Braunlehm remains a (B)-horizon. Humus-sol eluviation does not enter into this bleaching, for there is no dystrophic humus-form to generate acid sols. The high colours of the iron-minerals are replaced in the A-horizons by pale brown (humus) or grey (de-ferruginized quartz) shades, while the deeper (B) retains its original colour.

Type: Rotlehm (German = red loam). Like Braunlehm, Rotlehm is a sub-tropical to tropical soil-type, with the difference that its characteristic colour, due to dehydrated iron-minerals, is produced in dry seasons alternating with the wet, while in Braunlehm, since the soil is continuously moist, no such dehydration is possible.

Rotlehm is formed on silicate rocks by intense chemical weathering and leaching, so that it is entirely decalcified, still rich in silica and colloids, but with plentiful ferric-oxide concretions and precipitates.

In Europe, it is widely found as a relict soil.

Sub-type: Typical Rotlehm. If still *in situ*, the soil has a complete A(B)C profile, the A-horizon poor in humus (though this is mull), the (B)-horizon frequently quite shallow. Accumulations of colluvial rotlehm are not uncommon. They display no differentiation into horizons and are predominantly (B) materials divorced from their true C-horizon.

Bleaching by eluviation sometimes occurs and a B-horizon of enrichment forms within the (B). Though very poor in bases and leached, there is still plenty of silica present and free alumina may be altogether wanting, so that there is no approach to lateritization as in the alumina-rich roterde. This preservation of silica seems to be due to the density of the soil as a whole. Percolation takes place mainly in channels formed as drying-cracks, and even these tend to become blocked by siliceous and ferruginous gels, precipitated from the mobile colloids through dehydration during the dry season. The interior of the largely clayey masses separated by these cracks is, therefore, inaccessible to any considerable volume of water, except to that taken up by capillarity and strongly held in the pores, so that it remains saturated and almost stationary.

In thin section, the peptized iron with flow-structures is still prominent, but the numerous red concretions and precipitates are irreversibly dehydrated to haematite and give the pronounced colour.

Rotlehms are common in the Mediterranean countries, of local occurrence in central Europe and are generally replaced by braunlehms in the north and west.

A variety *Earthy Rotlehm*, is less plastic, readily permeable owing to coarser grain-size of the parent rock, and has lost much of its silica, with consequent iron-enrichment. It represents a transition from rotlehm to roterde.

Class C G Latosols (Ferruginous soils)

Type: (Lateritic) Roterde (German = red earth). The type corresponds, on silicate-rocks, to Allitic Terra rossa on limestones. It is silica-impoverished, iron-cemented, alumina-enriched, porous and non-plastic when wet.

Under crossed nicols the thin section is very dark owing to lack of quartz or other anisotropic minerals or the birefringent silica-iron colloid flow-structures. The dehydrated iron oxide is almost opaque to polarized light, brilliant red in ordinary light.

Roterde is exclusively tropical, representing the end-point of chemical weathering under alternating hot/wet and hot/dry conditions. It is of interest to us solely as a fossil or relict soil.

9

Classification of Soils (iii)

+‧+

Class C H Brownearths

Type: Braunerde (German = brown earth). An A(B)C soil without distinct boundaries between the horizons, neither strongly acid nor strongly alkaline. Colloids are flocculated and immobile, so that the (B)-horizon is not an horizon of enrichment. The reaction is generally close to neutrality.

Increased acidity, on the one hand, will make the soil tend to change in the direction of a podsol; on the other, in the presence of plentiful calcium carbonate, as on loess in the moist climates of Western Europe, to acquire a rendsina-like crumb-structure. Any peptization of ferric hydroxide, as is likely in the warmer parts of the oceanic-climate zone, will cause changes towards braunlehm. Waterlogging will introduce gley-features.

It is essentially a soil of moderately moist climates with relatively cool summers and without a regular dry season. It is seldom more than intermittently and superficially frozen. Given this climatic environment, the Braunerde type varies widely in character, chiefly in accordance with the availability of bases in the parent rock. On the borders of the Mediterranean and continental climatic zones, increasing summer drought and reduction in total precipitation yield somewhat impoverished varieties, which are due to restriction of chemical weathering and soil-life by lack of moisture, or regular winter freezing, which has the same effect.

Sub-type: Central European Braunerde. In nature, this is the soil of the temperate deciduous and mixed deciduous/coniferous forest zone. Owing to clearances by man, this zone is, today, often under arable cultivation or more or less artificially-maintained pasture. Moist all the year round, even under snow, it is seldom subject to drought in summer or to freezing. Even snow-cover thaws intermittently during the winter. This (Kubiena's) description, with minor modifications, covers the conditions met with as far west as Britain. The differences are mostly of degree, owing to the generally moister and more equable conditions experienced here. One important difference is, perhaps, the usual absence of snow-cover, save for very short periods in most years. This works in two opposing ways:

(1) If it is due to winter temperatures generally above freezing-point, it permits sustained chemical and biological activity throughout the winter.

(2) In the event of exceptionally wintry weather, with north-east winds, the absence of snow favours freezing of the soil to a depth of at least some inches, perhaps a foot or so, occasionally for several weeks together. Though of benefit to the gardener and farmer, as breaking down clods to a fine tilth, it is a serious check to biological activity under natural woodland. Snow would prevent this in most cases, but north-east winds from the Continent bring us frost, but seldom much snow, which generally comes from the north-west, if at all.

Varieties of the Central European Braunerde are mainly controlled by the nature of the parent material.

Variety: Eutrophic Braunerde (nutrient-rich). This is the most productive natural soil of the Braunerde type, ideally formed under deciduous forest on base-rich parent rocks such as basaltic lavas. It is dark brown in colour, of a sepia rather than a red-brown shade, with plentiful well-humified plant-remains above and a marked crumb-structure and porosity due to earthworm activity. Plentiful iron, derived from the dark ferro-magnesian minerals of the bedrock, is entirely flocculated and immobile. On this flocculation depends the stability of the crumbs when wet, so that they do not break down into dense, loamy, impermeable masses. The degree of flocculation varies with the soil-climate, being particularly favoured by warm, dry summers, as in eastern central Europe, on the borders of the steppe zone. Even where the base-status of the underlying rock is satisfactory, colder and moister conditions, as in the Atlantic zone, adversely affect the iron flocculation, giving heavier, more loamy soils.

There is little visible differentiation into horizons, the surface litter passing imperceptibly into mull-rich porous mineral soil of some 50 cms in depth, below which comes a marked (B)/C-horizon with physically-comminuted rock-fragments. Such a soil combines a large water-capacity, yielded only slowly in drought, with excellent aeration and enables deep penetration of the varied fauna and flora.

Not only is Eutrophic Braunerde not widely and typically developed in nature in western Europe, owing to the cool, oceanic character of the climate, but large outcrops of suitable parent rocks are found in these islands (in particular) only in northern Ireland. The Lowland Zone of Great Britain occupies an area of geologically younger sediments, many of them already weathered both before and since their deposition. Even the Highland Zone consists overwhelmingly of ancient sedimentary formations, from which felspars and ferro-magnesian minerals (the chief sources of plentiful bases for the soil) have long since been weathered away. Our natural brownearths, therefore, are generally by nature less fertile than Eutrophic Braunerde, though good husbandry with applications of mineral and organic fertilizers make our best agricultural soils little inferior to the ideal Central European type. In one respect, depth, they are frequently better, since solid hard rock, even at as much as half a metre from the surface, limits rooting-depth seriously, whereas, in our looser sediments, there is often no practical limit.

Variety: Oligotrophic Braunerde (deficient in nutrients). This is the soil, in moist-temperate climates, of silicate or silica rocks of low base-status, e.g. granite, or other 'acid' igneous rock, sandstones, schists and already-weathered sediments such as quartz- and flint-gravels, sands etc.

The Central European variety, as described by Kubiena, generally formed on hard rocks, is, on the whole, a poorer soil than most of our chemically-comparable soils on sediments. A base-deficient igneous rock may even be poor in iron, so that, here, the colour may be pale, whereas sandstones and siliceous gravels are frequently rich in iron at least.

The profile is A(B)C, shallow on hard rocks, the texture dense and not crumbly, stony and even the A-horizon deficient in humus. When cultivated, the A-horizon is somewhat mixed with the (B) and scarcely recognizable. Soil-life, in comparison with the eutrophic variety, is restricted almost entirely to the litter layer. In the dry-summer belt this variety is often deficient in moisture, owing to shallowness and low humus-content. The humus-form, despite considerable acidity, is mull, in drier regions.

Under more oceanic conditions, even on silica sediments, the situation is better than that described by Kubiena. Forest-soils may be deep and their humus plentiful, even if not base-rich. Rainfall is almost always adequate to preserve moisture throughout the year, though light soils on coarse sediments dry out readily. Our brownearths often tend rather to the *mesotrophic* state, intermediate between eutrophic and oligotrophic Braunerde. In the more acid, the humus remains as moder, since soil-life and humification are restricted. In agricultural soils these are much improved by treatment with lime and fertilizers.

Variety: Calc-braunerde (calcareous brownearth). Where the parent rock is calcareous, as on limestone, marl, calcareous sandstone or loess, the climax-soil in Central Europe may be a Braunerde, developed in the first place from a rendsina, which, as it deepens, loses calcium carbonate from its upper part. In some few cases it is due to secondary enrichment of a Braunerde with calcium carbonate washed or blown from a nearby calcareous outcrop.

The profile is A(B)CaC, the A- and (B)-horizons generally decalcified, save where there is renewal from the surface, when the A-horizon may remain rendsina-like. There may be a B/Ca 'pseudo-mycelium' layer, especially on loess, like that of a Chernosem, followed by a distinct horizon of calcium-carbonate illuviation. A good crumb-structure with mull-humus is generally observed.

Further west, with increasing availability of moisture, no Ca-horizon can be formed permanently even at depth, for percolation takes place right through the profile and leached-out calcium carbonate is lost in the drainage. Thus, in Atlantic Europe, complete decalcification is the eventual fate of mature rendsina and calc-braunerde alike, with evolution of a neutral or slightly acid braunerde of ordinary type, of which the base-character—eutrophic, mesotrophic or oligotrophic—depends on whatever minerals, other than calcite, the parent rock may provide. A calcareous sandstone, for example, will yield, on decalcification, a more or less pure quartz sand and the braunerde first developed will become poorer and poorer in bases and evolve along the line: Oligotrophic Braunerde—Podsolic Braunerde—Podsol. If, on the other hand, there is available a variety of other minerals, an Eutrophic Braunerde may persist for a long time before the base-reserves are used up, even in an oceanic climate. It is nevertheless not, with us, a climax soil.

Variety: Ferritic Braunerde. This is confined to particularly iron-rich bedrocks, containing much siderite ($Fe_2(CO_3)_3$), limonite ($2Fe_2O_3$. $3H_2O$) and ferruginous limestones. It is crumbling and, according to clay content, variably, but not generally very plastic. Kubiena describes it in Mediterranean and Central European environments only, though he says that it occurs in northern Europe also. The iron hydroxide is completely flocculated. Decalcification takes place, but not podsolization. This may be due to lack of silica in the parent material. A soil consisting of little but iron hydroxide has nothing to form the fabric of a bleached horizon, even if humus-acidity should rise sufficiently to mobilize the iron itself!

Type: Meridional Braunerde. In the absolutely drier areas of southern Europe, climax brownearths may be formed on silicate rocks, of which the further development is retarded by shortage of moisture. In these conditions, vegetation-cover is discontinuous with a shrubby growth of Ilex (*Quercus ilex*) and Juniper (*J. oxycedrus*).

The soil is siliceous, dense and dries out hard, owing to cementing by colloidal silicic acid. Flocculated ferric hydroxide is locally seen in the thin section, but there are also braunlehm characteristics—peptized and mobile silica-iron sols with the typical flow-structures in conducting channels. The colour is generally light and the A-horizon very shallow, both being due to lack of moisture, resulting in incomplete chemical weathering and poor plant-growth. The braunlehm features are due to high temperatures in the presence of the intermittent moisture, but desiccation is rapid and physical comminution plays a larger part than chemical action.

Class C I Gley-like soils

Type: Pseudogley.

Sub-type: Krauss' Pseudogley. Formed on silicate sediments in a temperate-continental climate, the appearance of the soil is gley-like, though it is not saturated with groundwater. The reduction-phenomena are due to temporary surface saturation, owing to poor drainage through the dense clayey subsoil-material, though the silty upper portion is reasonably pervious.

The gley features are superimposed on some normal variety of the Braunerde, generally formed on fairly fine-grained sediments, so that, after rain, vertical drainage is impeded by the subsoil and what water does not escape as surface run-off moves slowly downhill laterally, if there is any slope. In many cases the terrain is almost level.

The basic profile is A(B)C, with a dark, generally shallow A-horizon and moder humus. Below this follows a g-horizon (pseudogley, as contrasted with a true gley G-horizon). This may be thick, pale grey or greenish, with root-holes and channels containing oxidized iron-compounds. It merges into the (B) via a fairly well-developed layer (g/(B)), which shows some grey flecking of the normal (B), lying on a dense, generally clayey siliceous parent material.

The g-horizon, as is shown by its generally pale colour, is not only reduced by periodical water-saturation, but has suffered some impoverishment of iron-compounds. On drying out, which takes place chiefly by capillarity towards the surface, the ferric hydroxide is precipitated in dark brown flecks and streaks, not only in such fissures and channels as exist, tending to block them, but in the silty fabric itself. These concretions are diffuse and of irregular outline, unlike the well-defined, rounded concretions of Braunerde proper. Some iron is probably carried away laterally.

The soil, though too wet at times, loses moisture readily by capillarity in dry summers and has no capacity for water-retention owing to the dystrophic humus and lack of crumb-structure. Humic-acid sols and the presence of tannins in the litter from the usual oak-forest cover are the agents which mobilize the iron. The soil is typically, but not exclusively, developed in north-west Saxony. It is here found on London Clay (and other heavy acid bedrocks) under mixed oak forest on slopes.

Sub-type: Marbled Pseudogley. This is a soil of temperate deciduous forest on fine-grained acid silicate sediments, especially of oak- and hornbeam-forest which yields plentiful tannins, capable of peptizing and reducing iron. On the whole it resembles the Krauss' Pseudogley closely, save that the mineral material is more clayey and permits less lateral drainage. Root-holes and drying-cracks admit acid humus and tannate-sols, which reduce iron and locally bleach the walls of the conducting channels. The appearance in section is, therefore, veined and marbled and there may be a leached g-horizon, where the marblings have coalesced, with blackish iron-concretions. There is no B-horizon of enrichment, for the iron moves only a short distance, even laterally, and scarcely at all vertically. The reaction is very acid, as low, on occasion, as pH 3.6, owing to the tannins, which are phenolic in constitution. It occurs in both central and northern Europe.

Class C J Podsol Class. A B C soils with true B-horizons

Type: Semi-Podsol. A soil in which leaching of iron is hardly apparent to the eye, but which shows a distinct ABC profile, and enrichment of the B-horizon on chemical analysis. Drainage water from it may be brown with leached-out humus sols.

Sub-type: Podsolic Braunerde, superficially like Braunerde, but with incipient humic eluviation of iron.

Variety: Eupodsolic Braunerde. A soil, moderately acid in reaction, generally developed under coniferous forest, with dystrophic moder humus, on base-poor, relatively coarse, mainly siliceous parent material. The acidity is sufficiently advanced for humic percolation to attack the iron compounds in the A_1-horizon and to begin to form bleached discontinuous flecks, or even a thin A_2 bleached seam, at the summit of the still-ferruginous (B)-horizon of the parent Braunerde.

Still lower, there is distinct iron and clay enrichment, so that this becomes a true B_2-horizon, of denser consistency. There is no separate accumulation of humus material in a B_1-horizon.

This variety is formed as a climax-soil in the Alps, under spruce-forest at 700-1500 m. elevation. The climate of this zone is so cool as to check the decomposition of plant-remains and somewhat to favour their accumulation, but not wet enough to lead further to the massive eluviation of iron hydroxide, which characterizes the true Podsol in the more oceanic northern and western regions. It may be found as a transitional stage from Oligotrophic Braunerde to true Podsol, on the boundaries (either climatic or due to variation of parent rock, and hence base-status) of the Braunerde zone with that of the Podsol.

Variety: Stesopodsolic Braunerde (Braunerde with arrested podsolization). The principal feature of this variety is its dense, loamy to clayey texture. Though rich in acid humus-sols and the colloids peptized thereby, the density of the fabric prevents much percolation.

Immediately below the A-horizon, which is clearly divided into A_0 (fermentation) and A_1 (humus) layers of the dystrophic moder, comes a marked B_1-horizon, in which humus sols are able to move only by capillarity. There is no apparent bleaching. The B_1 is chocolate coloured and often several cms thick. Iron-enrichment takes place in the B_2, below this again, which is ochreous yellow or brown in colour.

The soil is typical of sub-alpine spruce-forest in the eastern Alps, and at lower levels in northern Europe.

Type: Podsol (Russian = ash [-grey] soil). The type is a strongly acid soil of ABC profile with dystrophic moder or raw humus. The most striking features are a well-marked bleaching of the A_2 by removal of iron through humus sols and a correspondingly enriched B-horizon, sometimes with distinct B_1 (humus) and B_2 (iron) concentrations. Drainage-water is generally brown-stained with extracted humus.

It is typically the soil of northern and western cool-temperate regions with plentiful rainfall to develop the characteristic leaching. The acidity is due in part to base-deficient parent rocks (principally siliceous sands, gravels, sandstones and the more acid silicates), partly to the comparatively low temperatures prevailing, which check decomposition and oxidation of organic matter, and, further, to the intrinsically acid-forming nature of the fibrous plant-remains from conifers, birch, heather, bracken, bilberry and the rest of the acid-tolerant plant-assemblages, which flourish in such conditions.*

Sub-type: Gley-Podsol. A typical Podsol above, with A_1 (humus)-horizon, a bleached A_2 and B-horizon merging, below, with a gley. It is necessarily rather local in occurrence, for the normal A-horizons denote leaching and uninterrupted downward percolation of moisture, while waterlogging is confined to the deeper layers. This can only occur in a fairly restricted zone on the flanks of valleys, just above the maximum normal height of the water-table. The soil is generally sandy and open-textured.

The B-horizons may include humic layers, but are chiefly marked by well-developed water-table hardpans (see p. 89) of ferric hydroxide derived from the A-horizons. The exact situation of these depends on the local groundwater level, both at present and in the past. 'Fossil' (today inactive) iron-pans may indicate higher water-levels of the past. The iron may be mobilized as ferrous bicarbonate and be re-precipitated by oxidation, but mere dilution of percolating sols by groundwater at a higher pH than 5.6 would have the same effect (see p. 89).

Sub-type: Molken-Podsol (Central German peasant name = milky podsol). Close in character and appearance to Pseudogley, this is a sub-type of heavier, more clayey, acid soils and is a true Podsol, because there is actual leaching and translocation of the iron, though the dense texture prevents such complete bleaching as would be found on coarser mineral material.

The profile shows a brown A_0 of coarse moder on a darker, blackish, A_1, formed of animal droppings but almost amorphous. The somewhat bleached A_2 has some infiltrated humus sols above, making it markedly

---

* The influence of the vegetation itself on the soil has been strikingly illustrated by Dimbleby & Gill (1955) who show that even oak and beech by themselves can initiate podsolization. The role of the understory flora, and especially the holly, in producing and maintaining mull humus even on base-poor subsoils like the New Forest Plateau Gravels, is of great theoretical interest and of the highest importance in forest ecology.

sticky when wet. The mineral fabric is reduced and pale bluish or greenish in colour. The remainder of the A_2 is pale yellow or grey (the 'molken'-layer) with some humus distributed in flecks by capillary movement of fluids rather than percolation. There may, also, be dark brown ferruginous concretions. The resemblance to the g-layer of a Pseudogley is evident.

The B-horizon is marked, above, by humus and iron deposition, the $B_{1/2}$ dark brown and dense in texture, the B_2 of a high-coloured red-brown due to ferric hydroxide alone. This proves that movement of humus and iron takes place in a downward direction only, though slowly, whereas, in the Pseudogley, upward capillarity brings solutions back towards the surface in dry weather.

The constantly moist and cool climate and the dense-textured but acid parent rock are responsible for these features.

Sub-type: Humus Podsol. Since humus-sol podsolic eluviation carries down iron from A-horizons to be deposited in the B, an obvious Podsol, showing little iron-eluviation, can be formed only on an acid rock which contains little iron in the first place. The Humus-Podsol is the sub-type formed under heaths on aeolian sands or other coarse siliceous sediment, which is by nature very clean and non-ferruginous.

The A_0 and A_1 are fibrous and dark grey in colour, such sand-grains as they may contain—and most of their material is raw humus—being bleached quite clean. The A_2 is pure white incoherent sand. The coffee-coloured B_1 and the lighter brown B_2 are humus-illuvial horizons. They are sometimes followed by several irregular thin bands of illu-viated humic material which penetrate the otherwise unaltered C-horizon. These humic veins and bands are often to be seen in the sections of barrow-mounds on sand, especially in the Low Countries, where they have been described as 'fibres' (Modderman, 1954).

The startlingly clearly-defined dark and light layers of such a humus podsol are very seldom horizontal or uniform in thickness, for the permeability of the sand varies considerably from place to place in the same section.

Rain-water extracts from the raw humus colloidal sols of some of the acid bodies present, forming brown or yellow solutions. These soak into the deeper layers and yield their solids again when the soil dries, which it readily does by drainage and evaporation from the surface. The solubility of these substances is quite small so that, once deposited, they are not readily conveyed further, for subsequent percolation from above is generally already saturated with them. After unusually heavy and prolonged rains, it may be that the soil is thoroughly wetted to a greater depth than is commonly the case, and with percolating water which has not had time in passing through the A_{0-1}-horizons to take up its full quota of organic matter. Some of the already-accumulated amorphous humus of the B-horizons may, in such a case, be taken into solution and carried still deeper. This perhaps explains the subsidiary 'fibres' in the C-horizon.

Apart from a very little humus actually in transit, the bleached A_2 shows nothing, under the microscope, but clean quartz-grains. It is therefore very loose and incoherent. The illuviated humus, on the other hand, embeds and clothes the grains of the B-horizons so that they are somewhat cemented together. When dry, these coatings shrink and 'craze', much as the glaze on a pot sometimes cracks in all directions on firing. Under the microscope by reflected light, this appearance is very typical.

Not only humus-substances but any fine mineral particles also tend to be physically washed out of A-horizons in coarse, sandy podsols. The B-horizon may show, on mechanical analysis, an enrichment, as compared with the A, of finer material.

The sub-type is most typically developed on the Atlantic, North Sea and Baltic seaboards of northern Europe, but occurs inland anywhere in the podsol belt where non-ferruginous sands afford suitable parent material under heath vegetation.

When cultivated, the A_1 and A_2-horizons are mixed, giving a typically ash-grey colour, but the B-horizons are generally too deep to be involved, and are readily recognized. The numerous bleached sand-grains in the surface soil are well seen under a hand-lens.

Sub-type: Iron-Humus Podsol. This is, perhaps, the most widespread sub-type. The A-horizons are very like those of the Humus Podsol, with marked bleaching of the A_2. The B-horizon is normally clearly differentiated into B_1 (humus, dark brown or sepia) and B_2 (iron, ochreous yellow to rust-coloured), but they may be confluent, or so close together as to form but one recognizable layer. The warmer brown colour generally betrays the presence of iron mixed with the humus, but chemical analysis may be necessary to show the presence of iron when it is not large in amount. Such combined horizons are often more firmly cemented than is humus alone. In all other features the soil is closely like the Humus Podsol.

The preferred parent-materials are more or less ferruginous sands and gravels, but any markedly acid siliceous rock, such as mica-schist, acid gneiss or granite, may give rise to a Podsol, generally under heath vegetation, but also under (chiefly coniferous) forest, high on mountains in the south, down to sea-level in the oceanic north.

In the warmer, but moist, surroundings of the Cantabrian Mountains of North Spain, a variety, the Asturian Podsol, is formed. This has dystrophic moder instead of raw humus. Chemical weathering is very intense and some eluviation of silica as well as of iron takes place. This is redeposited between the B_2 (iron) horizon and the bedrock, much as a Ca-horizon forms on calcareous material, re-cementing the grains.

Sub-type: Iron Podsol. This is a soil of northern forests, especially of spruce and pine, formed on quartzose rocks deficient in bases. The less complete humification and predominantly fungus soil-life are the result of the lower temperatures and slower chemical decomposition in higher latitudes.

The soil differs from the two previous sub-types in having a deep accumulated litter (A_{00}) and a well-developed fermentation-layer (A_0), with only a slight coprogenic and well-humified A_1-horizon. Coarse moder and some raw humus are present. The formation of humus sols is thus sufficient to peptize and move iron, but there is no large excess of them, as in Humus and Iron-Humus Podsols. The B-horizon shows only iron illuviation and is yellow to rusty in colour, but there is no pan-formation, save for water-table hardpans, when groundwater is close enough to the surface. Owing to reduction by the humus and restriction of aeration by the deep, moist raw-humus layer, some ferrous compounds are formed, of which the presence can be shown by reddening of the apparently clean, bleached A_2 layer, when ignited in air in the laboratory (p. 154).

Part III

TECHNIQUES OF SOIL-INVESTIGATION

H

10

Physical Methods (i)

✦✦✦

SEVERAL ENTIRE BOOKS could be written on this subject without exhausting it, for, in the nature of things, our theoretical and practical knowledge are advancing all the time and Science is continually devising new tools for research, many of which could be usefully applied to the solution of archaeological problems.

Chemical analysis, in particular, has been revolutionized in the past twenty years by the introduction of new, and often expensive, optical, electrical and electronic equipment for the routine analysis of very small samples with great rapidity and accuracy. At present, the use of many such devices in our field is uneconomic, for workers are few and, though there is plenty of material awaiting investigation, the budgets of archaeological research institutions will not stretch to expenditures of hundreds or thousands of pounds on apparatus which may actually be in use on only a few days in the year. Were there more pairs of hands available to operate the equipment, such mechanization would perhaps become worth while, but Universities, though not averse from capital expenditure, within reason, on buildings and apparatus, think twice before committing themselves to recurrent payments such as additional salaries unless a very urgent case can be made for the increase. Archaeological investigations do not qualify as work of National Importance!

Liaison between archaeological researchers and other departments who may possess advanced equipment for their own work makes it possible for occasional special inquiries to be carried out elsewhere, when the urgency of the case or the labour involved in older methods make the use of the most modern methods necessary.

This section devoted to methods, therefore, confines itself on the whole to experiments which can be carried out with relatively simple traditional apparatus, often with no more elaborate equipment than a bench, a sink and a gas-point for a bunsen burner, with a few inexpensive items of laboratory glassware and common reagents. Methods described are, further, restricted on the whole to those of which the writer has personal experience. Others may prefer to use their own approaches to the same ends.

Even in this narrowed field, treatment is not exhaustive. There are, for example, several established methods for mechanical analysis of finer sediments. Only one, the hydrometer method, is here described in detail, as that found most generally useful. To do otherwise would be to write a textbook of sedimentary petrology. This has already been done very adequately by numerous specialist authors, to whose works (see Bibliography) the technical inquirer is confidently referred.

The methods fall conveniently into two groups: the physical and the chemical, though these two aspects of soils are closely interdependent and some overlap is inevitable. The former methods are concerned, for example, with sampling, grain-size estimations, physical condition of mineral grains, visual methods for the study of individual grains, the morphology of soils as seen in thin section and the physical separation of heavy minerals and other interesting constituents. Chemical methods are used both to show the presence of particular substances (qualitative) and, where necessary, to estimate the amounts present (quantitative analysis).

Sampling

The amount of a sample depends on the nature of the material and on what is to be done with it. Of course, a larger amount must be taken to ensure that all particles are fairly represented for quantitative purposes. For some purposes a single sample of a deposit may suffice, but we are generally concerned with its relations with what lies above and below it, so that it is more often necessary to take a whole series of samples from a section.

Since archaeological deposits often consist of fairly fine material, a reasonable sample from any layer would weigh, say, $\frac{1}{2}$ lb. or 250 gms.

The spacing of samples in a section will depend on what the inquiry is expected to reveal. In general, a single sample of each distinct layer is enough, but in searching for, say, a buried surface or occupation horizon which is not distinctly shown, the samples will be taken at arbitrary close intervals, as at every foot, or even every few inches. On occasion, samples may be taken in the horizontal plane to delimit the extent of an area of occupation or to identify from its surroundings a burial-pit under a barrow. In this case a grid of mesh as close as is necessary or practicable will first be laid down and the samples be taken at every intersection.

When it is only a question of determining the nature and mode of formation of a particular deposit, a 'spot' sample will generally be sufficient.

In any case, a sample should be sufficiently large to afford material for any laboratory work envisaged, for repeat experiments on occasion and to leave over a reasonably large amount for storage and future reference. It is easy enough to throw away samples later, if they are not needed for the collection. It is much more difficult, sometimes, to get repeat samples if the original was not large enough for all purposes.

Samples are taken in the field from the carefully-cleaned face of a section by cutting out a solid block with a trowel or other tool, carefully cleaning the tool before taking the next. If the material is loose or stony, the best that can be done is to collect a quantity, omitting the larger stones if a grading test is not contemplated, and ensuring that there is enough fine matrix for all tests. The first sample should be taken from the bottom of the section, working upwards for the rest. This prevents samples being contaminated with loose material falling from above.

They may be packed in any convenient container. Screw-topped jars are perhaps the best, but heavy to transport. Boxes and tins are suitable, if strong and clean. Incoherent materials may be collected in glazed linen or canvas bags. Untreated paper bags are nnsuitable, save as a temporary measure. Soils are nearly always moist and the paper or the adhesive holding the bag together are liable to give way in transit. Samples once mixed or contaminated are quite useless. Close sealing should be avoided, especially of moist material. Polythene bags are ideal once the sample has been dried. Unless the samples can be dealt with immediately moisture will encourage the growth of algae or moulds if the soil is not allowed to dry in store. For the same reason written labels should not be placed inside the containers unless these are porous. They are certain to go mouldy and to be illegible after a short time, not to speak of contaminating the sample!

Care should be taken not to touch the samples with the fingers, or even to breathe on them, lest their chemical reaction, which is an important diagnostic feature, should be changed.

Labels should be outside the container. Stick-on labels adhere well to glass, but not to tin. On tins they should be taped down with 'Sellotape' or tied on with string. In the case of bags, a tie-on label threaded on the string tying the neck of the bag is quite safe.

Samples taken, *faute de mieux*, in paper bags or wrapped in paper should be transferred to more permanent containers immediately on reaching home. In any case, containers should be allowed to stand open on arrival for at least some days to enable the samples to become air-dry. While drying, they must be protected from dust. They may then be stored and will keep indefinitely.

In the laboratory, the amount of material needed for each experiment is generally of a few grammes weight, sometimes as little as 1 gm. only. This ought to be as representative as possible of the deposit as a whole. In the case of sand, or finer sediment, this will present no difficulty, but if the material is a stony loam, for example, it is the matrix, not the flints, which is of chief interest, from the chemical point of view. Considerable stones should be excluded from the weighed-out quantity. The same would apply to lumps of limestone in a rendsina sample. The matrix might well be almost decalcified, but if a 1–gm. sample contains a limestone pebble weighing half of the total, a quite wrong idea of the calcium carbonate content of the soil as a whole will be obtained. Properly, therefore, in the presence of large stones, several kilos of the material should be finely ground (imagine doing this with Clay-with-flints or a boulder-clay!) and the 1-gm. sample weighed out from the carefully mixed powder. This is obviously impracticable in many cases without removal of the harder rocks. In practice, therefore, one sifts out stones larger than 6 mm., or even 2 mm. in diameter to obtain some 100–200 gms. of the finer grains, which are then treated as follows.

'Quartering'. The dry fines are spread out over a circular area on a large sheet of paper, well mixed and a fair distribution of the larger particles obtained by eye. The circle of spread is then divided with a spatula into four quadrants and the material of alternate quadrants set aside. The remaining two quadrants, if still too large in amount, may then be reunited, mixed, spread and again quartered as many times as may be necessary to reduce the bulk retained to the required proportions.

For sands, loams, silts etc. even this is unnecessary. Provided that there are not many grains over 1 mm. or so in diameter, any 1-gm. sample weighed out is reasonably representative of the whole. With ill-sorted deposits, however, it is well to be on guard against sampling errors and for chemical work it is as well to grind 10–20 gms. and quarter before weighing out small quantities for particular experiments. For grain-counts, sieve-analyses or for qualitative examination of grains there must, of course, be no grinding. A sufficiently large sample must be faithfully split down to the required size, if the grading of the material demands it.

Such splitting must avoid selection of grains of any particular size, shape or density. To pour the desired amount of coarse sand for microscopical examination and grain-counting off a paper on to the slide would, for example, favour the selection of larger and better-rounded grains at the expense, say, of mica particles. Special devices exist to obviate this difficulty, but care to obtain a truly representative sample, with this possibility of error in mind, will generally enable a fair subdivision to be made by hand.

Good sampling lies at the very root of all quantitative work. No matter how carefully the eventual determination of a quantity is carried out, if the sampling is untrustworthy the results will be equally un-reliable. The proof of a good determination is its repeatability. Without fair sampling results will never be repeatable, and no valid conclusions can be drawn from them unless they are.

Colour-description of soils and deposits

The colour of a soil or sediment is an essential physical characteristic, of some value in determining its nature, condition, history and constituents.

A soil which is pronouncedly red almost certainly owes its colour to anhydrous ferric oxide, the presence of which may indicate a marked degree of weathering, that the material has been heated, as in a fire, or that it is derived from a geological deposit which is already red.

To say that a soil is red is to indicate such possibilities, but to describe in words, exactly yet briefly, the quality and degree of redness, so that another person can accurately visualize or reproduce the colour and compare it with the redness of soils known to him, is almost impossible by the use of words alone.

Some colour-standard, taking into account both quality of colour and its depth and intensity, is required. Many colour-charts and standards have been devised and used for different purposes. A set specially developed in the United States for work on soils, which has proved itself to be useful, is the Munsell Soil Color Charts*.

In these, a letter- and figure-notation is used to specify three variables of colour: 'hue', the basic spectral colour; 'value', its quality of lightness or darkness; and 'chroma', its purity of hue, the degree in which it departs from neutral grey.

Hue. The whole spectrum is divided, on this system, into ten sections, ranging from red-purple (RP) through red (R), yellow-red (YR), yellow (Y), green-yellow (GY), green (G), blue-green (BG), blue (B), purple-blue (PB) to purple (P). Each of these sections is again subdivided into ten parts, signified by figures from 1 to 10, so that 1R is a red bordering on red-purple, 5R a mid-red and 10R a red bordering on yellow-red.

Value. Colour may be dark or pale, as neutral greys vary between the extremes of pure white and dead black. The position of a particular shade in this range is indicated by a figure between 1 (black) and 10 (white).

Chroma. This is the quality of pureness of colour. Most soil-colours are somewhat adulterated with grey. A colour of chroma 1 differs only slightly from a neutral grey, of chroma 0; one of chroma 9 is almost pure, whatever its depth or value.

Any shade of colour may thus be briefly described by a formula, such as '10R 3/4' (red bordering on yellow-red, value 3/10, chroma 4/10). This particular example connotes a deep-toned, somewhat greyish brick-red.

Nearly all soils are comprised within the range of hue 10R to 5Y (a mid- or canary-yellow), passing through the yellow-reds. A set of seven shade-cards at intervals of 2.5 degrees of hue, cover this range closely, each card giving the possible variations in value and chroma at that degree. A close match can thus be found for almost any soil-colour of the wet or dry sample and from such a quoted formula any worker can reproduce the colour specified easily and quickly, if he has an identical set of charts for comparison. The use of such a system enables accurate communication as to exact colours between workers with normal colour-vision and almost eliminates the subjective factor.

The use of the Munsell charts is becoming almost standard practice,

* Munsell Color Co., Inc., 10 E. Franklin St, Baltimore 2, Maryland, U.S.A.

in Britain as well as in the U.S.A., among soil-workers, geologists and others. Archaeologists would do well to adopt the same standard descriptions for deposits at their sites.

An attempt has recently been made (Carter, 1956) in the south-western United States to correlate the colour of archaeological deposits with the length of time taken to produce the observed weathering. In order to reach valid conclusions as to such a correlation, the other soil-forming factors (parent material, climate, exposure, etc.) had to be kept constant, so that the study was confined to a comparatively small area. The results cannot, of course, be compared directly with those from any other, where circumstances are significantly different. With these limitations, however, some interesting facts emerged, and it was shown that greater age could be correlated, on the whole, with more pro-nounced reddening, so that, for the particular region studied, the likely relative date of a weathered deposit of unknown age could be deduced from its colour-formula, as given by the Munsell charts.

Texture-description for soils and deposits

A range of eighteen textural descriptions for soils, corresponding approximately with their physical (particle-size) composition, has been designed and is widely used by pedologists. It is based on quite empirical data, which may be estimated in the field by simply handling a moist sample of soil and judging the proportions of the following qualities represented:

(a) Gritty feel, incoherence, cleanliness (not staining the hands)—*sand*. (Particles between 2.0 and 0·06 mm. diameter).

(b) Silky feel, incoherence, staining hands—*silt* (0.06—0.002 mm.).

(c) Cohesiveness, resistance to deformation, polish obtained by smoothing with the finger—*clay* (< 0.002 mm.).

No natural soil is a 'pure culture' of sand, silt or clay (though some consist overwhelmingly of one of these grades, with only small amounts of any other). The handling test aims at estimating rapidly the approxi-mate proportions of each present. When none of the main qualities—grittiness, silkiness, stickiness—is specially apparent, the soil is a loam—a fair mixture of all three. By handling a moist sample an appreciation of the mechanical composition can be obtained and the soil assigned to one of the standard textural descriptions:

1–4. Sand, coarse, medium, fine, very fine (silt + clay $< 15\%$).
5–8. Loamy sand, coarse to very fine (silt + clay 15%–20%).
9–12. Sandy loam, coarse to very fine (silt + clay 20%–50%).
13. Loam (silt + sand 30%–50%).
14–15. Silty loam, silt-loam ($> 50\%$ silt).
16–17. Silty clay-loam, clay-loam (20%–30% clay).
18. Clay ($> 30\%$ clay).

As for colour-description, the use of these systematic textural descriptions by archaeologists would greatly enhance the value of excavation-reports, substituting, for example, 'Deep red (10R 3/4) coarse sandy loam' for the 'reddish clay' or 'puggy soil' (without an attempt at colour-rendering) of all too many writers. A more exact description might suggest to a reader who had never seen the material something of its character and origin which might be important from the archaeological standpoint.

Gravel analysis

Rock-material from 200 mm. down to 2 mm. particle-diameter is considered as 'gravel', subdivided into cobbles (200–60 mm.), coarse (60–20 mm.), medium (20–6 mm.) and fine (6–2 mm.) gravel between these limits.

Since gravels often contain the implements of Palaeolithic man, who was the witness or the immediate forerunner of their formation, their study is of some importance for indicating the environment in which they were laid down.

For a quantitative grain-analysis of any sediment, it has been shown that at least 1,000 separate particles must be examined for different constituents to be fairly evaluated. The coarser the material, therefore, the more bulky is the necessary sample. For pebbles between 15 and 20 mm. in diameter, some 7.5 Kg. (16½ lbs.) would be needed to provide this, while only 25 gms would do so for the 2–3 mm. grade. It follows that the finer grades are more conveniently sampled and transported, but it is sometimes necessary to examine the sizeable rock-fragments also, and this is best done in the field.

The material to be examined is subdivided with suitable sieves into grades and the particles of each constituent are counted, either with the naked eye, with a hand-lens, or, for the finest grains, under a binocular microscope.

Zeuner (1932) has described the technique and the presentation of results.

The method is, unfortunately, unsuitable for use in our Lowland river-basins because the gravels consist of little else but flint. It could probably be usefully applied in the Highland Zone of Britain, as by Zeuner in Silesia, to elucidate former courses and catchment areas of rivers, estimation of their volumes and current-velocities at different times and hence of their contemporary climatic environments.

Orientation of pebbles

Since pebbles in fluviatile gravels tend to come to rest with their longer axes parallel to the current (in which position they offer the minimum resistance to the current and the maximum to further transport), a statistical analysis of the orientation of pebbles in ancient gravel-deposits is capable, within limits, of showing the direction of flow of the current in which they were laid down, should this be in any doubt. The method has been applied to glacial deposits, with a view to determining the direction of movement of the ice. In this way, West (1956) has studied the boulder-clays of East Anglia and has recognized the existence of distinct main directions for the ice-streams in his region, perhaps attributable to two distinct glacial phases, though the deposits cannot confidently be distinguished lithologically. It is, of course, necessary to distinguish between contorted bottom-moraine and true, englacially-transported material deposited by the melting of the ice. Only the latter will show significant and consistent orientation of the pebbles, while in the former they may be distributed in quite haphazard fashion, or even at right angles to the ice movement!

In the special case of roller-shaped pebbles in beach deposits, it has been found that these tend to lie with their long axes parallel to the shore-line. Observation of the average orientation of such pebbles would indicate the general trend of the contemporary coastline, if the lie of the ground left any doubt as to the relations of an ancient beach-shingle.

Shape-analysis

Methods have been devised to give quantitative expression to the degree of roundness of the particles in gravels and shingles, which is a measure of the attrition to which they have been subjected by rolling in the bed of a stream or on a beach. They are all extremely tedious, depending on the measurement and comparison of the areas of profiles, perimeters and angles, and the compilation from these data of indices of angularity, sphericity and so on. Measurements are carried out on individual particles, either directly, or, in the case of the finer sediments, by using their magnified images obtained with a micro-projector. Such an analysis may be used to define and delimit two deposits which, to the eye, are indistinguishable. If, for example, an archaeologically-important difference in age were suspected, it might be worth while to undertake a shape-analysis of the grains in the hope of establishing a significant difference. Cailleux (1945) has contributed a valuable paper on shape-analysis, whereby it is claimed that non-fossiliferous marine and fluviatile deposits can be distinguished.

Erratics

Study of the content of far-travelled stones in a gravel will sometimes reveal the temporal relationship of an ancient terrace to a particular glacial deposit. Should the foreign material prove to be derived from a boulder-clay or outwash-fan entering the basin of the river from outside, and be of a character not normally met with in that basin, any deposit containing such erratics must be later in date than the glaciation to which the ice is attributed.

Recognition and determination of erratics is a task for a competent petrologist. Not many archaeologists will be prepared to spend the time necessary to acquire the art, which would be useful chiefly to students of the Palaeolithic period.

11

Physical Methods (ii)

+ +

Mechanical analysis of finer sediments

BY THE BRITISH STANDARDS definition, 'gravel' includes all particles of
a sediment of a size ranging from small boulders down to stones of a
mean diameter of 2 mm. Below this particle-size the material is 'sand',
grading down to 'silt' at a diameter of 0.06 mm.

These terms refer exclusively to grading, and have no implications
as to the chemical nature of the particles. We think of 'sand' as being
predominantly quartzose, of 'clay' as chiefly complexes of silica and
alumina, but a sand can consist of little else but calcite, and so on. It is
'sand' because the particle-size falls within the arbitrary limits we may
impose for the term.

The British Standards metric scale of grades, widely recognized, even
internationally, is as follows:

Stones or cobbles		> 60 mm.
Gravel		60—2.0
Coarse		2.0—0.6
Medium	sand	0.6—0.2
Fine		0.2—0.06
Coarse		0.06—0.02
Medium	silt	0.02—0.006
Fine		0.006—0.002
Clay		<0.002

These divisions are based on a logarithmic scale, but the grade-
limits chosen are slightly irregular, since the ratios between adjacent
grades alternate between 3.0 and 3.3. The small irregularity has the
advantage of greater simplicity and of convenient round numbers which
are easily remembered and does not interfere with easy plotting of
results on a logarithmic curve.

Separation into grades of the finer gravel and sand material in a
sediment is most readily achieved with a suitable range of wire-mesh
sieves. For the silt and clay, sedimentation methods are called for
(see below p. 125).

Any scale of grades cannot but be arbitrary, since the material to be
subdivided consists of particles varying in size by infinite gradations.

Since the weight and volume of grades consisting of equal numbers of
particles depend on the mean diameters of the particles composing
them, a geometric scale is desirable. Fair sampling of a sediment depends

on the number of particles examined. The number of them available, in a sediment containing equal volumes in all grades, increases disproportionately if an arithmetic scale of grades is used, so that, the finer the particle size, the closer should become the subdivision of grades. A difference of 0.1 mm. between adjacent grades represents 10% in particles of 1 mm. and only 1% in those of 10 mm. diameter. Thus the volumes and weights in different grades should bear a roughly linear relationship to one another when plotted on a logarithmic scale, and this makes for ease of plotting results.

Sieve-analysis for sand-grades

British Standard millimetre sieves, having apertures of 2.0, 0.6, 0.2 and 0.06 mm., based on the logarithmic scale, are convenient for the subdivision of the sand-grades. All material smaller than 0.06 mm. (silt and clay) passes through them.

If, and only if, the material is clean and incoherent (i.e. is free from fine dust of the silt and clay grades) dry sieving is permissible. Where there is finer material, it tends to form aggregates which remain with the sand instead of passing the finest sieve and the sand-grains themselves may be masked and coated with such dust, so that their nature is not easily seen under the microscope. Moreover, much fine dust will certainly be lost during the sieving of the dry sample. For most soils and sediments, therefore, wet sieving is necessary, whereby the crumbs and uncemented aggregates of fine material are broken down and the larger particles washed clean. It is absolutely essential for quantitative work.

Owing to the probably friable nature of many of the most significant remains which the soil may yield on sieving, only agitation and jarring are permissible for dry sieving and washing with a not too powerful jet of water in the wet method. Pestling, kneading with the fingers, or even brushing, may damage or destroy microfossils and other organic evidence of value for study. After the washing and drying of the sieve and retained sample, it is permissible to jar the sieve slightly in order to allow to pass some smaller particles which may have been held in the mesh, when wet, by the surface-tension of the water.

Particles of the sand-grades are easily examined, and counted if quantitative relationships are to be determined, under the binocular microscope at magnifications of x10–x25.

Bones of small rodents and other animals, smaller molluscs and Foraminifera, plant-remains, including seeds, fragments of charcoal and other materials indicative of human occupation and activities may be recognized by this means.

From the mineral grains themselves something may often be deduced as to the sources of the parent materials, the manner of their transport and accumulation at the site and, therefore, about the conditions prevailing at or near the site at the time of deposition.

The actual percentage distribution among these grades of the material of a soil-sample may throw light on the nature of the deposit, though this consideration applies especially to the more general distribution between the sand, silt and clay grades.

Whilst the majority of sandy deposits is water-laid, sand-grains larger then 0.06 mm. may be transported by wind. If so, they travel in a series of leaps, of longer or shorter duration depending on their dimensions and on the wind-force. Dune material has often not travelled very far from its original source.

Silt and clay grades

Once the silt-grade is reached (below 0.06 mm.) a moderate wind is able to transport the grains, bodily suspended, for long distances, even hundreds of miles. The very finest material, of the clay grade, settles out only slowly, even in still air, so that it may, by turbulence, reach the upper atmosphere and eventually be deposited grain by grain and widely dispersed, mingling with more rapidly-forming sediments. In any case, it is thus lost as an entity, at least in terrestrial and marine shelf deposits, though deep-sea clays, forming extremely slowly far from sources of water-borne terrigenous sediments, are often mainly composed of air-borne dust, frequently of volcanic or meteoric origin also.

The silt is heavy enough, in relation to its surface-area and friction with the air, to settle out fairly rapidly whenever the wind-force falls below a certain moderate limit. The enormous and widespread loess deposits, occurring in the Pleistocene periglacial regions, were formed in this way, at some distance from the ice-margin, whence the prevailing winds blew and where the rock-floor, prepared by ice and frost, was plentifully exposed to its action. A loess, therefore, (or any wind-borne —as opposed to wind-transported—sediment) has the property that the majority of its constituent grains falls within the silt-grade, 0.06–0.002 mm.

Water-borne silts fall into two classes: those which are primary, consisting of weathered material washed out of the parent rock direct, and those, especially flood-loams, which contain as a secondary addition some material derived from earlier loess. The latter may still show something of a loess grading, though it is not loess *in situ*, but wind-sorted material which has in some way been caught up by flowing water and redeposited. Many of the loess-like materials found in this country fall into the second category, for though they have the typical sorting of loess they are clearly stratified or laminated by subsequent water-transport (Fig. 1, p. 28).

Particles of a mean diameter of less than 0.002 mm. fall within the clay-grade. This classification, though arbitrary, is not without a foundation in physics, for below this upper limit of size particles begin to be subject to the laws governing the behaviour of colloids. In particular, the enormous increase in their surface in comparison with their volume and weight brings into play phenomena like adsorption, which is concerned in the formation of the 'clay-humus complex', so important in soil-fertility, but whose actual constitution and nature is so little understood. The small size of clay particles renders them more responsive than those of the coarser grades to minute electro-chemical and electro-static forces, which, under some conditions, favour the formation of aggregates and, in others, prevent settlement of solids in suspension because of the mutual repulsion of the particles.

Even the slight viscosity of air prevents the ready settling of dust-particles of colloid dimensions and, in so relatively dense a medium as water, they may remain almost indefinitely suspended, unless con-vection-currents and other movements of the fluid are prevented.

Owing to close packing and the consequently minute interstices between the constituent particles, clays, while being avid and retentive of capillary water, are almost impervious to its passage as a body of fluid.

These characteristics of small particles make for some serious diffi-culties in the qualitative and quantitative mechanical analysis of soils containing a considerable clay-fraction. The tiny particles tend to form tenacious aggregates in the presence of electrolytes, and especially of calcium-ions, not only themselves adhering together, but coating some of the larger grains. Mere washing is not always sufficient to separate them and prolonged agitation with water or chemical treatment to remove or neutralize calcium ions may be necessary to disaggregate the sample completely.

For our purposes physical dispersion with the addition of a small amount of deflocculant is generally all that is necessary.

Methods of separation of the silt and clay fractions into grades depend on the different rates of sedimentation of particles of different sizes in a fluid (water or air).

Stokes' Law. The basic law governing rates of settling of spherical particles in a medium was first enunciated by Stokes, as long ago as 1851, and bears his name. It states that the velocity of sinking, under gravity, (v) of a given solid particle in a given fluid depends on the difference in density between particle (d_1) and fluid (d_2), on the radius of the particle (r), the viscosity (η) (eta) of the fluid and the acceleration (g) due to gravity.

Mathematically stated, this then reads:

$$v = \left\{ \frac{2}{9} \frac{(d_1 - d_2)\, g}{\eta} \right\} r^2$$

If the value of g is expressed in cms/sec./sec., that of r in cms, then v, the sinking velocity, is expressed in cms/sec.

This all looks very formidable to the inquirer who is an archaeologist rather than physicist or mathematician, but may be greatly simplified for practical purposes. The expression in wavy brackets is a constant for given experimental conditions, represented by C. Stokes' Law then reads: $v = Cr^2$—i.e., the velocity of sinking (in a given set of conditions represented by C) is directly proportional to the square of the radius of the particle. Given r, therefore, the value of v may be read off a table for computed values of C.

Where the fluid is water at 20°C and the particles quartz (specific gravity 2.65) the constant, C, is calculated to be 3.57×10^4, whence it is easy to compute the sinking velocity of particles under the given conditions.

Observed results, in the range of particle-diameters 0–0.06 mm. with which we are concerned, agree surprisingly well with the theory, despite the assumptions that the particles are smooth spheres (which is evidently not the case with soil-particles) and that all particles have the same density. As to the latter assumption, it appears, in practice, that some 95% of most samples consists of quartz (S.G. 2.65) and felspars (S.G. 2.6), so that a mean value of 2.65 or 2.7 will allow for the usually small proportion of heavier minerals present.

The viscosity of water falls about 50% in the temperature-range 0°–30°C, so that sedimentations should be carried out with some temperature-control to avoid fluctuations and errors arising from this cause. Provided the temperature variations are not frequent or of important extent, a numerical correction for changes in viscosity of the fluid may be applied, which dispenses with the necessity for maintaining strictly the standard temperature during an experiment.

Tables and other devices for the use of workers in mechanical analysis have been compiled, taking all the variables into account. One which is generally useful is the nomogram due to Crowther, which enables settling-times of various particles, according to Stokes' Law, to be read off directly in two operations by placing a straight edge across three scales. (See Brit. Standards Inst., 1948.)

Numerous techniques have been proposed and tried for the separation of finer sediments into grades and some involve complicated and expensive apparatus, mainly aimed at saving time without loss of accuracy.

There are at least half a dozen different approaches:

(a). Decantation—allowing part of the sediment to settle and pouring or drawing off the fluid with the remainder still in suspension;

(b). Elutriation—washing or blowing the lighter fractions away from the heavier by a continuous stream of fluid;

(c). Continuous sedimentation—weighing the sediment at intervals during sedimentation by a balance-pan immersed in the suspension;

(d). Hydrometer methods—Measuring the changing density of the suspension as fractions of the sediment settle out;

(e). Pipette methods—direct sampling of the suspension at a stated depth after stated times by means of an inserted pipette, the solids being separated and weighed from the measured volume of suspension;

(f). Visual methods—micro-measurement of particles removed by sampling the suspension, or optical measurement of the cloudiness of a sedimenting suspension.

No method is free from all objections. For our purposes, three factors are of importance in making a selection: simplicity, rapidity, sufficient accuracy for relative comparisons. This rules out at once both the very simplest, but time-consuming methods, such as Atterberg's (a), and the very highly mechanized, such as Odén's Balance, (c), above, or the Heywood Sedimentometer (f); these on grounds of expense. The apparatus is costly in both cases and would not be an economic investment unless analyses were being carried out continuously as a matter of routine.

Atterberg's method, a modification of simple decantation, probably gives the results which are most accurate in the absolute sense. A single experiment, however, takes about a fortnight! It has also the advantage that the grades concerned are separated and can be examined microscopically if required. Its greatest use is as a check, when doubts arise about results by other methods.

Hydrometer method

The method of choice, for our purposes—cheap, rapid and sufficiently accurate—is the hydrometer method. This is designed to estimate the quantity of solid material in a settling aqueous suspension by measurement of its density at a stated depth and point in time after shaking the suspension. Its cardinal virtue is that readings may be repeated, if results are dubious, without loss of the sample. Apparatus is simple, manipulation calls for no particular skill, but there is no final separation of the grades. The calculations involved are somewhat daunting to the non-mathematician, but are soon mastered by practice and may be simplified by the use of mechanical aids such as the slide-rule or Crowther's nomogram.

The method has been standardized (British Standards, 1948), but some slight departures from the standard method have been found advisable for the present purpose. The preliminary oxidation of organic matter and decalcification prescribed in the standard procedure constitute an artificial 'weathering' of the soil, which, in our context, evidently defeats the object of the investigation in many cases.

After the removal of material coarser than 2 mm., 50 grams of the sample are dispersed in distilled water, either mechanically, using the electric stirrer, or by a hand procedure, triturating with water in a mortar, using a rubber pestle. The latter process is only to be recommended when the mechanical stirrer is not available, for the pestling inevitably breaks down some small cemented calcareous aggregates, which are an integral part of the soil.

The suspension obtained is transferred without loss to a 1000 ml. graduated cylinder and the liquid made up to the mark with distilled water. The temperature should stand within a few degrees, one way or the other, of 20°C. After thorough shaking, end over end, and standing to settle, readings of the density are taken at stated intervals, timed by a seconds timer, and appropriately recorded. The temperature is also recorded at the time of taking each density-reading.

Readings of the hydrometer are taken at 0.5, 1, 2, 4, 8, 15 and 30 minutes, 1, 2 and 4 hours after shaking. A certain amount of practice is required to shake a litre-cylinder without loss, set it down, start the clock, wipe the neck of the cylinder internally, insert the hydrometer and obtain a confident reading of the rapidly-falling density within 30 seconds after setting the cylinder down. Thereafter, readings are very simple. Should any mistake be made, or doubt arise as to the accuracy of a particular reading, it is easy to re-shake and repeat the experiment as often as may be necessary, and this involves no great loss of time, for it is only the first few readings about which there can be any doubt. For the rest, there is ample time to steady the hydrometer and check readings as thoroughly as necessary.

By the use of tables or the nomogram and a suitable form for recording the results the calculation of the size of particle falling past the point of effective depth of the hydrometer at the given time and the percentage of the sediment still in suspension at that moment are easily calculated. The speed of calculation is soon improved with practice. Corrections have to be made for changes in temperature and the consequent changes in density and viscosity of the water and in buoyancy of the hydrometer, and for the reading of the hydrometer at the meniscus instead of at the true surface of the cloudy suspension. The resulting figures for particle-size and summation percentage of the sample remaining in suspension are plotted on semi-logarithmic graph-paper.

The sedimentation-cylinders used and the hydrometers are calibrated and the data recorded once and for all. These figures are used in every re-calculation of results obtained with these particular instruments. All details may be obtained from the British Standards booklet referred to (Brit. Stand., 1948).

When the silt and clay curve has been obtained, the contents of the cylinder are poured off without loss through a nest of sieves of 0.6, 0.2 and 0.06 mm. mesh. These retain the sand fractions, allowing the silt and clay to run to waste. The sand is washed on each sieve with tap-water, rinsed with distilled, dried and weighed. The weights are then inserted to give three or four more points on the cumulative curve, which should connect smoothly with the silt-clay curve if no mistake has been made, or washing of the sand not been completed. The form of the curve, thus obtained, may afford valuable indications as to the nature and mode of formation of the sample.

An ill-sorted flood-loam, for example, having some fraction coarser than 2 mm. and equal amounts of sand, silt and clay, will give a curve which is almost a straight line, crossing the form diagonally. At the

I

other extreme, a fresh loess, with more than 70% of silt and only small amounts of sand and clay, will give an S-shaped curve, of which the middle part will be very steep, between the silt-limits, flattening out rapidly at both ends. Infinite gradations between these two extremes will be encountered and their interpretation is not always easy, though some general principles to be taken into account are indicated in Chapter 17, p. 185 ff.

Some soils, generally owing to the presence of calcium carbonate, tend, even in distilled water, to form aggregates and flocks requiring chemical treatment for their dispersion. A few ml. of 10% sodium hexametaphosphate ('Calgon', used for water-softening) are generally effective in this. In extreme cases, where the soil contains much humus or, in some from arid climates, gypsum, even this will not prevent flocculation and washing of the sample is necessary before the hydro-meter experiment can be carried out. This is a tedious process, but presents no particular difficulty. Neither humus nor gypsum is very soluble, and large volumes of distilled water may have to be used for their extraction. Washing may be done on a filter until the percolate is colourless or free from more than small traces of sulphate, but the fact of persistent coagulation is generally not discovered until the weighed sample has been dispersed and transferred to the cylinder for sedimen-tation. In this case, it is easier to siphon off the supernatant water when settling is complete, to refill with fresh distilled water and to repeat the process until coagulation no longer takes place within four hours, the usual duration of the hydrometer experiment. Washing in this way may take several days, depending on the amounts of the unwanted constituents present, but the experiment need only occupy attention for a few minutes daily and other things may be done while it is in progress.

Lais on cave-sediments

The writer has been concerned with mechanical analysis chiefly to characterize loesses and other wind-sorted sediments and to dis-tinguish in sections of loamy material any evidence of chemical weather-ing, as indicated by a reduction in particle-size from the silt to the clay-grade.

Lais (1941) has used mechanical analysis for the investigation of cave-sediments, with a view to drawing conclusions as to the climates contemporary with their formation. The grade-subdivisions used by him approximate to the British Standards grades used here as follows:

    Lais' Grade I   = clay + fine silt + medium silt
            II = coarse silt
            III = fine sand
            IV = medium + coarse sand

He plots curves for each of these grades present in the different layers of the cave-deposit, interpreting an increase in the finer grades as an indication of chemical weathering and therefore of temperate climatic conditions. Increased coarse grades, on the other hand, suggest frost-weathering, and indicate a cold period for the formation of the deposit in question.

Subdivision of cave-sediments into the full scale of B.S. grades would give a more detailed picture, but Lais' rougher classification seems to yield satisfactory results (Fig. 6).

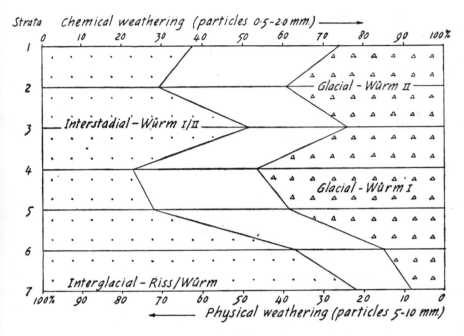

Kartsteinhöhle, near Eiserfey

FIG 6. Mechanical analyses of cave-deposits and their climatic interpretation (after Lais).

In addition to the laboratory work, he determines on the site the proportion of material in a deposit greater than 10 mm. in diameter, by coarse sieving. He thus reduces the sample to be taken for the laboratory determinations to manageable dimensions—about 1 lb. only.

Lais found that, in practice, the curves for the different grades followed each other so closely in most cases that even only two grades, greater and less than 0.5 mm., respectively, gave an intelligible picture for climatic determination. It seems, however, that the further sub-division of the loamy material would often be informative, by suggesting the proportional part played by wind in the formation of the sediment.

Cailleux on marine and fluviatile sediments

Cailleux (1947) has applied mechanical analysis and the resulting particle-size distribution-curves to distinguishing between fluviatile and marine sediments, not only in the pebble-grades, but also in the sand and silt sizes. His paper is valuable not only for the results, but for the discussion of the theoretical considerations attending their graphical presentation.

12

Physical Methods (iii)

◆◆◆

Heavy-mineral analysis

THE GREATER PART of most finer sediments of temperate climates consists of quartz and other forms of silica, because of their superior hardness and resistance to chemical attack in these conditions. Quartz is sometimes associated with variable amounts of felspars and other 'light' minerals, having a specific gravity of less than 2.89. When this light fraction is separated, the small residue of 'heavy' minerals can be more easily examined and identified.

The character and quantity of the heavy minerals from a 'drift' deposit depend on the nature of the 'solid' rock from which the sediment was derived by weathering and transport. Either the species of heavy minerals, alone, or the relative proportions of them present may be characteristic of a particular deposit and distinguish it sharply from another adjacent to it, but not, to the naked eye, very different in appearance. For this reason, it may be important, in an archaeological context, to examine the heavy-mineral content of a sediment, in order, if possible, to characterize it, to determine its provenance, mode of transport and deposition. Its history, if thus discernible with any degree of probability, may be of value in dating archaeological remains associated with it.

There are, for example, in East Anglia, two different series of glacial deposits, with which Palaeolithic industries are associated. The earlier is attributable to an ice-sheet which, developing in Scandinavia, crossed the North Sea basin and deposited boulder-clays, with their associated outwash formations, both of which contain a characteristic suite of heavy minerals originating in the igneous rocks of Scandinavia. Later ice reaching East Anglia arose rather in the highland areas of Britain, so that its moraines and outwash-deposits carry an entirely different series of heavy minerals, corresponding with the different rocks exposed in the areas where it developed and in those which it traversed in its advance (Solomon, 1932).

While the boulder-clays of these two ice-sheets may be readily identified in the field by their larger erratics and contained derived fossils, sands and finer water-laid deposits derived from them may have no evident macroscopic distinguishing mark. Nevertheless, their assemblages of heavy minerals remain distinctive and make their derivation from one or the other ice-sheet reasonably certain.

While conditions are not often as clear-cut as in this example, analysis of heavy minerals can often suggest, if not prove, the source of the material of which a sediment is composed and enable it to be distinguished from similar deposits of a different age. An instructive example concerned the dating of the Oldoway skeleton from Tanganyika, associated with mineral grains characteristic of a bed later than that in which it lay, thus proving the find to be an intruded burial from a younger surface with some admixture of minerals from later beds in the grave-filling.

The arbitrary line of demarcation between 'light' and 'heavy' minerals depends on the most widely-used method of effecting a primary separation from the lighter, by the use of heavy liquids. Bromoform, $CHBr_3$, a chemical relation of chloroform, is a heavy liquid with a specific gravity of 2.89. If a dry sample of a sediment is well mixed with this liquid and the vessel allowed to stand, the mineral grains having a specific gravity less than 2.89 will float, while those of 2.9 and over will sink, and are thus readily separated from the bulk of the sample. Further subdivisions of the heavy fraction may be separated in the same way by the use of still heavier liquids, such as acetylene tetra-bromide (S.G. 2.96), methylene iodide (3.3), thallous formate (3.4) and thallous formate-malonate (4.3). None of these is cheap, and some are exceedingly expensive, as well as having technical disadvantages such as chemical instability and volatility.

A simple apparatus for mineral separations by heavy liquids consists of a stoppered separating-funnel arranged in a retort-stand above a filter-funnel and paper draining into the stock-bottle for the liquid. The filter serves to hold the heavy-mineral 'crop' while allowing the liquid to drain away for re-use, the actual separation of the sunken fraction taking place by simply opening the cock of the stoppered funnel and allowing the sediment and some of the liquid to escape on to the filter-paper below (Fig. 7). The liquid must first be tested with a hydrometer to ascertain its exact S.G., a quantity is introduced into the separating funnel, the dry sediment sample added, the funnel well shaken and allowed to stand for some minutes for the heavy fraction to sink before drawing off the sunken fraction below. Several such operations may be needed for complete separation, for some grains inevitably adhere to the inside of the separating funnel after shaking and some of the heavier grains may be prevented from sinking on first standing through being floated by numerous surrounding lighter grains. The heavy fractions are united on the filter, a fresh filter substituted and the light remainder also collected by rinsing down with additional small quantities of liquid. Both fractions are washed on their respective filters, with alcohol in the case of bromoform, and allowed to dry by evaporation of the alcohol. The washings are saved for recovery of the bromoform, which is relatively expensive. This is done by repeated shaking of the alcoholic washings with a large volume of water, decanting off the greater part of the water and separation of

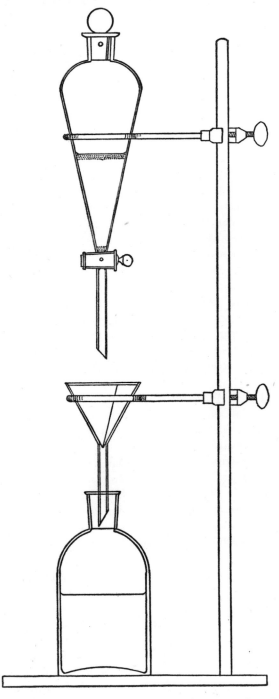

FIG 7. Simple apparatus for the separation of heavy minerals by bromoform or other heavy liquids.

water and clean bromoform in the separating funnel (the bromoform of course sinks and being relatively insoluble in water forms a distinct layer below, whence it is easily run off completely). The recovered bromoform is saturated with water and appears cloudy. It is de-hydrated and rendered fit for re-use by adding solid calcium chloride to take up the water. After standing for 24 hours over calcium chloride, it is clear and may be decanted off. Its S.G. should be checked after recovery (2.89) before restoring it to the stock-bottle. There is, of course, always a small wastage by evaporation and solution in the washing water, but the process of recovery is nevertheless economi-cally worth while.

After drying of the heavy-mineral crop, it should be weighed and the weight expressed as a percentage of the total sample.

Unless the operator is himself a competent mineralogist, this is the point at which he hands over the concentrated heavy minerals from his sample to the specialist. The preliminary separation saves the latter a considerable amount of labour and he will be all the more likely to render his report expeditiously. The identification of sedimentary mineral grains under the microscope requires considerable training. Any reader with an ambition to acquire the necessary skill and having access to a petrological microscope is referred to the numerous standard works on mineralogy and sedimentary petrography for information. As in most other trades, an ounce of practice is worth a ton of theory and his first steps should be taken with skilled advice.

Visual examination for inorganic and organic inclusions

At all stages of soil-examination the pocket-lens, with a magni-fication of about x 10, and the low-power binocular microscope (about x 25) are valuable instruments.

The coarser constituents of soils, such as stones and pebbles, bones, shells or macroscopic plant-remains are easily sorted out and individu-ally examined with the naked eye, but the sample is very likely to include admixtures in the finer grades also, which will be at least equally interesting and as important as the larger remains in determin-ing the nature, mode of formation and the environmental significance of the soil.

Preparation of a sample for low-power visual examination consists, first, of passing it, dry, through a sieve of 2 mm. mesh to remove particles of the gravel grades. Soft aggregates of over 2 mm. in diameter should be noted with the coarser material and then gently crushed with a rubber pestle or with the fingers to enable their constituents to be seen separately. The resulting finer grades are then washed with a jet of cold water on a 0.06 mm. sieve, until the silt and clay fractions are also removed. Only the jet should be used: rubbing and pestling to assist the washing will, perhaps, grind down organized structures and render them unrecognizable. Unless this washing is done a coating of fine dust may mask the character of the grains. After drying the lower surface of the sieve with an absorbent cloth, complete drying may be assisted by placing the sieve with the sand-grades in a warm (not hot) oven.

Once dry, the sample is spread out on paper of a contrasting colour (e.g. black for clean quartz sand) and lighted somewhat obliquely with an intense beam of light from a microscope-lamp. Daylight suffices for the hand-lens, but is generally not intense enough at the higher magnification of the binocular and is, in any case, too diffused to accentuate the surface-texture of the particles and to facilitate their recognition.

Examined in this way, the nature of most of the sand-grains will be evident. In most samples, quartz and other varieties of silica will predominate. The special examination and interpretation of quartz sands is dealt with below. Any non-quartz mineral grains which appear to be of interest may be segregated by hand, using the point of a damp camel-hair brush to pick up individual specimens. They may then be separately identified under the petrological microscope or by other tests.

Grains suspected of being of a calcareous nature may be treated on a slide under the low power with a drop of hydrochloric acid, when their effervescence will betray their nature. A similar test may be carried out, but to identify amorphous particles of organic matter by warming the slide with a drop of hydrogen peroxide. (In neither case should the objective of a good microscope be brought close to the reagent spray from the reacting particles. The binocular has a sufficiently long working distance to be out of harm's way, but a short-focus objective (1″ or less) should be protected with a large cover-slip cemented with mountant over the bottom lens.)

Charcoal is a frequent accompaniment of soils from archaeological sites and, where it derives from rain-washing of hearths, it may not always be present in fragments of a size to be determined with the naked eye. Among it may sometimes be found carbonized seeds, fruits and grain. Chemically it will be recognized by its resistance to concentrated reagents, so that, when present, it will invariably be found with quartz and other resistant silicates in the acid-insoluble residue (see below, p. 138) of a soil. If not already used, hydrogen peroxide will eliminate non-carbonized organic matter and, when the residue is ignited at a low red heat over a flame, the carbon-grains will be seen to oxidize with small bright flashes. If the presence of carbonized bone is suspected, but no fragments large enough to be identified from the structure are found, the ignited residue should be tested for phosphate.

Small organized particles, such as plant-seeds, Foraminifera, the smaller species of molluscs and immature individuals of larger species, separate bones and teeth of small land mammals, fish and amphibia will be recognized by their form and structure and may be picked out with forceps or the brush-point for detailed study.

Some inorganic inclusions of artificial origin, such as grains of burnt clay, pottery, brick, plaster, small beads, fragments of metals and their corrosion-products may also be seen, extracted and more clearly identified by suitable tests.

The character of many samples will be obscured, in the fresh state, by the presence of much calcareous or clayey matter. Thorough washing on a sieve will remove much of the latter, but the presence of much calcium carbonate, iron and manganese salts, often secondarily recrystallized and acting as cement between the more siliceous particles, will make the recognition of these, without further treatment, difficult, if not impossible.

Dilute hydrochloric acid in the cold suffices to dissolve calcareous cements, but if magnesium carbonate is present in any quantity, it will resist this treatment but dissolves on heating. Iron and manganese salts require concentrated acid and even prolonged heating on the water-bath for their complete removal. When their solution is complete, the dish is flooded with water and the residue is then panned, as in separating gold-dust, with several changes of water, to remove soluble salts and the finer insolubles. When the coarser solids settle, leaving the washing-water clear after a pause of 5-10 seconds, the residue may be washed on the finest sieve (0.06 mm.), dried and examined under the microscope. The preliminary dilution washing and panning is necessary so that excess acid does not come in contact with the fine brass-wire sieve.

Not only sand-grains, but siliceous and aluminous aggregates, and, as already indicated, charcoal grains, survive this process and may be properly examined individually.

Microscopic determination of plant-remains or pollen lies outside the scope of the soil scientist proper, but, as with the heavy minerals, if there seems to be an assemblage of botanical material which could be determined, a somewhat enriched sample may be prepared for submission to a competent botanist. Enrichment may be by hand-separation, if the remains are large enough to handle with forceps or brush, or by some kind of physical separation. Carbon tetrachloride (sold under the trade-name 'Thawpit'), among others will serve as a heavy liquid to float organic particles while allowing the minerals to sink. The technique is the same as that used for heavy minerals, only, here, it is the floating fraction which it is desired to separate for examination.

Sand-grain analysis

Cailleux (1942) made a special study of quartz sand-grains with a view to recognizing those which indicated transport by wind and evaluating them quantitatively as indices of periglacial conditions in the past. He showed that, far from wind action being confined to hot deserts, it is a constant feature of periglacial regions also, even where there is considerable precipitation.

He confined his attention to quartzes between 0.4 and 1.0 mm. in diameter, those above this size not being readily transported while those smaller are of too small a mass to have experienced to the full collisions with other grains and with fixed obstructions which give their character to the larger wind-transported grains. Intensity of wear increases with the size of the particle so that fairly narrow limits of grain-size must be set for any comparative study.

Cailleux distinguishes four types of quartz-grains:

(1). Unworn and angular. These are the product of recent comminution by weathering agencies and their relative youth is seen by their sharp edges and freshly-fractured surfaces;

(2). Worn, or rounded, and glossy. These are typically water-borne grains. Abrasion takes place by rolling on the bed of a stream and by friction with other grains. Owing to the hydrostatic loss in weight in water, adjacent particles have only slow, light rubbing contacts with one another. Corners and sharp edges are blunted and rounded but there is seldom any approach to a spherical shape. In time, all surfaces receive a high polish, but the acquisition of this may take thousands of years, so slight are the abrasive forces.

(3). Clean, well-rounded, matt-surfaced. These are the wind-rounded grains, and are typically spherical, ovoid or lentoid in shape. The matt surface is due to a multitude of bruises, evenly distributed all over the grain, sustained by repeated collisions at speed with other grains and fixed obstructions. Some few rounded grains, having fallen into water and being further transported may eventually lose their matt surface and receive the gloss of water-wearing.

(4). Dirty, rounded and matt-surfaced. These grains, with adhering traces of cement, are recently derived from older sandstones and their wind-rounded character was acquired before the deposition of those beds.

Examination under these heads, therefore, shows rather the total history of the grains examined than the immediate origin of the deposit from which the sample is taken. If, however, the proportions of the above four classes of grain in various deposits are determined, some interesting results can be obtained from their comparison.

The sample is cleaned by washing with water, panning off the finer material, acid-treatment if there is any cement and careful washing and drying. Grains coarser than 1 mm. are removed by sieving. A specimen is mounted in a cell formed by a $\frac{3}{4}''$ hole punched in a slip of heavy cardboard sandwiched between two $3'' \times 1''$ glass slides.

Examination is by low-power binocular microscope by reflected light incident at a low angle, against a black background. Under these conditions the individual grains can easily be assigned to one of the classes referred to. Counts of the different sorts of grain in the samples are expressed as percentages of the whole number counted. These are then mapped.

Cailleux' study was concerned with evidences of aeolian action in the Pleistocene of western Europe. He showed that Pliocene deposits contained very few wind-rounded grains, but that these increased in proportion with cooling climate in the early Pleistocene. In Britain, he found percentages as high as 25%-35% of wind-rounded grains only in the eastern counties, where they were derived from Scandinavian glacial deposits. In the areas of our local ice-sheets the proportions were very small, no more than 5%.

The method may be applied with caution to British deposits in an archaeological context, for today, there is practically no wind-action save in drier coastal areas. Our moist climate favours a close vegetation cover almost everywhere, so that, if an ancient deposit yields even 5% of wind-rounded grains, it is reasonable to conclude that conditions attendant on its formation differed in the direction of less moisture and perhaps lower temperature, or, at least greater extremes and perhaps greater continentality.

Several other workers have attacked the problem of the immediate origin of sands from different points of view. It is suggested for instance that marine sands are locally better sorted in grain-size than river sands and more distinctly rounded and polished (Guggenmoos, 1934). The methods for determining these features quantitatively are extremely laborious and belong rather to studies in sedimentary petrology than to those devoted to archaeological deposits.

The techniques have been tentatively used from time to time, but with no results to date of archaeological significance.

13

Physical Methods (iv)

✦✦✦✦✦✦✦✦✦✦✦✦✦✦✦✦✦✦✦✦✦✦✦✦✦✦✦✦✦✦✦✦✦✦✦✦✦✦

Microscopical examination of
undisturbed fabrics in soils and sediments

IF A SMALL fragment or crumb of a sedimentary deposit is examined under the microscope by reflected light, something may be seen of the grains composing it, of the way in which they are cemented together and the presence or otherwise of fissures, root-holes or voids. The walls of the latter may be coated with deposited mineral salts or organic matter and suggest the manner of formation and the dynamic changes at present taking place in the fabric. Owing to these possible coatings, however, and to the fact that the broken surface of the crumb is irregular, the grains themselves are hard to identify and the small depth of focus of even the lower powers of the microscope makes it impossible to keep more than a small part of the field of view in focus at the same time.

While such episcopic examination, either with a hand-lens or a low-power microscope, is helpful in visualizing the fabric of the specimen in the solid, and should not, therefore, be omitted, the exact information to be obtained about the specimen by this means is somewhat limited. The characteristic 'waxy' appearance of the walls of conducting channels in soil-types with much peptized and mobile iron (p. 98) is well seen and is very distinctive of these types. This is, of course, a surface-phenomenon and is not to be seen in the thin section.

If a smooth plane section of the fragment were prepared and examined in the same way, by reflection, under a powerful beam of light, a little more detail might be visible and the whole field of vision could be focussed at once, but even so, the material being often rather dark in colour, there is difficulty in lighting a specimen well enough for much more detail to be seen by reflection only.

The best method is, evidently, to cut a section of the sample thin enough to *transmit* light, like those made of hard rocks in petrology, but, with a relatively incoherent sediment or soil, sectioning presents some difficulties unknown to the worker on (say) igneous rocks.

Preparation of thin sections of incoherent materials*

The specimen must first be impregnated with some material which will hold the grains firmly in place during the grinding and polishing

* I am indebted to Mr E. O. Rowland, of the Geology Department, King's College, London, for much help and practical advice on this matter.

processes. Three materials have been found suitable for this purpose, in differing circumstances: Gum dammar,* a natural gum-resin from various Asiatic and Australian conifers (*Dammara* spp.); Santolite MHP, a synthetic resin,† and Lakeside 70C cement‡, a preparation made in the U.S.A. but obtainable in London.

Dammar is cheap and the most generally useful impregnator. It melts to a viscous fluid at about 100°C and becomes quite thin and mobile at about 150°C. It penetrates even the more fine-grained sediments adequately, but shrinks on solidifying and is very hard and brittle. It does not adhere well to glass or to coarser quartz-grains, so that these are rather liable to tear out during the grinding process. It is best used for all finer sediments. It is somewhat soluble in paraffin (kerosene).

Santolite MHP has a rather higher melting-point, impregnates nearly as well as dammar but is more tenacious when solid, though it still does not adhere strongly to glass. It is suitable for medium-grained material and the less dense fabrics.

Lakeside 70C is very tenacious, holding even coarse quartzes and flints extremely well, but it does not penetrate the sample as readily and, if heated for long at (say) 140°C in order to make it mobile enough for good penetration, it tends to undergo chemical change and to become rubbery. It is then practically insoluble in the usual solvents. It is therefore best suited to impregnating material of coarser grain which it can penetrate quickly and easily in a melt at low temperature thinned with solvents.

All three materials are soluble in xylol, toluol and acetone and their refractive indices are close to that of glass or Canada balsam, often used for microscopic preparations. Their refractive indices are not perceptibly altered by prolonged heating, even though some discoloration takes place in time.

Technique of impregnation

A dry fragment of the material is stood on a hotplate kept at 100°–120°C surface-temperature§, on which the impregnating medium is

* Gum dammar, obtainable from any chemical supplier.
† Santolite manufactured by Monsanto Chemicals Ltd, Victoria Station House, Victoria Street, London, S.W.1.
‡ Lakeside 70C, marketed by Cutrock Engineering Co. Ltd, Dollis Mews, Dollis Park, London, N.3.
§ The hotplate used by the writer is an ordinary 1.5 kW electric boiling plate with 3 × 500-w. elements in parallel and a 4-way (high-medium-low-off) switch. The 'low' switch gives a surface-temperature of about 140°C. Wired in series with the hotplate is a 10-w. double-slider resistance of 150 ohms. This is for use in conjunction with the 'low' switch only (with 'medium' or 'high' load, it would have to carry more than its rated current, would overheat and might burn out. It is therefore 'shorted' when the switch is used in 'medium' and 'high' positions). With the main switch at 'low' this resistance

melted in a small (e.g. 7.5 cms diameter) porcelain basin. When the plastic is melted the hot specimen is immersed in it. The time needed for impregnation depends on the density of the specimen and on its thickness. This is a matter requiring the exercise of judgment in each case, but an average sandy loam will be impregnated with dammar or Santolite in about ten minutes. If the sample is very clayey, half an hour would not be too long for a first trial. If unsuccessful, the impregnation may have to be repeated.

If practicable, the specimen should be roughly trimmed before impregnation to a tabular shape, using a coarse file, rasp or coarse carborundum stone, to a thickness of perhaps 5 mm. This is frequently impossible with the more friable materials and one must then select the most suitable chance fragment, regardless of shape. The tabular shape improves the chances of good impregnation, especially of fine-grained samples. In the case of the coarser, it will save much labour in coarse-grinding later.

When impregnated, the specimen is half lifted out of the molten resin with a glass rod, picked up gently with forceps and laid on a clean sheet of paper to cool. Until it is cold, it acquires little additional strength from the impregnation, so must be carefully handled. If properly impregnated, it should be strong and quite hard when cold. With Santolite the same treatment serves, save that the temperature of the resin could be a little higher (say 150°C) with advantage. If too hot, the resin may froth over the edge of the basin, so it should be watched until the process is going on quietly. Some evolution of bubbles is, of course, necessary.

Using 'Lakeside', unless very porous material is to be impregnated, it is best just to melt the plastic and then to add about an equal volume of solvent (50/50 alcohol/acetone) with stirring. The vapour given off is inflammable, so no naked flame should be near during this proceeding. The basin should be covered with a clock-glass between stirrings to avoid too rapid loss of solvent. When all is dissolved to a clear melt, the warm specimen is immersed in cold solvent before putting it into the resin solution. The clock-glass is then removed and all the solvent allowed to evaporate off slowly with the hotplate at about 90-95°C. This may take an hour or more. The process is complete when a drop of resin taken up on a glass rod is hard and brittle

gives perfect control of surface-temperatures of the hotplates between 65° and 140°C, at a room-temperature of about 17°C (63°F). The temperatures are read with a mercury-in-glass laboratory thermometer laid on the plate, graduated up to 200°C (the surface temperatures of course greatly exceed this maximum with the switch in 'medium' and 'high' positions).

Since three separate elements are accommodated below the plate, of which only one is in use at the 'low' switch-position, the surface-temperatures of different parts of the plate vary quite widely. This is a useful feature, and one soon learns where to obtain the temperature desired without having to adjust the resistance for minor differences.

when cool. If this drop remains at all plastic when cool, there is still solvent present and heating must be continued. When all the solvent has gone, the specimen may be fished out gently and cooled, as before.

First grinding and polishing

One flat face is ground and polished on the impregnated specimen. The largest surface which can be mounted on a 3″ × 1″ slide should be obtained. Obviously, mechanical aids such as power-driven diamond laps or carborundum wheels greatly reduce the labour of grinding, but excellent results can be obtained by hand-grinding with a circular motion on cast-iron or glass plates, using successively finer grades of carborundum powder lubricated with paraffin oil (kerosene). If the specimen is perfectly impregnated (or in any case with Dammar) the rough grinding may be done with water and this makes cleaning the specimen easy, for all that is necessary is to hold it under the cold tap and perhaps brush slightly. However, since clay-minerals swell with moisture, water is better avoided, at least in the final stages, and the writer uses paraffin for all but the coarsest stage of grinding save with dammar-impregnated specimens. The specimen is rinsed for inspection in a small quantity of oil in a basin.

When a flat face has been rough-ground, the specimen is carefully cleaned of coarse abrasive and transferred to another plate with the next finer grade of abrasive. If a single grain of coarser carborundum finds its way on to a plate used for a finer grade, deep scores may be cut in the already smoothed surface and the second plate will have to be cleaned off completely, a clean lot of fresh abrasive added and the smoothing begun again. Care in cleaning the specimen and the fingers (not forgetting the finger-nails!) between grades is well worth while and prevents damage and repeated work.

The smoothed face is again cleaned meticulously and the polish completed on yet another plate with the finest abrasive. A high polish, such as is required for metallographic specimens, is not necessary. Only four grades of abrasives are generally needed: '400', '3F' and '600' carborundum, and '600' Aloxite (alumina) for the final polish. For very thick quartzose specimens, a grade even coarser than '400' would speed rough grinding, but is seldom required in practice.

Cementing to the slide

The first ground-and-polished flat face is cemented to a 3″ × 1″ glass microscope-slide. Lakeside 70C is the best cement, because of its strong adhesion to glass.

The clean slide is laid on the hotplate at about 95 °C and a small amount of Lakeside applied by melting from the stick on its hot surface. Some bubbles may first form and these must be allowed time to disperse. The polished face of the cold specimen is laid in the cement on the hot slide, allowed to rest for a few seconds, the slide then taken off the plate on to a pad of paper and the specimen pressed firmly down so that no air-bubbles are trapped between its face and the glass. This requires a little judgment and timing. The specimen must not be heated through, or it may spread or crack when pressed down. On the other hand, if the slide is too quickly removed some bubbles will be trapped. At all costs overheating of the specimen must be avoided, or the impregnating plastic may generate bubbles of vapour between the polished face and the glass. Should this happen (and everybody makes mistakes sometimes!), the specimen should be quickly slid off the glass, be allowed to cool and mounting again be attempted at a somewhat lower temperature. The lowest practicable temperature— about 90 °C—is the best for mounting. At the same time, a somewhat higher temperature (say 110 °C) assists the cement to flow and to expel the bubbles quickly. The same hotplate probably affords areas simultaneously at these optimum temperatures, and these must be found by moving the bulb of the thermometer about from place to place. The pre-heating of the cement can then be done at one spot and the slide moved to one somewhat cooler for the actual mounting.

Second grinding and polishing

When the slide has cooled after cementing, the specimen is ground and polished on the other side to a transparent slip with a second flat face parallel to the first, having a standard thickness of 20-30μ (m$\bar{u}$) (0.02-0.03 mm.), determined optically under the petrological microscope.

Rough grinding is carried out as before, the slide being hand-held parallel to the abrasive surface to obtain even thickness. Parallelism should be obtained at the earliest possible stage. Any departure from it is harder to correct as the specimen grows thinner, but final adjustment is possible only when the preparation becomes translucent and the optical test can be applied. With practice, however, quite surprising accuracy is obtainable merely by eye. The slide should be frequently turned end for end during grinding, in order to distribute any consistent variation in pressure applied by the hand. A stop at intervals to cast an eye along the slide as held will enable corrections to be made as grinding proceeds.

When the specimen first begins to transmit light through cracks and root-holes, it is cleaned and grinding continued on the plate with the next finer grade. A single stray grain of coarse abrasive at this stage may ruin the preparation. The scratch of such a grain can be felt by the hand. If so, specimen and plate must be carefully cleaned and recharged with abrasive. This precaution becomes ever more necessary the thinner the preparation. As it becomes thinner it should be wiped clean from time to time (a special cloth for each grade, so as not to introduce any coarser grains!) and inspected for uneven thickness under the microscope, first in ordinary light, later between crossed

K

nicols in polarized light. Extra pressure is applied to thicker areas by tilting the slide slightly.

The approach to the correct standard thickness is seen by change in interference-colours of the quartz-grains between crossed nicols (Fig. 8). High-order colours are pale pinks and greens, those of the first order (indicating increasing thinness) clearer and more intense: green, blue, magenta, red, orange, yellow, grey, in descending succession of thickness of the specimen.

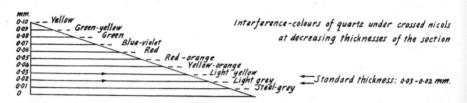

FIG 8. Diagram showing change of quartz interference-colours under polarized light with decreasing thickness of the section.

When the quartzes show blue-magenta (70-60μ), a change should be made, after careful cleaning, to Aloxite '600'. The desired end-point is reached when the quartzes all show grey under crossed nicols, or at the most a very pale yellow (30-20μ). This point must be approached with great caution, with only a few light rubs on the finest abrasive between inspections under the microscope. If too great haste is shown towards the end, the preparation is only too easily ground away completely—and all our labour is in vain! (This, too, happens to everyone at some time.) One fiftieth of a millimetre is a very thin slip, to be treated with extreme gentleness until it is safely under the cover-glass. Indeed, if the specimen is not ground quite parallel with the face cemented to the glass, one side of it or the other will begin to disappear before the rest is thin enough. Some adjustment is possible even up to the end, but becomes progressively more difficult.

When the preparation is thin enough, it is finally cleaned up by washing with paraffin, using a camel-hair brush cut to a stub, to remove the last traces of mud and abrasive. Excess cement is then carefully scraped away round the section with the point of a penknife or razor-blade until the slide and mount are quite clean. As much paraffin as possible is mopped off with a linen cloth or (better) a natural sponge, which does not leave lints. It is finally inspected before covering, for, once covered, the removal of any dirt or foreign bodies is a major operation and hazardous for the section.

Mounting

Cold mounting is preferable to the use of Canada balsam if there is no particular hurry to complete the slide, as for transmission by post.

'Permount'* is a colourless clear plastic dissolved in xylol, which takes a few days to dry and some weeks to harden completely. By its use, there is no danger of melting the impregnating or cementing media, introducing bubbles or otherwise spoiling the section, which has already cost some trouble to prepare.

A few drops (3-5, according to the size of the finished section and that of the intended cover-slip) are spread carefully over the section, one more placed in the middle of the clean cover-slip and the latter inverted and gently lowered on to the section. Slight pressure with a finger or a rubber-tipped pencil on the centre of the cover-slip spreads the mountant and the excess, with any bubbles which may have been trapped, is squeezed out from its edges. If there is a large excess, through misjudgment of the amount of mountant required, it may be quickly removed with a fine brush dipped in xylol, but it is generally better to do no more to the preparation until it is dry. It is better to use rather too much mountant than too little, or there is danger of incomplete sealing of the edges of the cover to the slide. The slide may be inspected directly it is mounted, taking care in moving it about not to get Permount on a short-focus objective from the excess of mountant round the edges. The preparation is greatly improved in transparency and brilliance by mounting, and this puts a very satisfactory finishing touch to a carefully and well-made preparation.

When the mountant is *hard*—some weeks later—the excess may be scraped away cleanly and a final cleaning with a rag dipped in xylol completes the job. Beware of attempting this before the mountant is really hard and brittle. If it is still 'cheesy' in consistency, the force necessary to remove it may shift or even break the cover. Removing the debris and re-mounting is a messy and dangerous job and puts off for another period of weeks the completion of the preparation. Once hard, the mountant will chip off cleanly and easily.

'Permount' cannot be 'cooked' like balsam before covering. Loss of solvent from the surface, even in the cold, causes the formation of a skin over the exposed solution which prevents the quick wetting of the cover-slip immediately it is applied. In this case there is danger of trapping air-bubbles, so that mounting should be completed as soon as possible. Moderate warmth, up to blood-heat (37 °C), may be used to accelerate drying *after* mounting.

Mounting in balsam

If a quickly-finished slide is needed Canada balsam may be used to mount it, but the process, involving heating the slide and finished section, is rather more hazardous and open to fatal mistakes.

Before using balsam it is recommended that the clean polished section be brushed gently over with a dilute solution of 'Durofix' (Nitrocellulose adhesive) in amyl acetate and be allowed to dry. Should

* Manufactured by Fisher Scientific Co., Pittsburg and New York.

the cement or impregnating resin melt during 'cooking' of the balsam, this adhesive film will hold the section together. Without this it would almost certainly 'spread' under the pressure of the cover-slip during mounting.

A few drops of Canada balsam dissolved in xylol are placed on the section and the whole slide laid on a *cool* hotplate (not more than about 80°C) together with a clean cover-slip having also a drop of balsam at its centre. The xylol evaporates slowly, leaving the resin soft and melted but ready to harden at once when allowed to cool. Complete evaporation may take some time at this low temperature. This is shown by dipping a glass rod in the warm balsam, which should draw out a long thread as it is removed, the drop on the rod and the thread hardening when cool. When this stage is reached, the cover-slip may be inverted, placed gently on the section and pressed down cautiously to expel bubbles and the excess of the balsam. The slide is then taken off the plate and allowed to cool. The balsam sets hard directly and the excess may be scraped off and the mount cleaned with a rag moistened with xylol.

A few practical hints may be useful for the prevention of imperfections in the partly-ground section at different stages.

If very fine-grained, the original fragment of soil, although prepared in rough tabular form, may not be completely impregnated at the first attempt, even with dammar, so that only a crust has been hardened (Fig. 9a). In the preparation of the first 'flat', if the specimen is ground beyond the plane represented by the dotted line, a central unimpregnated area will be exposed, which will grind hollow, owing to the rubbing out of some uncemented grains (Fig. 9b). If this is overlooked and the specimen is cemented to the slide, when grinding is completed to standard thickness the centre of the section will be ground completely away, leaving a hole in the preparation (Fig. 9c). There is only one cure for such 'soft spots'—re-impregnation and continued grinding until a perfect plane surface is obtained. As soon as the floor of the pit is reached, the specimen should be finished and cemented to the slide, for continued grinding is likely to expose more unimpregnated material at the centre. If there be any doubt as to the efficacy of the first impregnation, it is generally as well to be content with a smaller area of section rather than to grind through to an unimpregnated zone in an effort to obtain a larger section.

The converse condition—a lentoid form of specimen—occurs if too much pressure has been applied round its edges (Fig. 9d). This is often due to over-correction of errors of parallelism during the second grinding and results in a 'high spot' in the centre of the section. Unless this is carefully reduced to a true plane before the standard thickness is too nearly approached, the edges of the preparation are in danger of being ground away before the centre is thin enough. This can also happen when the grinding-plate becomes worn into depressions after prolonged use and uneven distribution of the wear. The best cure is to get a new piece of plate-glass—or simply to turn the old one over on to the other, unworn, side!

Some silty and clayey materials may have few or no reasonably large quartzes by which to judge the progress of the grinding in the final stages. Any which can be found should be studiously watched, for the greater part may be so fine as not to exceed the 30-20μ standard thickness, and these will appear grey between crossed nicols although the section as a whole is still too thick. The interference-colour of the *thickest* quartz-grains is the only guide. Thus, before the section is approaching the standard thickness, and many of the quartzes still show high colours, a few may appear grey and therefore suggest that the section is nearly thin enough. These paler grains are those which are not resting on the lower polished surface but are somewhat perched above it. On continued grinding, they will be removed altogether, showing what lies between them and the glass slide.

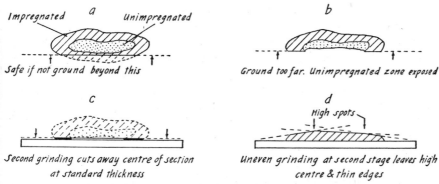

FIG 9.   Some avoidable imperfections in the preparation of thin sections.

In a few soils, notably those of Roterde type (see p. 102), there may be few, if any, quartzes at all. This is because, under the seasonally-moist tropical conditions of their formation, silica has been leached out, leaving little but clay and dehydrated iron oxide. The latter is extremely opaque under crossed nicols, so that the section will appear very dark and so seem still to be very thick, when in fact, it is close to the standard thickness. Great care must be exercised in the final stages of grinding and polishing and any quartzes, however insignificant in appearance, should be closely watched. Otherwise there is great danger of going too fast and too far and of losing the preparation altogether. In ordinary light the section of such a soil shows bright red when it is thin enough and a rather dark brownish red when the grinding has still some way to go.

Generally it is as well to obtain a specimen as large as can conveniently be mounted, say about $1'' \times \frac{7}{8}''$, as this facilitates grinding the second face parallel with the first. Often, however, the sample will not afford fragments as large as this. Several smaller crumbs may be mounted together if no larger pieces can be found.

Occasionally, as in podsol A$_2$-horizons, it is almost impossible to obtain crumbs at all, for, lacking cement, the quartz-grains fall apart altogether when dry. Some impregnating technique, using 'Durofix' solution might be used in the field, if the section is dry enough, to consolidate a sufficient fragment of the sand. Alternatively a 'debris preparation' can be made—a sort of 'pudding' of loose sand with Lakeside 70C or other plastic, which can be ground as if it were a natural crumb when cool. The 'pudding' may be made in a glass tube and the tube broken to release it. In any case it cannot be made on the slide direct, for many of the grains will rest on the glass only by points and edges and when ground down to the standard thickness will disappear almost entirely. The solidified lump of sand must have one flat face ground, as usual, before cementing to the slide.

The general principles and details of some successful techniques having been described, one must experiment and extemporize methods to meet special cases that may arise. Practice and acquaintance with the properties of the materials available are the only guides to the preparation of successful thin sections—especially in knowing when to stop polishing, short of rubbing the section completely away!

The techniques and materials here recommended are by no means necessarily the last words on the subject. Others may well be tried and be found superior. These suggestions only represent the best advice, based on personal experience, which the writer can offer at the moment.

As may be seen, thin sections afford a valuable means of studying soils and sediments morphologically, as opposed to investigating their nature by chemical analysis. Two materials giving identical quantitative analyses might be distinguishable at a glance when their microscopic structures were compared. Such a difference will almost certainly be due to some difference in formative environment—one which it is impossible to appreciate using the chemical tool by itself.

Useful as it is and sometimes leading rapidly to valuable conclusions, sectioning still takes the specialist considerable time, unless he has at his disposal expensive machinery to do at least the rough grinding for him. Could the excavator or inquirer have adequate sections ready prepared for examination, he would be likely to receive a report on his soils much more expeditiously than is at present possible. Their preparation requires some little practice and judgment rather than any great skill, and is certainly not beyond the capacity of any reasonably deft-fingered archaeologist with the will to learn the trade.

Even a petrological microscope would not necessarily be essential to a section-maker. Excellent preparations could be made with nothing more elaborate than a hand-lens of x 10 to x 15 magnification, with provision of simple holders for the slide and a 'Polaroid' disc below it with another between the eye and the lens, replacing the Nicol polarizer and analyzer of the compound microscope. This low magnification would not be enough for the proper examination and interpretation of the section, but would suffice to enable most materials to be ground down to the proper standard thickness. Not even a stand would be needed. The whole optical assembly could be easily made to be held up in the hand against daylight or a table-lamp. A slight refinement in the shape of a stand like that of a low-power dissecting microscope would be very convenient.

This is not the place for detailed instructions in the use of the polarizing microscope. The theory and practice have been well treated in many works on mineralogy and petrology. A beginner would be well advised to obtain an hour or two of instruction from a skilled practitioner before attempting too much by the use of books alone.

14

Chemical Methods (i)

AS WILL BE CLEAR from our consideration of the processes of weathering and soil-formation (p. 76), physical investigations will generally have to be supported by some chemical evidence if we are to obtain any clear picture of what is happening, or has happened, in a soil-profile or deposit associated with archaeological remains.

The total quantitative analysis of samples would nearly always be a waste of time (*pace* the few excavators who still send in isolated samples without specific queries to be answered but with a general request for them to be 'analysed'!)

We need, at first, some information, of no great exactitude in most cases, on only a few important points. Having considered the results from these, it will then appear what further, more accurate, determinations are likely to be useful, in view of the questions posed by the archaeological circumstances.

The range of significant substances to be found in most natural soils is not large. 'Trace-elements' are of great importance for the study of plant and animal nutrition, but the presence or absence of very small traces of these is, as far as our present knowledge extends, of no assistance in interpreting archaeological stratification.

The conclusions which we may be able to draw from analytical results are, in most cases, necessarily rather general, and we delude ourselves if we imagine that very accurate determinations will greatly enhance their exactitude. One might say, for example, that a layer in a section containing three times as much humus as any other was perhaps the A-horizon of a buried soil. This conclusion would be neither strengthened nor invalidated if we were to determine the exact proportion at 2.836 times—it could be anything between 2.0 and 4.0 without in the least affecting the issue. Nor is there any great significance in isolated absolute values. The information that a particular sample contains $12\frac{1}{2}\%$ of calcium carbonate tells us practically nothing by itself of use in interpreting it as a member of an archaeological section, but if this result is combined with the fact that a sample from a layer a few inches above it has none, while that next below has 25%, we may justifiably begin to suspect that we have a calcareous brownearth forming on, say, a floodloam. We could then proceed to confirm this theory by humus-determinations and thin-sectioning. Almost any set of figures showing an approximate 0–1–2 quantitative relationship in respect of calcareous content would have served equally well.

We arrive, then, at three preliminary conclusions as to chemical methods applied to the investigation of soils:

(1). The substances to be sought in natural soils are not very numerous;

(2). Great accuracy in determination of any constituent is not only unnecessary in many circumstances—it may be positively misleading;

(3). It is the *relative* values from horizon to horizon of chemical constituents, rather than the absolute values, that are significant. The absolute figures are only of very local validity and are not characteristic of any type of deposit as such.

In view of the first of the above considerations, we may now list the significant soil-constituents as follows:

Metallic ions (cations) Group III*: Fe^{3+}, Fe^{2+}, Al^{3+}, Mn^{3+}

IV: Ca^{2+}

V: Mg^{2+}, Na^+, K^+, $(NH_4)^+$

Acid radicles (anions): $(CO_3)^{2-}$, Cl^-, $(SO_4)^{2-}$, $(PO_4)^{3-}$, $(NO^3)^-$

Organic matter: Plant-humus and perhaps animal matter;

Insolubles: Silica and silicate minerals generally, carbon.

Seeing that we are not solely concerned with natural soils, but with archaeological deposits in the widest sense, we must, on occasion, add to these some industrial materials introduced by man:

Metals of antiquity: gold, silver, copper, tin, lead, iron and perhaps zinc, with alloys of these like electrum, bronze, pewter and soft solder.

Non-metallic materials: Stone, wood, bone, ivory, pottery, faience, jet, shale, and various mineral pigments; possibly glass and amber; rarely, perishable organic materials such as resins, bitumen, leather and textile-fibres.

Obviously many of these would best be studied by specialists, but small fragments of any of them may, from time to time, be found in samples of archaeological deposits, so that the soil-investigator is (quite properly) expected to recognize their general nature. It is *not* part of his task to undertake detailed analyses. He would, for example, report: 'This fibrous substance appears to be hide or leather—suggest that it be submitted to X for special examination'.

Some quick preliminary tests may be adopted, as routine procedure for all samples examined:

1. *Visual examination of sand-grades.* A small amount, about a teaspoonful—say 5 grams—of the sample is washed on the finest (0.06 mm.) sieve. This removes silt and clay, which frequently obscure the larger grains. After drying, the coarser residue is examined under the hand-lens or binocular microscope. This gives some idea of the

* The Groups designated by Roman numerals are the main subdivisions in the classical scheme of wet separations. Any textbook of qualitative inorganic analysis would give the full scheme, with operational details.

mineral composition and will indicate the presence of any intrusive materials of human use or manufacture, such as charcoal or metallic corrosion-products.

2. *Acid-insoluble residue*. The washed sample is treated with concentrated hydrochloric acid with heating, is washed, dried and re-examined. (Details on p. 138).

3. *Ignition in air*. When heated gently over a flame, and finally held for half a minute or so at a bright red heat, on a silica crucible-lid or platinum foil, certain informative changes may take place. Any un-carbonized organic matter first chars and may emit fumes or vapours of a nature approximately identifiable by their smell. The colour darkens. At a low red heat (c. 800°C), charcoal grains oxidize with small bright flashes. The ferric iron salts present in most deposits will be dehydrated, the yellow colour of limonite being changed to the brick-red of haematite. If any ferrous compounds are originally present (black, grey greenish or bluish colour), they will be oxidized to the ferric state and give eventual pink or red colours to the ignited residue. A refinement of this rough experiment is described below (p. 168).

4. *Presence of calcium carbonate*. A pinch of each sample is dropped gently into a basin containing cold, dilute hydrochloric acid. There will be vigorous effervescence if calcium carbonate is present. The slow emission of only a few bubbles is probably due only to air included in the dry sample. If in doubt, the reaction should be watched under lens or binocular, when any distinctly-effervescing grains will easily be recognized. Equal pinches of several samples in fairly quick succession will give a rough, but fair, idea of the relative amounts of carbonate present. The open basin facilitates this comparison and is speedier than separate tests in tubes.

5. *Presence of humus*. If a small amount of the dry sample is boiled briefly with caustic soda over a small flame, a yellow to brown, or even black, solution will be obtained. This is due to an alkali-soluble fraction of the organic matter and is regarded as a measure of total organic content. Seeing how little is known about the chemistry of soil organic matter, this is perhaps an unwarranted assumption, but it must be made for want of more exact information. Since a quantitative experiment to determine this fraction (see below, p. 176) is almost always necessary in soil investigations, this rough qualitative test may frequently be omitted. It is, however, useful for establishing quickly the predominantly organic or other nature of any dark-coloured deposit or body, of which the composition is in doubt.

6. *pH*-determination*. Treatment with 'universal' indicator or pH test-papers, to discover the approximate range in which the absolute acidity or alkalinity of the sample falls. Once more, it is routine with the writer to test the pH of all samples with some accuracy, using the

* An explanation of the meaning of the quantity designated by the symbol 'pH' is given below (p. 163).

electric meter (see p. 165). In the absence of a meter, the colorimetric determination is well worth doing.

A crumb of the material to be tested is wetted with distilled water and a few drops, as free from sediment as possible, are transferred to a glazed porcelain dish or a watch-glass resting on white paper. To this is added the liquid indicator (one or two drops) or the liquid is taken up in the absorbent test-papers. The colours assumed are indicative of the soil-reaction, and on this feature many soil-processes are directly dependent (see p. 193).

When these few rough tests have been applied, much has already been learned about the general character of a sample or group of samples. Indications will probably have emerged as to lines of further inquiry which could profitably be followed. In many cases of samples submitted by excavators accompanied by specific queries, these tests may provide an answer outright, or at least indicate where one may be found.

When the interest of the question warrants it, as, for example, when a conclusion of more than local importance hangs on the answer, more detailed and exact investigations are required. At one time or another the writer has found it necessary to identify, and sometimes to estimate quantitatively, nearly all the metals, radicles and other substances listed above, so that some suitable methods and materials must now be described.

Qualitative analysis for metallic ions (cations) in soils

The ordinary Group and intra-Group separations by wet methods for metals and radicles are long-established, widely known and reliable. This is not to claim that they are the only suitable ones, even among the classical methods. It happens that the writer is most familiar with these and so has used them with satisfaction, but doubtless others have been developed which might be superior. The archaeologist cannot at the same time be in the front rank of chemical research, so he must use the tools he has and be grateful for hints on improved methods from specialist chemical colleagues.

Unless it is a question of identifying a metal or alloy, Groups I and II in the analytical scheme are not generally significant and, once it has been established that these metals are absent, the examination can proceed at once to those of Group III, some of which are almost certain to be present in natural soils.

A difficulty at once presents itself. Phosphates, at least in small amounts, are almost inseparable from sites of human occupation. In many cave-earths, for example, bone-remains contribute massive amounts of phosphate to the deposits. Even in a phase of desertion by human inhabitants, bat-guano and the castings of owls and other birds of prey may add to the concentration.

For qualitative purposes, therefore, iron may be identified in the ferric state by a spot-test in acid solution with potassium ferrocyanide, when phosphate does not interfere. A drop of an acid (HCl) extract of the soil is placed on a filter-paper or white glazed tile and a drop of the reagent added. A very strong blue coloration (prussian blue) shows the presence of ferric iron. If there is not an excess of phosphate present, alcoholic alizarin will give the characteristic pink lake with aluminium, tested in the same way and finally exposed to the fumes of ammonia by being held over the unstoppered ammonia-bottle. If an excess of phosphate is suspected, or known to be present, the phosphate precipitate obtained on making the test solution of Group III metals alkaline with ammonia should be filtered off, redissolved in dilute acid and the aluminium test made with the solution. Though iron interferes, the two tests may be made on the same paper, by first precipitating iron with ferrocyanide and then treating the diffusing fluid beyond the blue zone with alizarin, when the red lake of aluminium will be obtained. These tests are very delicate and reliable. If, on the other hand, the metals of Groups IV and V are to be sought in the same solution, it is necessary to remove phosphate and the iron group in the usual way, as basic ferric phosphate and as the hydroxides respectively. In this case, no abbreviation seems possible.

Of the iron group, manganese presents no problem if no other metal is sought. Even, as is usual, in the presence of much iron, fusion of the dry soil with excess sodium carbonate on platinum foil or crucible-lid (nickel will serve if platinum is not available!), followed by extraction of the melt with dilute sulphuric acid, gives the purple colour of sodium permanganate at once. Even the deep blue-green colour of the cooled melt (sodium manganate) is specific, being quite unlike the apple-green of ferrous iron, which is sure to be there also. The permanganate colour is evanescent if excess iron is present, so that this method will not serve for quantitative work without prior separation of manganese from iron by the standard method.

Calcium is the only member of Group IV important here. Occurring chiefly as the carbonate, its presence may be relied on if there was any effervescence with acid in the preliminary tests. In the absence of more than traces of phosphate, sulphate and magnesium, it can be quantitatively estimated, if somewhat roughly, as the carbonate. The presence of phosphate and/or sulphate, the only other calcium salts likely to be present, may readily be recognized in the acid extract of a soil by ammonium molybdate and barium chloride reagents respectively. An elegant and reliable estimation of calcium is, however, described below (p. 169).

Magnesium is rather more difficult, but, save in areas where the Magnesian Limestone has had a part in the formation of the soil, the metal is not likely to introduce serious inaccuracy into the estimation of calcium by carbonate.

Wood-ash contains perceptible quantities of magnesium, so that habitation and industrial deposits are likely to show some small amount of the metal, unless subsequently decalcified. Should there be any doubt regarding the presence of magnesium, it will be necessary to carry out the full calcium and magnesium estimation by titration with sodium versenate, as described on page 169. This is much more rapid than gravimetric methods.

The flame-test (brick-red flame when a platinum wire wetted with an acid (HCl) solution of the unknown is held low on the margin of a blue bunsen flame) will, of course, show calcium by itself, if present in fair quantity, but is likely to be masked by the intense yellow sodium flame, if that metal is present in more than traces.

The alkali-metals, sodium and potassium, though ubiquitous as traces, have salts too soluble for preservation in important amounts at archaeological sites, at least under our moist climatic conditions. In arid climates they do, of course, play an important part in soil-chemistry. Even wood-ash, a likely source of potash on inhabited sites, seldom proves to have survived unleached. If exposed to the weather, the first downpour will dissolve out most of the potassium carbonate. Once more, the flame-tests are useful (yellow for sodium, lilac for potassium) if calcium is first removed. The flame-photometer, for the estimation of these three bases in a mixture by the intensities of their flame-colorations, is referred to below (p. 171).

Ammonium compounds, like those of the rest of Group V, are usually of no great significance because of their great solubility in our climate. They are gradually formed through the breakdown of animal and vegetable nitrogenous organic compounds (largely proteins) and therefore constantly accompany man, animals and plants, wherever they live or die. For this reason, the test for ammonia on boiling with caustic soda should not be omitted. In the examination of organic matter, nitrogen estimation by Kjeldahl's method has proved itself in the examination of the Piltdown remains, as well as on other occasions (see p. 178).

Qualitative analysis for acid radicles (anions) in soils

Among the acid-radicles, chloride and nitrate, because of their solubility, seldom persist in any quantity. Nevertheless, as for ammonium and the alkalies, the respective tests with silver nitrate and the brown-ring test are quick and worth making if the result seems likely to be significant. One should bear in mind that any traces found have a good chance of having been recently introduced rather than representing an original feature of the soil.

Carbonate has already been referred to. Its estimation is dealt with below (p. 171ff.).

Sulphate, usually present as the calcium salt, is not uncommonly found on ancient sites, where it occurs as a component of wood-ash and, in the case of more advanced civilizations, as wall-plaster. Another possible source should not be over-looked. Modern farm fertilizer, ammonium sulphate from the gas-works, is a common nitrogenous 'artificial' on cultivated land. Nor is sulphate in the soil necessarily due to the activities of man, whether ancient or modern. Selenite and gypsum (calcium sulphate) are common minerals of the Trias and of drifts derived from this. Marcasite and pyrite occur widely as nodules in the Chalk and elsewhere, and sulphates are sometimes readily formed by weathering and oxidation of these sulphides. Sulphate associated with elementary carbon is an indication of wood-ash. Sulphate is readily detected in acid solution by the addition of barium chloride, giving a white crystalline precipitate of barium sulphate. For our purposes it may be gravimetrically determined by the same reaction, though for the most accurate results it is probably best to carry out a preliminary fusion of the soil with sodium carbonate, so as to remove all heavy metals, and, after leaching the melt with water and filtration, to use the resulting sodium salt for the sulphate determination.

Phosphate is of the highest importance. Of the breakdown-products of animal matter it, alone, may be relatively fixed and persistent in the soil, usually in the form of the calcium salt. In acid surroundings, however, and in all soils poor in bases, phosphates are likely to be washed out also. The quantitative method, by colorimetry, is dealt with more fully below (p. 174 ff.), but the mere presence of phosphate can easily be shown in an acid extract of the soil by boiling with ammonium molybdate and nitric acid, when a voluminous canary-yellow crystalline precipitate is formed even with small quantities. This is a simple and most delicate test. The test-solution being acid, nothing else is likely to interfere.

Silica and silicates are almost universally present in soils of temperate regions, owing to their hardness and chemical stability. The chemistry of rock-forming silicates is a subject on its own (see Groves, 1951) and does not closely bear on most human problems posed by soils from temperate climates. In tropical conditions, however, where, at the higher temperatures prevailing, silica may become mobile in the soil, the relation between silica and the sesquioxides of iron, aluminium and manganese is a valuable index of the degree of weathering under-gone by the soil in comparison with the parent rock.

The subject is not irrelevant even in our regions, for climates of the not too remote geological past have caused some tropical weathering here also. Such ancient soils, or their redeposited remains, may sometimes be associated with the works of prehistoric man and require interpretation.

Silicate analysis by gravimetric methods is very time-consuming and, on the whole, unproductive of commensurate results in our con-text. Silica, free and combined, may be rapidly estimated by loss in weight on repeated evaporation of a sediment in a platinum vessel with excess hydrofluoric acid, which does not attack the remaining soil-constituents, in particular, the sesquioxides.

Since hydrated silica and some silicates are appreciably soluble in dilute acids and tend to remain in colloidal solutions, an acid extract of a soil to be examined for metallic ions may well contain some quantity. If present, they will be precipitated by ammonium chloride and interfere in the Iron Group (III). Repeated evaporation with concentrated hydrochloric acid converts them into insoluble silica. The solution containing the metals should, therefore, be prepared at the outset by boiling with concentrated acid and evaporating to dryness. This operation should be carried out on a water-bath, as overheating may render other constituents insoluble also.

Carbon and total organic matter

Elementary carbon is a regular accompaniment of human habitation and funeral ceremonies, being derived, generally, from the incompletely-consumed fuel of hearths and from burnt bones. The possibility of naturally-caused forest and heath fires must also be borne in mind. Sizeable pieces of charcoal can be used to identify tree species of the time, but tiny crumbs occur frequently, and often in quantity, in archaeological deposits.

Owing to its resistance to concentrated reagents, carbon is found, during chemical investigations, with the insolubles, where it is easily recognized visually. Its estimation is not so easy, however, for the situation is almost always complicated by the presence of uncarbonized organic matter also. Simple ignition and calculation of the loss in weight will not do, for the uncarbonized fraction is also destroyed, water of hydration will certainly be lost from some of the mineral components (as, for instance, the iron oxides) and any ferrous iron will be oxidized to ferric, with an unknown gain in weight. If humus, ferrous iron and combined water are also known from other experiments the loss in weight on ignition can be made to yield a figure for free carbon, but this involves four separate determinations. It is possible that some quantitative method of physical separation, such as froth-flotation or a heavy-liquid separation (p. 139) might be devised to segregate free carbon for estimation.

Uncarbonized organic matter is estimated by one or other of the 'wet-combustion' methods (see Wright, 1939, for details)—oxidation with hydrogen peroxide, potassium dichromate or potassium permanganate. The first is the simplest—heating with an excess of H_2O_2 made just alkaline with ammonia, filtering, washing, drying and reweighing. Frothing is hard to control (alcohol, of course, cannot be used to kill the froth) and it is difficult to say when the reaction is complete. Permanganate is easier from this latter point of view since the persistence of a pink colour shows when the oxidation is complete, but the residue of brown Mn_2O_3 must be taken into account in the final weighing, for treatment with acid to remove it would remove other materials, such as iron oxides, naturally present. Ferrous iron is also oxidized with the organic matter, and this disadvantage applies equally to the dichromate-oxidation. In view of these various objections, therefore, the estimation of the alkali-extractable part of the uncarbonized organic matter, taken to be a fixed proportion of the total, is usually relied on. The assumption may well be unwarranted, but we have at present no yardstick by which to criticize it. The method is more fully described below (p. 176). It has hitherto yielded reasonable and satisfactory results.

15

Chemical Methods (ii)

✦✦

Qualitative analysis for the metals of antiquity

THE QUANTITATIVE ANALYSIS of ancient metallic objects, the detection of traces of impurities and the analysis of corrosion-products and metallurgical wastes (slags) are all tasks for skilled specialists, but because fragments of all such materials are found from time to time in samples of archaeological deposits it is useful to be able roughly to characterize them.

Owing to the limited number of industrial metals available to the ancients (see list, p. 153), their identification under these circumstances is not difficult.

Gold. If present in appreciable quantity, it should be visually recognizable as the metal, save in the case of very thin leaf gilding, when the decay of the underlying base metal may have caused the gilt to break up into finely-divided powder.

The sample is evaporated almost to dryness on the water-bath with concentrated nitric acid. There may be an insoluble residue. If black, this may consist of carbon or finely-divided gold. In the latter case, it should be separated, washed, dried, ignited and examined under the microscope. Ignition destroys carbon and, if the residue is still visually unidentifiable, a confirmatory chemical test for gold should be tried.

Tin. If the acid-insoluble residue is white, it probably consists chiefly of metastannic acid, derived from tin or bronze. There may be traces of arsenic, bismuth or other Group II metals. These are archaeologically irrelevant, being unknown to the ancients, and are usually too slight to interfere, so they may be neglected.

The acid extract is diluted with 4-5 times its volume of water and boiled. Repeated filtration, using macerated filter-pulp and a heavy-weight filter-paper (Whatman No. 42) may be necessary for the separation of the metastannic acid, which should be washed with dilute HNO_3. (If water is used for the washing, the insoluble tends to peptize and will continue to pass the filter as a colloidal sol.) The residue is reduced to metal with zinc and dilute HCl. On dissolving the metal in cold HCl of sufficient concentration to give a clear solution, stannous chloride is formed and the presence of tin may be confirmed by the Herberg-Meissner flame-test.*

This procedure has the great advantage of separating tin at the outset, thereby enabling bronze to be quickly differentiated from copper. In the more usual extraction of the sample with dilute HNO_3, tin is not available for confirmation until after the separation of Group IIb, which calls for considerably more time and manipulation.

The filtrate from the metastannic acid separation then contains any other metals present.

Copper will, almost certainly, be immediately identifiable by the light blue colour of its nitric acid solution. The green corrosion-products or the pinkish-red of cuprous oxide next to the unchanged metal surface will have removed any doubt about this in the first place, in the case of bronze-corrosion.

Silver and lead, if present, are quickly and easily separated by their chlorides in Group I; tin having already been identified, copper remains the only metal of Group II. After precipitation and separation of copper sulphide there may remain iron and zinc.

Ferric iron shows readily by its yellow chloride, but if organic matter has not first been destroyed in the sample before the first acid extraction, a yellow acid-soluble fraction of the humus may simulate iron at this point, if present in sufficient amount. Iron is precipitated with excess NaOH, zinc, if present, being separated by filtration as zincate in the excess. The yellow humus-fraction, being also soluble in alkali, passes the filter with the zinc. Unless its existence is taken into account it will puzzle the chemist why some of the 'iron' appears, against all the rules, to be unprecipitable by excess soda! One forgets the ubiquitous humus when performing an *inorganic* analysis.

In the case of slags from ancient metallurgical operations, these may consist of glassy silicates and will probably not readily yield metallic salts to acid. Even if they do so, silica will almost certainly interfere in the separation of Group III. In this case the slag must be finely ground and be fused with an intimately-mixed large excess of sodium carbonate. On extraction of the melt with water, the insoluble carbonates of the metals may be separated and examined as above. Beyond this, the

* Herberg-Meissner test. A test-tube filled with cold water is dipped in the solution and immediately held and rotated in a small blue bunsen flame. Bright blue flashes appear at the cold surface of the tube, indicating the presence of tin. No other metal interferes. The blue colour of tin is distinctive and cannot be mistaken for the normal colour of the bunsen flame. A *small* flame is essential, otherwise the temperature of the surface rises too quickly and the test will fail even in the presence of much tin. A fair concentration is, in any case, necessary, for the test is not very delicate.

analysis of slags, corrosion-products and alloys is properly the field of the metallurgist.

For the identification of single metals, the dry method, fusion of the unknown substance with sodium carbonate on carbon before the blowpipe, is a valuable tool, as are the borax beads and flame-tests. They are not so useful for the somewhat complicated mixtures often found in our particular circumstances.

Quantitative determinations

The rough preliminary tests and the qualitative examination having given some indication of the general character of a series of samples from an archaeological section, it will often be the case that more detailed, and especially quantitative, information about certain features indicated will be of value in interpreting the section. In any one case, only a few quantitative experiments will be required, but there is quite a variety of estimations which may have to be carried out on particular occasions.

Hydrogen-ion concentration (pH)

The chemical 'reaction' of a soil-sample frequently determines the sort of changes which can take place in it and is a quantity which it is generally desirable to know at the outset of any chemical examination. More exactly, the reaction is expressed by the hydrogen-ion concentration, denoted by the symbol 'pH'. This is a measure of the absolute degree of acidity or alkalinity of a solution, and is the negative exponent of the actual concentration of H^+-ions in grammes per litre.

Pure water contains only 10^{-7} (1/10,000,000) grammes of H^+-ions per litre, and is the standard of chemical neutrality (neither acid nor alkaline), expressed as pH 7.0. More H^+-ions than this in a solution confer on it an acid reaction. Thus, 10^{-6} grammes/lit. (pH 6.0) would be the measure of a slightly acid solution, so that *decrease* in the pH figure denotes *increasing* acidity. pH values higher than 7.0 denote alkalinity.

In practice, the pH scale ranges from 0 to 14, the range found in moist-temperate soils varying between about 4.0 (very acid) to something over 9.0 (strongly alkaline), the great majority giving values between 5.5 and 8.5.

Various methods exist for the measurement of pH values, of which two recommend themselves for the present purpose.

Colorimetric method using the B.D.H. 'Capillator'* A few drops of aqueous solution are prepared from the soil with distilled water, to which is added an equal volume of a coloured indicator solution. The whole is mixed, taken up in a capillary pipette and compared for

* Obtainable from Messrs British Drug Houses, Ltd, Poole, Dorset. Outfit with complete directions.

colour with a ready-made range of similar sealed capillaries, containing solutions of the same indicator at known pH's, each labelled with its appropriate value. Several different indicators are provided, each covering part of the pH range to be tested. A preliminary test with an 'universal' indicator shows the part of the range in which the value for a particular sample falls. The appropriate indicator is thus chosen for the more accurate test by colour comparison. The same 'Universal' Indicator (B.D.H.) has already been referred to in connection with the preliminary tests (p. 154). The fine capillary tubes used minimize the difficulty arising from the unavoidable turbidity of unfiltered solutions extracted from soils, which would otherwise make the colour comparisons very difficult.

The 'Capillator' outfit is packed in a case small enough to be accommodated in a large pocket and could be used in the field under favourable conditions. Experience has shown, however, that it is better, and more economical of time on the site, to collect samples and take notes in the field and to defer pH- and other determinations to a later time, when they can be carried out at leisure and under more propitious conditions.

Drawbacks of the method are the time consumed in testing considerable numbers of samples, owing to the constant 'washing up' and rinsing with distilled water of the tiny glasses and capillaries. Without this care, no degree of accuracy can be assured. The temptation to hasten unduly is very great and, in any doubtful case, a repeat test with carefully-cleaned vessels is the only check possible.

Properly and systematically carried out, the method has proved, by comparison with results obtained with the direct-reading meter, to be perfectly adequate for our purposes.

pH test-papers* (**simplified colorimetric method**). Small books of absorbent test-papers, designed to cover the normal range of soil-reactions, are now obtainable and make the measurement of pH, even in the field, a very simple matter. A pinch of soil is moistened with distilled water on a watch-glass, saucer or other carefully-cleaned vessel and a few drops of liquid taken up in the paper torn from its book. The colour assumed by the indicator with which the paper is impregnated is matched with the colour-scale printed on the inside cover and the corresponding pH-value read off.

As most of the writer's work has been done in the laboratory and with the assistance of an electric pH-meter, no great experience has been obtained with this method. Its simplicity and the fact that it could easily be used in the usual hut provided for tools and drawings on an excavation suggest that it might be useful to many archaeologists on the site, where the highest accuracy would not be required. A bottle of distilled water, a glass pipette with a rubber teat and a watch-glass would be all the apparatus required.

* Supplied by Messrs Johnson & Sons, Hendon, Middlesex.

Electrical method. The direct-reading meter. This is, without question, the method of choice, but is clearly only available to workers having a well-equipped laboratory. It would only be worth its comparatively high cost if pH determinations are required in numbers.

The apparatus relies on the potential difference set up between a calomel and a glass electrode immersed in the solution under test. The resultant E.M.F. is measured by balancing it against that given by a standard solution of known pH, adjusting a potentiometer until the galvanometer shows no deflection when switched successively into the two circuits. The potentiometer is calibrated to read directly in pH units.

Standardization of the known E.M.F. is effected, before each batch of readings, by setting one potentiometer to pH 3.57 and balancing this against another until a nil deflection is obtained when the electrodes are immersed in a freshly-made saturated solution of potassium hydrogen tartrate (KH$\overline{\text{T}}$). This has been shown to yield a solution in distilled water of constant pH 3.57 within very narrow limits. Having well rinsed the electrodes with distilled water and substituted a solution of unknown pH, the potentiometer is again rotated to obtain a nil deflection, when the unknown pH may be read from the dial directly.

Proof of the reliability of this instrument is obtained by the fact that, after testing a series of unknowns, when the standardization is checked again by the KH$\overline{\text{T}}$ solution, a reading correct within about 0.02 pH units is given.

The instrument is designed to be portable and to run off dry batteries. Its portability, however, is limited and it would be unthinkable to attempt to use it in the field! In the laboratory, mains-operation is obviously desirable in the long run and the makers* have provided at small cost a transformer and rectifier with a smoothing circuit, which has proved entirely satisfactory. A small grid-bias dry battery requires replacement from time to time.

Some precautions have to be observed. A few minutes must be allowed, when first switching the meter on, to allow the valves to warm up to a constant temperature, before a steady reading is obtained. If very widely different pH's are successively measured, the electrodes require a minute or two to settle down. All electrical connections must make good contact. The E.M.F.'s measured are in millivolts and without good contacts the very sensitive instrument becomes unstable. The glass electrode, especially, is very fragile and must be used and handled with extreme care to avoid breakage, for replacements are not inexpensive. The water used for pH determinations must be of a high degree of purity. The best is provided by percolation through a bed of the new ion-exchange resins in a de-ionizer† made entirely of

* Messrs Doran Instrument Co. Ltd., Stroud, Glos.

† De-ionizer, using ion-exchange resins, supplied by Messrs Elga Products Ltd, Railway Place, London S.W. 19.

polythene. The freshly-percolated product is tested by a built-in resistance-meter and the low conductivity obtained is a proof of its purity. It could be used with confidence to standardize the meter at pH. 7.0, a course which would be hazardous if single-distilled water from the ordinary laboratory still were relied upon.

Preparations for a series of tests are extremely simple. About 5 grammes of each of the samples are placed in freshly-rinsed 100-ml. beakers and some 75 ml. of de-ionized water added to each. The contents are well stirred, the electrodes are immersed in the solution and a reading taken. The electrodes are rinsed after each test with a jet of de-ionized water from a wash-bottle with a CO_2-trap of soda-lime. Readings can be taken, apart from the brief preparation of the samples, at the rate of one every minute, unless there are very wide variations in pH between them.

Iron

(1) **Ferric Iron.** Total iron, in the ferric state, is estimated colorimetrically, using thioglycollic acid.

An extract of 1 gm. of dry soil is made by heating it with 10 ml. of conc. HCl and a few drops of conc. HNO_3, to ensure complete oxidation. After adding an equal volume of water, the solution is filtered and the insolubles twice washed on the filter. The filtrate is diluted to 100 ml.

1 ml. of this x 100 dilution is taken in a tube, to which are successively added, with mixing after each addition:

Citric acid (20% w/v)	..	0.5 ml.
Thioglycollic acid	..	1 drop
Ammonia (1:3.3 v/v)	..	1 ml.
Water to	.. ..	10 ml.

The depth of violet colour obtained is measured, using filter 626, in an EEL colorimeter.* This valuable instrument measures the intensity of a beam of light falling on a selenium cell after absorption on passing through the tube of coloured solution, in comparison with that due to a similar, blank, tube containing only water or the reagents without iron. The deflection of the galvanometer is noted and the corresponding concentration of iron read from a curve plotted once and for all by readings taken from a series of known dilutions of a ferric iron salt (Fig. 10).

In the absence of a colorimeter, the unknown may be compared with a freshly-prepared range of standard colour-intensities due to known concentrations of iron. The concentration of the unknown corresponds with that one of the standards which it most closely matches. Standards containing ferric iron equivalent to 1.0 to 10 mgs Fe_2O_3 in 10 ml. afford suitable depths of coloration either for calibration of a colorimeter or for direct matching with unknowns prepared as above. The

* Manufacturers: Evans Electroselenium Ltd, Harlow, Essex.

concentration in an unknown found by the colour is then multiplied by a factor (100 in the above case) corresponding to the dilution, giving the concentration of iron as Fe_2O_3 in mgs per 100 gms of dry soil.

When there is much iron in the sample, the depth of colour obtained with 1 ml. of x 100 dilution may be too great for estimation with the instrument or by direct comparison. In this case a greater dilution must be made before adding the reagents—x 2, x 5 or even x 10. The value read for the coloured solution must then be multiplied by this additional dilution-factor to obtain the concentration in the original soil.

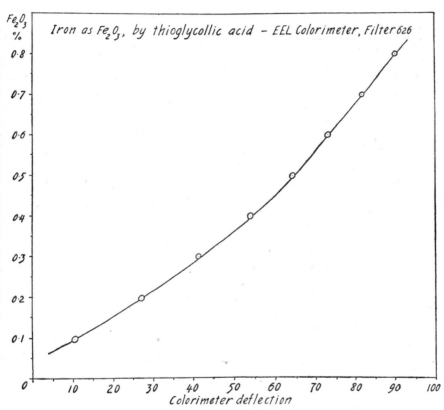

FIG 10.   Ferric-iron colorimeter-curve.

(2) **Ferrous iron.** A volumetric method (Groves, 1951), using standard potassium permanganate solution, has proved satisfactory.

Some samples which are incompletely aerated (e.g. of gley soils) may contain considerable amounts of ferrous iron compounds.

About 0.5 gm. of the sample, finely ground, is weighed into a platinum crucible fitted with a lid. Some 100 ml. of freshly distilled (or de-ionized) water, saturated with boric acid, in a 250-ml. beaker and a

50-ml. burette filled with standardized N/10 KMnO$_4$ are prepared beforehand.

The sample in the crucible is moistened with water and about 4 ml. of 50% H$_2$SO$_4$ and an equal volume of redistilled hydrofluoric acid are added. The crucible, standing on a silica triangle, is quickly heated to boiling with a bunsen held in the hand, so as to have complete control of the heating and to avoid loss by boiling over. As soon as the first jet of steam issues from under the lid of the crucible, the heating is controlled so as to keep the contents just boiling gently for 3 minutes. The crucible, lid and contents are then quickly transferred to the beaker and the titration completed as quickly as possible. The end-point is marked by a pink coloration of excess permanganate persisting for 30 seconds.

1 ml. of permanganate (N120) is theoretically equivalent to 8·9775 mgs. of FeO. The particular solution used should be standardized against a known concentration of ferrous sulphate and its exact equivalence noted on the label.

If there is much uncarbonized organic matter in the sample it will also be oxidized by the permanganate and give an unduly high figure for ferrous iron. Since we cannot find the oxidation-equivalent of the soil organic matter alone, it is hard to make any numerical allowance for this error. The determination of alkali-soluble humus will, however, give an indication of the amount of organic matter present in a particular case and show whether the error in the ferrous-iron estimation from this cause is likely to be large. For our purposes it is not so necessary to know exactly the proportion of ferrous iron as to compare the total reduction-potentials of different layers in a section. This is accurately given by the experiment.

(3) **Comparison of iron-colour by ignition.** Total iron, whether ferrous or ferric, can be compared, as between one horizon and another, by igniting the samples and comparing the colours shown by the different concentrations of ferric oxide produced. In podsols, for example, the migration of iron from the A to the B-horizons can be clearly and rapidly shown by this means, which destroys the masking humus and permits visual comparison of the impoverished and enriched layers with the concentration present in the unaltered C-horizon. One fact of note has emerged from experiments using ignition, which is that even the pale, leached A-horizons of podsols contain a certain quantity of iron, in transit or residual, which must be largely in the ferrous state in the soil because its colour does not become manifest until it is oxidized and dehydrated by ignition. This is of interest in considering the chemical problem of translocations of iron in soils.

If the ignited samples are finely ground and the powder evenly spread over an adhesive surface, permanent 'colour-cards' of sections can be prepared, of which the colours may be judged by means of the

Munsell charts (p. 119*). Quantative estimation should be possible by preparing a range of standard iron-colours with known Fe_2O_3 concentrations in a colourless vehicle. Once standardized, the Munsell descriptions could be used for quantitative work or colour-cards be compared directly by reflection-photometry using an appropriate colour-filter.

Calcium and Magnesium

A delicate volumetric method, originally devised for the estimation of hardness in waters (Schwarzenbach, 1946; Betz, 1950), has been adapted for soil-work. I am indebted to Mr Bruce Proudfoot, of the Queen's University, Belfast, for introducing me to the technique.

The method depends on the formation, with Ca^{++} and Mg^{++}, of un-ionized complexes with sodium versenate. These do not affect dyes which themselves form characteristically-coloured complexes with Ca- and Mg-ions. A solution is prepared as follows:

1 gm. of dry soil is extracted with 10 ml. of 3N HCl and a few drops of conc. HNO_3, in the cold at first, then over a flame, boiling off CO_2 when any effervescence ceases. The acid mixture (unfiltered) is then made alkaline with ammonia and about 0.5 gm. of solid NH_4Cl is added. The hydroxides of iron and aluminium, which would interfere in the titrations, are thus precipitated and removed in one filtration with the insoluble residue of the soil. The solution is boiled to drive off excess ammonia and filtered into a 100-ml. measuring-cylinder, the residue being twice washed on the filter. The neutral filtrate is diluted to the 100-ml. mark and carefully mixed. This is the sample-solution. Each ml. contains 1/100 of the Ca + Mg present in 1 gm. of dry soil. 1 ml. is taken for each titration and diluted to 25 ml. The procedure is then as follows (preparation of reagents and indicators page 170):

Titration (a) is for Ca + Mg. The solution is acidified with 1 ml. N/100 HCl, 0.5 ml. of buffer solution added and 5 drops of Erio-chrome Black T indicator, which forms pink-coloured complexes with Ca- and Mg-ions. This is then titrated with standard sodium versenate solution, which forms un-ionized complexes with Ca and Mg and, at the end-point, restores the true cold-blue colour of the uncombined dye.

Titration (b) is for Ca only. 2 ml. of N/1 NaOH and 0.2 gm. of the solid Ca-indicator (ammonium purpurate) are added to a fresh 25 ml. of diluted sample-solution. Titration with the standard versenate is continued until the pink-coloured complex is converted to the orchid-purple of the uncomplexed dye, as seen in a ready-prepared standard end-point solution. Each ml. of versenate required is equivalent to 0.1 mg. of Ca^{++} in 1 ml. of the sample-solution.

Magnesium is found by difference between the two titrations. Each ml. of difference is equivalent to 0.061 mgs. of Mg^{++} in 1 ml. of the sample-solution.

*This excellent notion is due to Dr G. W. Dimbleby of the Imperial Forestry Institute, Oxford.

Reagents

Standard sodium versenate (disodium salt of ethylene diamine tetra-acetic acid—versenic acid).

Sodium versenate 2·5 gms. Dissolve in 2 l. dist. water. Add 13·5 ml. N/1 NaOH and dilute to 2·5 l. Adjust by titration against standard Ca-solution (below), so that 1 ml. is equivalent to 0.1 mg. Ca^{++}, using Eriochrome Black T as indicator.

Indicator for Ca + Mg titration.

Eriochrome Black T	1.0 gm.
N/1 Na_2CO_3	1.0 ml.
Dist. water	30.0 ml.

Mix and make up to 100 ml. with isopropyl alcohol.

Buffer solution.

Borax	40 gm.	⎫
Dist. water	800 ml.	⎬ (1)
NaOH (pellets)	10 gm.	⎫
$Na_2S.9H_2O$	5 gm.	⎬ (2)
Dist. water	100 ml.	⎭

Mix and dilute to 1 lit.

Standard Ca-solution.

$CaCO_3$	0.125 gm.
Dist. water	100 ml.
N/10 HCl	25 ml.

Mix and dilute to 1 lit. (Equiv. to 50 mg./lit. Ca^{++})

Caustic soda solution.

  N/1 NaOH

Calcium (only) indicator (solid).

Ammonium purpurate	0.2 gm.
NaCl	100.0 gm.

Grind together in a mortar and keep dry. Measure as required with small glass spoon made to hold about 0.2 gm. when full.

Standard end-point.

Standard Ca-solution	10 ml.
Dist. water	90 ml.

Add 2 ml. $\frac{N}{1}$ NaOH and a spoonful of Ca-indicator, followed by 5 ml. standard versenate.

(As this colour fades, a permanent standard may be made to match this with dahlia violet in isopropyl alcohol and a very little methyl red.)

16

Chemical Methods (iii)

✦✦✦✦✦✦✦✦✦✦✦✦✦✦✦✦✦✦✦✦✦✦✦✦✦✦✦✦✦✦✦✦✦✦✦✦✦

Estimation of potassium and sodium

THE CLASSICAL GRAVIMETRIC methods of estimation for the water-soluble bases in soils and silicates* are so slow and tedious that they are seldom used unless there is a very compelling reason to undertake such a major operation of analysis.

A modern physical method has completely replaced these where alkali-determinations are required as a matter of routine. The flame-photometer† measures separately the intensities of the characteristic flame-colorations when a solution of alkali salts is atomized into the stream of gas reaching the burner. Even small traces of potassium may be estimated by this means in the presence of large amounts of sodium, using suitable light-filters. So also for calcium, but the sensitivity of the flame is much less in this case.

The amount of solution required for the flame photometer is very small—about 5 ml.—and the determination is as rapid as in colorimetry. A galvanometer is set to zero on the clean gas flame. The increased light-intensity in the given waveband (passed by a selected filter) is read while the solution is being injected. The reading is compared with a curve constructed by readings with the same instrument using a series of samples of known alkali-concentration.

The equipment is relatively expensive, however, and the writer has not had the use of this instrument, so cannot speak from personal experience. It is certain that potash, soda and lime determinations would much more frequently be undertaken were a flame-photometer available. Owing to the lesser intensity of the flame coloration due to calcium, the sensitivity for this metal is much lower. The versenate titration (above) gives excellent results.

Carbonate

The estimation of carbonate is by treatment of a weighed sample of soil with acid and either absorption and direct weighing of the evolved CO_2 or by loss in weight after the escape of the gas. The former, and more accurate, method involves a considerable drying- and absorption-train, so that considerations of space and rapidity make the estimation by loss of CO_2 the more convenient.

* For descriptions of these methods, see Groves, 1951.
† Manufactured by Evans Electroselenium Ltd, Harlow, Essex.

A small compact apparatus, the Schrötter flask (Fig. 11), is charged with dilute acid for the decomposition on the one side (Bulb A) and with concentrated sulphuric acid on the other (Bulb B) to dry the escaping CO_2. It is then first weighed empty, and a second time with the addition of the dry soil (about 0.5 gm.), carefully quartered and ground to ensure a representative sample.

The dilute acid is then admitted slowly to the body of the flask, when the evolved CO_2 escapes through the concentrated acid in the bubbler, which retains water-vapour. The flask is then heated over a flame to drive off dissolved CO_2, while being swept with a slow current of air drawn through it by an aspirator (see Fig. 11). The sweeping is continued while the apparatus cools again to room-temperature before being weighed finally. The difference from the second weighing is the weight of CO_2 lost by the sample.

Some precautions are necessary. The escaping gas must pass sufficiently slowly through the bubbler to be completely dried. A suitable rate is such that the bubbles may be counted easily. Sulphuric acid (3N) is used for the decomposition to avoid the loss which would be inevitable in boiling a volatile acid like HCl, but unless the soil is very finely-divided there is danger of incomplete decomposition of carbonates through formation on the particles of an insoluble crust of calcium sulphate. Too lengthy aspiration of air must be avoided, for there is no provision in this apparatus to prevent access of atmospheric moisture, which will be absorbed with the rest. About 300 ml. of air is sufficient for sweeping and should not be exceeded if possible. At the same time the apparatus must be fully cold before re-closure with the stoppers; otherwise concentrated acid will be sucked back into the reaction-chamber. Rapid boiling, on the other hand, may cause loss through blowing back of steam through the empty dilute-acid compartment. Though absolute results may be at fault by this method as compared with the absorption method, the relative values, which are more important to us, are sufficiently accurate provided care is taken to standardize the treatment of each sample—e.g. to boil and aspirate equally.

In a soil containing no important amount of magnesium, sulphate or phosphate the estimation of calcium carbonate by calcium alone will seldom be seriously in error. Where magnesium is present in more than traces there will be enough magnesium carbonate to upset the determination by calcium. The versenate method estimates both metals, so that, if there is no sulphate or phosphate, the carbonate will be equivalent to the total calcium and magnesium present. If there is sulphate and/or phosphate, there is no alternative to a carbonate determination. This applies also if there is appreciable soda or potash, as in soils of arid climates, for these, too, will mainly be present as carbonates unless the environment is total desert, so that chlorides and other very soluble salts can accumulate.

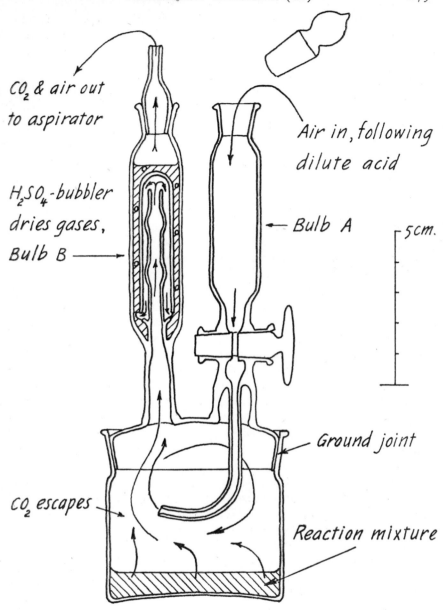

CO$_2$ & air out to aspirator

H$_2$SO$_4$-bubbler dries gases, Bulb B

Air in, following dilute acid

Bulb A

5cm.

Ground joint

CO$_2$ escapes

Reaction mixture

FIG 11.   Schrötter flask for carbonate determinations.

Sulphate

Where, as the result of a qualitative test, little sulphate is expected to be present in a soil, simple acid-treatment of a 1-gm. sample, finely ground, serves to extract all the sulphate, which is probably present as gypsum.

The sample is boiled for a few minutes with about 10 ml. of conc.

HCl, diluted with an equal volume of water and filtered. The residue is twice washed on the filter with boiling distilled water and the washings added to the filtrate. The filtrate is heated to boiling and an excess of barium chloride is added. The excess is proved by allowing the first-formed precipitate of barium sulphate to settle and by adding a few more drops of the reagent. There should be no further precipitate if an excess is already present.

The liquid and precipitate are transferred without loss to a filter and carefully washed until the washings give no precipitate, or only a slight opalescence, with silver nitrate. The filter is then folded and transferred to a weighed crucible, very gently warmed over the flame until dry and carbonized without flaming. The flame is then raised to the full and the carbon burnt off. When cool, the crucible and precipitate are weighed. The weight of $BaSO_4$ is converted to $CaSO_4 + MgSO_4$, the forms in which the sulphate was originally present.

If there is much sulphate, acid-extraction would require unwieldy quantities of conc. HCl and some calcium sulphate might be re-precipitated on dilution. Dilution is necessary unless a sintered-glass filter is available, for hot conc. HCl pulps a filter-paper.

A fusion is then necessary. The soil is intimately mixed with a large excess (5 to 10 times its weight) of sodium carbonate (anhydrous) and is fused in a platinum or nickel crucible over a Méker burner (the bunsen burner is scarcely capable of fusing the quantity required) or before a blowpipe. Fusion is continued until the melt ceases gassing and is quiet.

The melt is extracted with boiling water, when the carbonates of the heavier metals (chiefly iron and calcium) remain insoluble and are filtered off. The filter is washed carefully 2 or 3 times with dilute sodium carbonate solution. The filtrate is then acidified with HCl (avoid spurting!), evaporated to dryness in the fume-cupboard and the residue ignited. On extraction of the ignited residue with dilute HCl, silica remains insoluble. and is filtered off, again washing carefully. The filtrate then contains all the sulphate, with the other radicles, as sodium salts, and may be treated with barium chloride as before.

The estimation of sulphate is seldom necessary in the case of natural western European soils, because calcium sulphate is somewhat soluble in percolating moisture and is leached out of our soils within a few years. In drier or arid climates, sulphate persists, for the volume of percolation is insufficient to leach it right out. Its survival in archaeological contexts with us is usually due to accumulation of wood-ashes or importation of gypsum by man, as for wall-plaster. It may derive in part from the oxidation of organic sulphur-containing compounds such as proteins, or of mineral sulphides (e.g. pyrite).

Phosphate

Phosphate is determined colorimetrically by the molybdenum-blue reaction.

1 gm. of soil is digested in a boiling-tube with 20 ml. of 3N sulphuric acid on a water-bath for 15 minutes, with occasional shaking. The extract is filtered. To 5 ml. of the filtrate is added 20 ml. of Lorch's 'developer' and the tube is returned to the water-bath for a further 15 minutes.

If the solution is not too dense in colour, 10 ml. is then placed in a tube in the EEL colorimeter, using filter 621, and the depth of colour is compared with a zero set by a tube containing Lorch's reagent only. If much phosphate is present, a suitable dilution with the reagent is prepared to bring the colour within the instrument's range. The concentration of the test-solution is then read off the curve (Fig. 12), prepared from a set of standards of known phosphate concentration expressed as P_2O_5. If the test-solution is further diluted, the result must be multiplied by an appropriate factor.

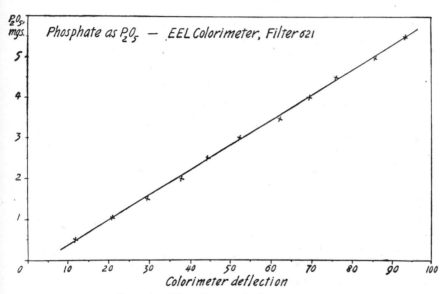

FIG 12.   Phosphate colorimeter-curve.

If no colorimeter is available, a range of standards prepared with sodium phosphate, at equivalent concentrations from 0.5 to 5 mg. P_2O_5 and treated in the same way as the unknowns, will be found satisfactory for comparison by eye, and stable, if well stoppered, for a period of at least some weeks.

For colorimetry by eye, a complication arises which, in using the colorimeter, is avoided by the use of the blue filter. Most soils contain a good deal of iron and the acid extract is inevitably of a somewhat yellow colour owing to the presence of ferric sulphate. Especially in samples with low phosphate, which are not much diluted, the iron makes the colour of the solution, after heating with Lorch's reagent, distinctly green and so not strictly comparable with the pure blue of the standards. The difficulty may be overcome by viewing both standards and the unknown, when comparing depths of colour, through a deep blue glass or gelatine filter, which cuts out the yellow. An alternative is to take with each developed unknown a tube containing an equivalent concentration of the original yellow extract from which it was prepared. By holding this in front of each blue standard when making the comparison, a shade of green exactly like that of the unknown is produced by the superimposed 'iron-correction solution'. This makes possible exact comparison.

Lorch's 'developer'*

Ammonium molybdate	12 gm.
Sodium sulphite	10 gm.
Hydroquinone	0.5 gm.
Water (distilled)	955 ml.
Sulphuric acid (conc)	45 ml.

Dissolve the solids in the water. Add the acid gradually and slowly, with shaking between additions.

Silica

If a platinum crucible is available, silica can be quickly estimated by loss in weight on evaporation of the soil with a mixture of sulphuric and hydrofluoric acids. This must be carried out in a fume-cupboard.

In some cases it is helpful to calculate ratios, such as those between silica and alumina or between silica and the sesquioxides. The exact determination of silica is by fusion of the sample with sodium carbonate, extraction of the melt with dilute HCl, filtration, evaporation of the filtrate and re-extraction with HCl. The united washed solids from the two filtrations are ignited and directly weighed as SiO_2 (details of both methods in Groves, 1951).

For many soils, however, which do not contain much alumina (clay-minerals) a quick approximation can be obtained by treating a weighed sample, first by ignition to destroy organic matter and carbon, then with boiling conc. HCl, followed by filtration, washing and drying. The insoluble residues of many sandy soils consist of little else but silica, even in the finer grades, so that reasonably close results can be thus obtained. If there is appreciable clay, or the soil contains undecomposed silicate minerals such as felspars or micas, this treatment will not serve and a fusion is indicated.

Alkali-soluble organic matter

As has been pointed out above (p. 160), the alkali-extractable fraction of soil organic matter is taken to represent humus as a whole, for want of a better yardstick.

* Lorch, 1940.

An extract of 1 gm. of dry soil is prepared by boiling it in a test-tube for a ½-minute with 20 ml. of 3N NaOH. The liquid is filtered and 10 ml. of the filtrate (or if too dark, a known dilution with the 3N soda) is taken for estimation of the colour-density in the EEL colorimeter, using blue filter 621.

A curve (Fig. 13) has been prepared for calibration of the meter from a series of standards containing 1-10 mg. of alkali-extracted peat-humus per 10 ml. The concentration found in the unknown is multiplied by 20 and by the appropriate factor if further diluted, to give mg./gm. of dry soil.

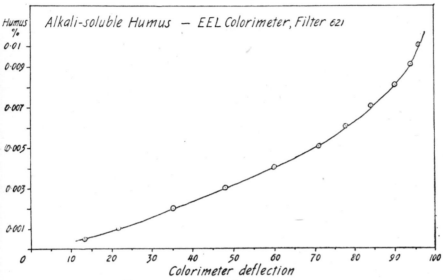

FIG 13.   Humus colorimeter-curve.

Unknowns may be directly compared with such standards if no colorimeter is available, but experiment has shown that their colour fades perceptibly on standing, so that standards must be freshly prepared if absolute comparisons are desired.

Preparation of humus-standards. About 5 gm. of dry peat is boiled for 15 minutes with 100 ml. of 3N caustic soda and the liquid filtered off, preferably with the help of a filter-pump. The extract is evaporated to dryness on a water-bath and the organic content of a small sample estimated by ignition. This amounted in a particular case to 28.4%. A solution of the whole extract in distilled water is then made to restore the alkali-concentration to 3N, and this is further diluted with 3N soda to contain exactly 0.5 % of organic matter. This is the darkest colour which is easily compared with that of an unknown. Dilutions down to 0.005 % are still distinctly coloured and distinguishable from distilled water by eye.

M

A quantity of the solid extract is kept for stock in a well-stoppered jar and is dissolved as required for making standards.

Nitrogen

Nitrogen occurs in our context chiefly in organic matter, where it is present in proteins and their degradation-products, mainly derived from plant-matter. On complete decomposition, the nitrogen is eventually reduced to ammonia in anaerobic conditions, or converted by oxidation to nitrates. Soil-nitrates are also produced by symbiotic bacteria in the root-nodules of leguminous plants, by fixation of atmospheric nitrogen.

Both ammonium salts and nitrates are very soluble in water and, if not taken up by plants, are eventually leached out in the drainage. In more complex organic combinations, nitrogen is not so readily available to plants and soil-humus represents a certain store of nitrogen which is slowly mobilized for use by the gradual processes of decay.

Estimation is by Kjeldahl's method of distillation and titration, perhaps on the micro or semi-micro scale, though the writer has no personal experience of these techniques, which have been largely developed by biochemists for work on minute quantities of material. Nitrogen-estimations on very small bone-samples have been thus carried out on Palaeolithic and later animal and human remains, notably in the case of the famous Piltdown exposure. The soil-investigator can generally obtain samples of adequate size, so that these refinements are not forced on him.

The principle is, in any case, the same. The original weight of dry organic matter (or the soil containing it) is broken down by digestion with concentrated sulphuric acid, whereupon nitrogenous materials form ammonium sulphate, $(NH_4)_2SO_4$. The mixture is then made alkaline with caustic soda and distilled, when ammonia, NH_3, passes over and is absorbed in the receiver in a known volume of standard sulphuric acid, re-forming ammonium sulphate. The excess acid is then titrated back with standard alkali solution, the difference from the original known excess being that part of the standard acid neutralized by the ammonia released from the organic matter. The amount of ammonia, and hence of nitrogen, in the sample is easily calculated. (See any textbook of organic analysis for details of this standard method.)

Part IV

INTERPRETATION AND EXAMPLES

17

Interpretation of Physical Results

◆◆◆

WE HAVE REVIEWED the principal tools of the soil-investigator. It is now necessary to consider how to interpret the results gained by their use.

The two most difficult parts of soil-work, both to carry out and to describe, are the economical planning of the experiments, so as shortly to get the greatest amount of pertinent information from the samples, and to render into terms useful to an archaeologist such conclusions as may be drawn from the experimental results.

The planning ought to begin in the field, when the site is visited and the samples collected, for a decision must be taken on the spot as to what questions can most usefully be elucidated by the methods at our disposal. This will govern our approach to the problems.

It is here that close understanding between excavator and soil-specialist is most necessary and valuable. The former must be able to state the problems clearly and the latter to assess how far his special knowledge and equipment may be capable of contributing to their solution. It is a counsel of perfection to enjoin on the specialist a visit to every site. Often this will be impossible and, though it is clearly a disadvantage to the man with the samples spread out on the bench before him not to have seen the deposits *in situ*, it need not be crippling if the excavator has previously consulted with him, or knows from past experience the sort of data that he will require.

The qualitative sort of questions: 'What is this stuff?' 'Why is it black?' 'Is this bronze-slag?' are often easily enough answered by the investigation of a single sample. The form of the question will usually suggest an approach to the problem.

'Is this the filling of a post-hole?' or 'How was this deposit formed?' afford no such positive suggestion, and the soil-consultant has to consider whether he is able to offer any answer at all and, if so, how to set about finding some evidence to support it.

The case of the post-hole is instructive. Obviously, there is nothing intrinsic to the single sample of material which will prove whether it is the remains of a post, unless soil-conditions are such that actual woody structures have been preserved. There is no law governing the absolute content of organic matter in post-hole fillings, so that a humus-determination, showing the presence of x% of alkali-soluble organic matter, would leave us no wiser than before. If, however, it can be shown that a sample from the supposed wood contains x times as much humus as one from the same level but a few inches to one side, this is good evidence that there was an intrusive mass of organic matter at that spot and so, under the circumstances, perhaps a wooden post.

Alternative possibilities must be considered; a rotted natural tree-stool, a filled root-hole, a rabbit-burrow, the natural filling of a solution-pipe containing humic soil from a higher part of the section; all these would show local concentrations of organic matter. Examination of the material *in situ* and of its stratigraphical relations with surrounding deposits will point to the likelihood of a human artifact providing the most plausible explanation of the observed phenomena. If the soil-specialist is unable to be present to assure himself of the exact situation, it will rest with the excavator, or whoever takes the samples, to make these observations and note what he can see in a sketch or memorandum accompanying the material sent for analysis.

Sketch-plans and sections should in any case be provided by the archaeologist to show the stratigraphical relations of all samples submitted and to illustrate the problems to be solved.

At any site it is as well to collect samples of a natural profile from nearby, where it is unlikely that the works of man have played any part. Much of the time we are looking for artifacts—human interference with the natural régime—so it is necessary to have some exact information about the natural soil in order to make it possible to detect minor evidence of human intervention.

Colour

One of the primary guides to the stratification of the site is colour. In natural sections, the colours exhibited are mainly due to humus and iron-compounds—most intense where these are concentrated.

The use of the Munsell Charts for colour-description has not long enough been established for a large body of comparative work to have been done on colour. Nevertheless, colour in natural soils is a valuable character in defining them. In general, yellow and brown shades are emblematic of relatively moist conditions of formation as in podsol and braunerde, because these are the colours of hydrated soil-minerals (limonite, etc.). Redder tones betoken some degree of peptization and dehydration of the iron and so suggest warmer, and perhaps seasonally drier, conditions (terra fusca, terra rossa), culminating in the brilliant reds of rotlehms, roterdes and desert sands. Possible derivation from some tropical relict formation must then be envisaged.

High temperatures alone do not produce redness. Braunlehm, with limonitic iron-minerals, is the typical soil of tropical rain-forest, where moisture is perennial. Irreversible dehydration (haematite, Fe_2O_3) depends on seasonal drought as well as heat. The condition of the iron compounds to be seen in the thin section is the final test. Even a very red soil (to the eye) may prove, on sectioning, to owe its colour mainly to the peptized iron hydroxide with some red concretions (terra fusca) rather than to precipitates of dehydrated iron oxide (terra rossa).

Humus contributes browner and, in calcareous or even more alkaline conditions, greyer shades. A light or bright colour, whether yellow or red, therefore, indicates immediately poverty in organic matter. Dark colours have the reverse significance. Both rendsina and chernozem are humus-rich and dark in colour, but where the chernozem zone merges into semi-desert, the red colour of the sun-baked iron salts becomes visible because the vegetation is reduced by aridity and the humus is not plentiful enough to mask the mineral colours (kastanosem).

Pale or whitish soils tend to be iron-poor (calcareous soils, marly clays and, even more, those saturated with gypsum or bleached by iron-eluviation, as in a podsol A_2-horizon). Greys, greens or blues suggest waterlogging, or at least air-exclusion, with some humus-deficiency. With plentiful humus, deep browns, greys and blacks mask the weaker iron-colours.

On occupation-sites, the natural colours are complicated by fallen structures, laid floors, hearths, charcoal, burnt brick etc. These often explain themselves to the eye of an experienced excavator, who should be at least as good at explaining visible stratification as the soil-investigator. When the explanation for a peculiar layer is not evident, the soil-man may be called on to intervene with instruments more specific than the eye to identify the peculiarity.

So various are the possibilities, that it is clearly impossible to make a complete catalogue, but the following list includes the more usual distinctively coloured substances.

White. *Calcium carbonate* (chalk, limestone), *calcium sulphate* (gypsum, plaster). Massive (alabaster), powdery, crystalline (selenite), silky (satin-spar), filamentous (pseudo-mycelium—see pp. 95–6, 105), efflorescent. Derived from lime-mortar, ash, chalk, marble, plaster etc. (Acid test— dilute HCl—gives effervescence and solution in the cold, $CaCO_3$— insoluble, $CaSO_4$.) *Calcium phosphate* (bone or bone-ash) does not effervesce but dissolves readily in mineral acids.

Silica. Quartz is crystalline, acid insoluble (hardness). White-patinated flint appears amorphous, porcellanous in texture. Hydrated silica (opal) possibly occurs in volcanic regions or near hot springs. Diatomite (floury, pure white) is a lake-sediment composed of the siliceous skeletons of diatoms (microscopic plants) (p. 40).

Silicates. Many iron-poor silicates are white (e.g. felspar, muscovite mica). China-clay (kaolin) is rare and industrially valuable, generally associated with granite, as in Cornwall. Acid pumice (rhyolite), near volcanic vents, may be almost pure white.

Water-soluble salts. Gypsum, common salt, borax and sodium carbonate occur naturally in soils in arid climates. The last two are strongly alkaline in solution (litmus, blue; phenolphthalein, magenta).

Grey. Impure forms of the above, stained with small amounts of humus, finely-divided charcoal or, if excluded from air, ferrous iron salts. Appropriate tests will show the nature of the impurity.

Black. *Carbon* (charcoal) is insoluble in acids, but burns with a bright glow and vaporizes, leaving only a fine white ash, when heated to red heat with access of air.

Humus with calcium carbonate, as in rendsinas. Hot dilute alkali gives a brown solution. So also for jet, shale, coal, bitumen, pitch. All these last give a smell of coal-smoke on burning and a smoky flame.

Manganese oxide or concentrated iron oxides, as in hardpans. These are soluble in hot concentrated HCl, giving a yellow (iron) or greenish-yellow (manganese) solution, losing its colour on slight dilution with water.

Iron tannates are inky blue-black, but appear black when concentrated. Formed in presence of oak wood or bark (and other timbers) with iron salts. Colour discharged on ignition, giving rusty brown or red of ferric oxide.

Freshly-fractured Chalk flint and crude glass (e.g. obsidian—natural glass) are smoky black (hardness). Flint has a matt, glass a polished, fracture-surface.

Metallic sulphides, formed by decay of organic matter in presence of (generally) iron salts with exclusion of air. May smell of H_2S (bad eggs). Yield H_2S with dilute acid. Brassy metallic lustre if crystalline.

Brown or Yellow. *Humus,* grey-brown if with calcium carbonate, otherwise chocolate-brown, as peat, lignite. Brown solution with boiling dilute alkali. Combustible.

Hydrated ferric oxide, carbonate (oxide dissolves in fairly concentrated acid, carbonate in dilute, with effervescence). Materials which are colourless when pure, heavily stained with iron or humus—clay, silt, sand or stone.

Mica, pyrite (pale golden, glittering). Former is markedly platy in form, light. Latter, generally cubic crystals, heavy.

Amber. Light, soft (scratches with pin), soluble in alcohol.

Red. *Anhydrous iron oxide* (Fe_2O_3). Burnt brick or clay with much iron. Yellow solution with hot, concentrated HCl. If natural loam or clay, probably derived from some Tertiary or more ancient fossil soil of terra fusca, rotlehm or roterde type—e.g. Permian or Triassic beds.

Any of the brown, yellow or grey materials after firing (or tropical weathering).

Pink. Naturally colourless substances (see under **White**), stained with generally only small amounts of ferric oxide (Fe_2O_3)—clays, gypsum (e.g. alabaster), felspars. Pink granite—colour mainly due to pink felspars. Some manganese compounds.

Green or blue. *Copper salts* (verdigris colour—copper carbonate, malachite) and *copper minerals*—some bright blue (e.g. sulphate, azurite).

Ferrous salts in general (indigo or sage-green), due to exclusion of air in waterlogged situations, especially in the presence of organic matter, as in lake-beds. Vivianite (china-blue) is a special case of this, a hydrated ferrous phosphate formed by iron (artificial or natural) in the presence of phosphates (bones or occupation-rubbish in general) under moist anaerobic conditions. Iron tannates (blue-black ink!) formed by iron salts in the presence of tannins (oak, willow etc. bark or wood). Basic igneous rocks (basalt, dolerite etc.—crystalline under lens) and ferro-magnesian minerals generally, contained in these.

Grade-separations

These are applicable, in our context, largely to distinguish wind-sorted materials (loesses and sands). Sieving, panning and elutriation serve to separate particles of any desired size-limits for closer examination. Shells, small bones, foraminifera, plant-remains, seeds and artificially-intruded particles such as microliths, beads and human teeth may be thus recovered.

The writer generally carries on field-expeditions a small home-made sieve of brass wire mesh (about ½ mm. aperture) soldered into the bottom of a 4-oz. tobacco-tin. Any deposit containing, for example, rodent remains, can be tested on the spot by washing a small sample on the sieve in a bucket of water, pond, stream—or even with drinking-water in a thermos-cap! One does not set out to extract or determine microfossils systematically on the site, but a test-washing is often worth while to see whether it is worth collecting a larger sample for proper examination in the lab.

The business of gravel- or cave-earth analysis involves great weights of the coarser grades (down to 6 mm.) and is best performed on the site to save the trouble of carrying away hundredweights of stones. Climatic conclusions of value can sometimes be obtained by this means. Laboratory methods for the finer grades have already been described and samples of sufficient size for these tests are easily portable.

Interpretation of mechanical analysis curves

With the particle-sizes on the horizontal axis and the summation percentages on the vertical, a steeply-sloping curve (Fig. 1, p. 28) indicates a concentration of particles in the sizes indicated by the projection on the horizontal of the steep portion. A perfectly horizontal section of any curve would stand for a total absence of particles in the range indicated. Thus, a gently-sloping, almost straight, line (Fig. 14) represents a sediment with equal weights in all grades—an ill-sorted deposit like a rainwash- or flood-loam.

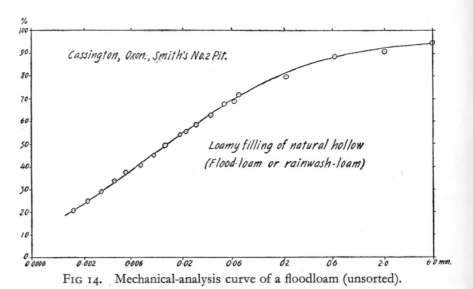

FIG 14.   Mechanical-analysis curve of a floodloam (unsorted).

Loesses and other wind-sorted materials have curves steep in the silt-grades (Fig. 15), levelling out above and to the right in the sand and below and to the left in the clay. A fresh (unweathered) loess contains some 70% or more of silt and no more than 20–30% of sand and clay taken together. After chemical weathering, as in the formation of a loess-loam (buried soil) the clay increases at the expense, chiefly, of the silt, though the whole curve may be shifted slightly to the left, i.e. into a finer grade, involving degradation of the sand also. Blown or water-sorted sand may show a main steep portion to the right of the silt boundary (0.06 mm.), in the medium and fine sand grades (Fig. 16). Any considerable fraction larger than 0.6 mm. is likely to indicate rain-washing or water-transport.

In general, deposits yield a smooth sigmoid curve, however slight the curvature in some cases of unsorted sediments. Any important nicks or bumps, not due to experimental or calculation errors, suggest superimposition of two or more maxima of sorting, i.e. probably a mixture of two distinctly-sorted materials. To track down the causes of such peculiarities may lead to interesting local environmental con-clusions, probably mainly of a topographical or geomorphological character. Any real anomaly of which no immediate explanation is forthcoming is worth a little study.

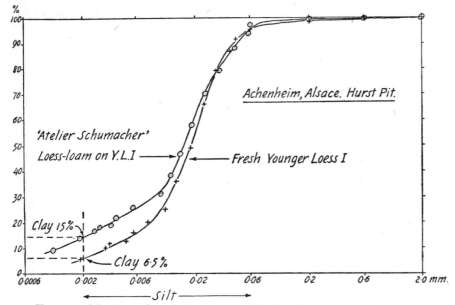

FIG 15. Mechanical-analysis curves of fresh and weathered loesses.

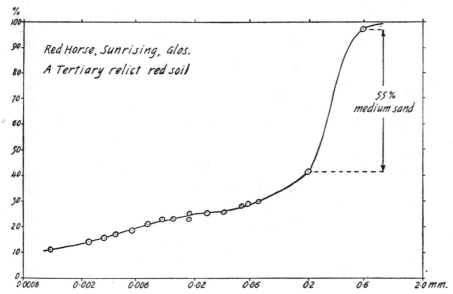

FIG 16. Mechanical-analysis curve of a loamy sand, showing marked sorting in the sand-grades.

With practice, one learns to characterize most sediments at sight from their curves and to recognize anything out of the ordinary. Exact comparison is facilitated by superimposing one curve on another held against a window or in front of a strong light. In this position, the points may be quickly transferred to the upper sheet if a permanent comparison of two or more curves on a single sheet is required.

Thin sections

While the preparation of thin sections of soils (pp. 141-51) is a matter of some manipulative skill not difficult to acquire with a little practice, the interpretation of the features which such preparations show under the petrological microscope requires not only experience but a considerable amount of theoretical knowledge. The works of Kubiena (see Bibliography, p. 222) are the main published guides, and any inquirer aspiring to use the valuable micromorphological tool with which he has provided us should first make himself familiar with them. The micromorphological features of the main types of soils have been included here with their macroscopic descriptions, but some general approach to the interpretation of unknowns may usefully be added here.

All natural classification is a human device to subdivide into categories for ready recognition the almost infinite variations with which Nature confronts us. The boundaries between adjacent classes are not naturally hard and fast and depend only on the arbitrary criteria chosen to define them, the number of such prominent characters being fairly small. Soils, archaeological deposits and the geological formations from which they are derived are no exception—there are, for example, infinite gradations between rendsina and braunerde and between braunerde and podsol. Untold varieties depend for their particular features on the nature of the parent material and on all the other variables which locally affect them.

Kubiena has selected the main subdivisions known to him which seemed to be significant and has described and illustrated typical examples. Many of his types do not occur at all, others only rarely, in these Islands. While the greater part of his European work has been done in eastern Central Europe (with a pronounced continental type of climate) and in Spain (largely under Mediterranean conditions), many of the soils which he describes have clear-cut characteristics, unlike those of the less well-defined climate which we enjoy in northwest Atlantic Europe. We must therefore first study microscopically our own varieties of the main types and classes before we can tell what is commonplace and what unusual in our particular modern environment. This micromorphological work has been actively progressing at several institutions in this country since the publication of *The Soils of Europe*, but little has yet been published.*

Nor is this the whole difficulty. At least in Lowland Britain, the main parent-materials of the soils of today are ancient weathered sediments and 'drifts', themselves largely composed of soil-material contemporary with, or even long antecedent to, the time of their formation. In these

*See Dalrymple, J. B., 1957, 'The Pleistocene deposits of Penfold's Pit, Slindon, Sussex and their chronology', *Proc. Geol. Ass.n* 68 (4), 294-303.

relict materials will be seen traces of their older weathering-histories, further changed by the conditions to which they have been subjected in more recent geological times. Kubiena's guidance nevertheless enables us to follow the general trend of what we see in a section under the microscope.

The British Isles, with a moist, cool-temperate climate, lie in the braunerde-podsol zone of north-west Europe. The most widespread climax soil-type, developed on a more or less siliceous bedrock, is the braunerde, varying from the rich eutrophic variety on basic igneous rocks to the oligotrophic on acid silicates, merging on the one hand with rendsina, developed on limestones, via calcareous braunerde, and on the other with podsol, developed on silica-rocks, via podsolic braunerde (see the table, p.87). So much for original soils. These types cover over 90% of them.

In Tertiary times, if no earlier, sub-tropical conditions here caused the widespread development on siliceous materials of braunlehms and rotlehms, with the likely accompaniments on limestones of terra fuscas and even terra rossas. Remains of these, not so much still in position (degraded or fossil) but derived (relict soils) have been incorporated in drifted parent materials serving as substrata for recent soil-formation. These often retain features of the climatic régime under which they were first formed, mixed, indeed, with fresh sediments in many cases, but still relatively unchanged in the new conditions, which have not yet endured so long as to reach a new equilibrium. This relates chiefly to the nature and disposition of their iron-compounds. We may, therefore, often have to take into account braunerde formations on pre-existing braunlehm material, for example.

Even earlier geological ages have contributed something to modern soils. The siliceous and aluminous acid-insoluble residue of a limestone often derives from contemporary silt- and clay-grade soil-material, airborne or water-borne from the land and incorporated on the sea-floor in mainly calcareous ooze of organic origin. Such particles are likely to weather out of limestones with their former colour and iron-content practically unchanged, having nothing to do, therefore, with the climate of the time when the cave-earth, of which they form part today, was being formed.

In considering the thin section of a cave-earth, or, indeed, of a buried soil from beneath a Bronze-Age barrow-mound, we have to take into consideration the possible parentage of the raw materials available to the weathering processes of the time. Despite these necessary precautions, it is often possible to draw some conclusions as to the conditions of origin of buried and fossil soils and archaeological deposits from their appearances in thin section.

Fabric. A glance at a thin section under low-power magnification (1″–2″ objective) enables an opinion to be formed as to its *fabric*, the arrangement of its fundamental constituents. It may be porous or dense, formed of relatively coarse mineral particles in a more or less fine matrix, of rounded crumbs or of angular aggregates. The presence or otherwise of conducting channels—root-holes, shrinkage-fissures, intergranular spaces—is informative, and whether these are empty or filled or lined with secondary deposits.

Open fabrics are those of podsol, eutrophic and mesotrophic braunerdes, rendsina and chernozem, for example (qq. v.).

Dense fabrics belong especially to rotlehm, braunlehm, terra fusca, gleys and pseudogleys and oligotrophic braunerde.

Plasma. Intergranular spaces and conducting channels may be filled, or partly filled, with colloids and precipitates, conveyed and deposited physically or chemically by percolating moisture. This is the *soil-plasma*, which constitutes in part the cement between adjacent grains and in part mere filling of available voids. Its nature is important for typing and interpreting the dynamics of the soil—the processes currently or recently at work in it.

On crossing the nicols, voids in the section will pass no light and show black, while any quartzes or other anisotropic mineral grains will be lighted and extinguish symmetrically on rotating the stage. The plasma, consisting of humus and other colloidal substances, iron concretions and precipitates, is mainly isotropic, not affecting the plane of polarization of the beam traversing the specimen, and so will remain dark. In the special case of iron-hydroxide sols, however, which may be protected from flocculation by silicic acid, and so be mobile in any conducting channels, an appearance of optical activity is simulated. If present, this mobile iron shines, in certain positions of the stage, with a bright golden-yellow colour ('egg-yellow'—Kubiena). A fairly high power (1/4"–1/8" objective) may be needed to observe this clearly if the structures are small. Though ferric hydroxide is not birefringent, reflections at the surfaces of innumerable flow-oriented sub-microscopic particles will affect and rotate the beam of plane-polarized light to produce the characteristic streaks and flow-structures. Where the plasma is peptized (colloidally dispersed) or containing bodies in true solution, it will spread over the free surfaces of cavities and grains, as does humus in a podsol fabric. When flocculated, on the other hand, the plasma will adhere only locally and be mainly concentrated in intergranular angles.

Concretions. Chocolate-brown isotropic concretions of rounded contour, composed of hydrated iron precipitated from the soil-solution, form among and actually embody some of the finer fabric-grains. They are typically seen in braunerde, braunlehm, terra fusca and other soils of moist environments, where they are deposited in drier, but not unduly hot, seasons, still fully hydrated, as limonite.

The brilliant colours of rotlehms, terra rossas and roterdes, soils of hot climates, are caused by concretions, flecks, 'scabby' or 'thrombus-like' precipitates of dehydrated iron oxide, haematite. These are isotropic (dark between crossed nicols), brilliant red in ordinary light, even at the standard thickness of $20-30\mu$, and even under high power. The colour is quite distinct from that of peptized iron (which may appear red at low power and in a section which is still too thick). In terra rossa, for example, the red precipitates may be associated with some yellow peptized iron in transit, not yet having been heated enough to lose its water of hydration. Any limonite concretions formed in the soil at an earlier stage of its evolution (terra fusca) will have 'aged' (i.e. become dehydrated), losing their youthful round or oval outlines by shrinkage and showing reëntrants and other irregularities. They are fully opaque in transmitted light, bright red of haematite by reflection.

Manganese concretions are always dead black, generally rather smaller than those of iron and of more irregular outline. They seem to be specially typical of colluvial (derived) material, for some reason still unknown.

'Sol lessivé' (French = leached soil). This is a type, formally a braunerde, with mainly immobile chocolate-coloured iron throughout the greater part of its fabric. Larger rootholes and other conducting channels are lined, and their walls impregnated, with yellow, peptized iron-sols, probably silicic-acid protected and introduced by the purely mechanical action of downward percolation. The phenomenon is typical of some interglacial and interstadial weathering-soils of loesses (buried loess-loams) and suggests an incipient transition from braunerde to braunlehm conditions of weathering—i.e. a climate perhaps somewhat warmer and equally moist, in comparison with the typical braunerde conditions.

In the extreme south-west of Britain, on drier slopes of limestone well exposed to the south, there are some terra fuscas (limestone braunlehms) which appear to be climax-soils at the present day (Dalrymple, 1955). Less favourably-exposed situations show braunerdes, which have developed out of rendsinas by decalcification and growth in depth of the soil. The terra fusca is obviously marginal here, confined to those situations which have a hotter and drier summer micro-climate, with some release of silicic acid, owing to the higher temperature, to protect the iron sols. The development of braunlehm weathering here is a parallel to sol-lessivé in loess-loams. It may well be that some such terra fuscas are fossil or degraded soils, buried in colluvial braunerde material or even with modern braunerde developed on the upper part. They occur at a little depth filling fissures in the limestone.

In considering soil micromorphology, we have paid little attention to different minerals, other than quartz, which may be seen in thin sections of soils, but to the end-products of their chemical weathering, iron hydroxide, calcium carbonate, silicic acid and so on. The same technique of sectioning can equally well be applied to more or less incoherent archaeological deposits which are not strictly soil-material. The problems of interpretation then become those of sedimentary petrology and mineralogy rather than of pedology. There is a wide field of fruitful investigation here for workers somewhat skilled in petrological techniques.

18

Interpretation of Chemical Experiments

+ +

pH

THE SOIL-REACTION, due to the presence of various constituents, acidic (chiefly carbonic and humic acids) or basic (metallic compounds), in varying concentrations, controls the processes of solution, eluviation, peptization, flocculation, precipitation and so on, which take place in a soil under the influence of weathering.

Some limiting pH-values are available* which greatly assist in the interpretation of pH figures obtained from unknowns:

	pH-value
Turbidity in colloidal ferric hydroxide	3.0
Humic acids (flocculated)	3.9
Precipitation of aluminium hydroxide	4.1
Peptization or re-flocculation of humic-acid sols	4.9
Precipitation of ferric hydroxide	5.5
Coagulation of colloidal ferric hydroxide	6.6
Aluminium hydroxide redissolves as aluminates	8.0
Precipitation of manganous hydroxide	8.4
Calcium carbonate in equilibrium with atmospheric CO_2	8.4
Calcium carbonate in absence of CO_2	9.0
Magnesium carbonate in equilibrium with atmospheric CO_2	9.5

As the pH values rise, these events will take place in one direction. If the change is in the opposite sense, the reverse event will ensue. For example, below pH 4.9 humic acids are flocculated and relatively insoluble; above that value they will peptize and go into colloidal solution. Below 8.4 calcium carbonate will dissolve, forming calcium bicarbonate (water-soluble) if the acidifying substance is CO_2, or a calcium salt of any other acid, e.g. the only slightly soluble calcium humates, in the presence of humic acids.

Thus, below pH 3.0, ferric iron (Fe^{+++}) can exist in true solution. If the pH should rise beyond this value, turbidity may be seen in the clear solution *in vitro* and a colloidal suspension of $Fe(OH)_3$ (ferric hydroxide sol) is produced. This consists of solid particles (micelles) of sub-microscopic dimensions (10^{-5} — 10^{-7} cms in diameter). In fully aerated surroundings, therefore, it is as a colloid that iron moves in the soil. Alumina ($Al(OH)_3$) is soluble at acid pH's below 4.0. It is precipitated between pH 5.0 and 8.0, but redissolves, forming aluminates of

* Correns, 1949, in part, partly own determinations.

whatever bases are providing the (OH)⁻ ions, at pH-values above 9.0. It is, thus, not mobile in soils with pH-values near neutrality.

At pH 5.5, ferric hydroxide is precipitated from colloidal sols, the micelles forming larger aggregates which fall out of suspension. At 6.6 the flocks are coagulated into a gel. On lowering the pH once more below 6.6 the gel will tend to disperse and at 5.5 it will again peptize to a colloid sol. Above pH 6.6, therefore, iron is generally immobilized, while it is not freely mobile in the finer intergranular spaces above 5.5.

It is notable that humic acids alone give a pH of 3.9, and are flocculated at this value. Peptization begins at 4.9, when humic acid sols become freely mobile and then can mobilize the iron. This action is specially powerful in base-poor surroundings, from which iron compounds may be almost completely washed out, as in podsols. In a soil with a pH above 5.5, therefore, podsolization and the mass movement of iron is impossible. It remains fixed in the profile, as in braunerdes.

Under certain circumstances, however, iron does move even at higher pH's than this, through the 'protection' given to particles of colloidal ferric hydroxide by coatings of silicic acid, which prevent flocculation due to alkalinity of the surroundings. Silica is least soluble between pH's 2–3 and its ability to form silicic acid sols rises steeply with rise in pH beyond 5.5. The solubility-curve also steepens greatly with rise in temperature, so that the colloid eluviation of silica as silicic acid in soils of warm climates is very much more pronounced than it is with us. Temperatures in our region are too low for the massive mobilization of silica and the accompanying protection by it of iron hydroxide colloids. It is in the warmer types of moist-climate soils— braunlehm, terra fusca, rotlehm—that the peptization of iron at pH's near neutrality (7.0) is most clearly seen.

Manganese hydroxide, frequently accompanying iron, is not fixed in a soil until the pH rises to 8.0 and over. It may, therefore, be expected to occur as a solid in alkaline soils only.

The presence of free calcium carbonate in equilibrium with atmospheric CO_2 (an excess over the humic acids present, which form calcium humates) gives a pH close to 8.4. Magnesium carbonate in excess raises it to 9.5. CO_2 is present in small amount in air (0.03 %) but is much more concentrated in soil-atmospheres, where it derives from the oxidative decay of organic matter. Dissolved in water, it forms a weakly acid solution (H_2CO_3, carbonic acid), which is capable of attacking calcium carbonate and converting it into water-soluble calcium bicarbonate. On rise in temperature or evaporation of the water, calcium carbonate is redeposited and CO_2 is released. Because of this reaction and because gases are most soluble in water at low temperatures, the solubility of calcium carbonate increases with decrease in temperature, provided that sufficient CO_2 is available to saturate the moisture. Decalcification is therefore more rapid in cool climates.

These processes, controlling or depending on the pH-value locally obtaining, determine the sort of weathering which can take place under given conditions, so that a knowledge of the pH-values at different levels in a soil-profile is useful in typing the soil and in explaining the translocation or immobilization of particular constituents.

The pH also has an influence on the preservation of phosphates in the soil—in particular of calcium phosphate, $Ca_3(PO_4)_2$, the principal mineral constituent of bone and the commonest phosphatic compound. This is attacked by humus and plant root-acids (mainly CO_2), with the release of free phosphoric acid, which, if not absorbed by plants and in the absence of sufficient bases (especially calcium and magnesium) to re-fix it as an insoluble, is leached out and lost in the drainage. The critical pH is close to 5.6, well on the acid side. Thus, if the pH of a soil is below this figure, its phosphate-content in the long run will be negligible. Negative phosphate tests, therefore, when attempting to locate (say) the site of a burial under a barrow constructed of acid soil-material, will prove nothing. There may well *have been* a body there.

Iron

Though the appearance of a profile in the field and that of a thin section under the microscope, together with a consideration of the pH-values, may lead to a suspicion that iron is being transported in it, only quantitative figures for the iron-content of different horizons will prove that this is the case, and show the extent of the movement. On occasion, as in the case of a podsolic braunerde, there may be no macroscopic signs and the chemical results will first indicate that there is some incipient eluviation of iron.

The situation is, of course, clearest in the podsol group of soils, but braunlehms can also be somewhat degraded, through eluviation of silicic-acid-protected sols, and support must be sought in the iron figures for the cause of any bleaching which is apparent.

With eluviation of bases and clay-colloids, there may be great concentration of the iron, so that the total observed in the weathered profile is greater than in a comparable thickness of unaltered bedrock. This need not mean, therefore, that there has been any extraneous addition.

In reducing surroundings, where air is excluded, there will be a high proportion of ferrous iron also, and this will probably be suggested by the colour. Ferrous-iron colours are less intense than the ferric, so that even the A_2 (bleached) horizon of a podsol may contain appreciable amounts of ferrous iron in transit, despite its pale colour. The presence of ferrous salts is easily shown by the ignition-test and they may be roughly estimated by colour-comparison after the ignition.

Bases: Potash, soda, calcium, magnesium

A base-rich fresh sediment exposed to weathering will, in our climate, first be leached by solution of the greater part of the soluble bases, potassium and sodium. After this first stage, which will be rapid, it will begin to lose some of the less soluble bases also.

A rendsina, for example, is fully saturated with calcium (and magnesium also, where this is available in the substratum), even in the uppermost part of the A-horizon, where, even if the carbonates have mostly been decomposed, the bases are held as humates, fixed by the humic acids. As soon as the profile becomes deep enough for the humic acids to form in excess of the available bases, the upper parts of the profile will become brown and begin to lose calcium and magnesium. The proof of the onset of this phase will be revealed by the calcium and magnesium analyses, through the profile, indicating some base-impoverishment above. At a later stage the calcareous braunerde formed may begin to show a Ca-horizon at some depth, due to re-deposition of eluviated salts, when their concentration will show in the analytical results and enable the soil-type to be recognized. Falling base-status, due to still further eluviation, will cause a transition through eutrophic to mesotrophic and oligotrophic braunerde—even to podsol, if the conditions are suitable. The base-determinations will enable the changes in this evolutionary series to be followed.

Acid-Radicles

The presence of *carbonates*, in our climate, is a measure, like that of the bases, of relative freshness. As suggested above, a rendsina A-horizon may still be base-saturated and yet have lost some carbonate, owing to the increasing humus. Carbonate-determinations in addition to those for calcium and magnesium will demonstrate this incipient impoverishment of the uppermost layer of the soil.

Sulphate, impersistent in moist climates, provides for us rather an indication of intrusive materials than a measure of soil-formation. In semi-arid conditions, where only the readily-soluble salts are first washed out, a series of sulphate-determinations in the profile would suggest the beginning of loss of the less soluble also, and thus be some measure of rainfall. Since calcium sulphate will be the compound chiefly concerned, calcium-determinations in addition to those for sulphate will make clear the distribution of calcium between sulphate and carbonate. In our climate perhaps indicates wood-ash.

Phosphate, it has been suggested, affords a measure of contemporary animal matter (unless a basic igneous bedrock or fossil bone-bed provides additional amounts). In base-rich soils, magnesium and calcium will combine to immobilize phosphoric acid, so that its vertical distribution will not greatly alter with time and weathering. The presence of a concentration of phosphate at any level in an archaeological section may be taken to represent a surface occupied by man or by animals—i.e. a buried soil, unless it is the floor of a dwelling.

Markedly acid soils, deficient in bases (pH < 5·6), have no power to fix phosphate, which will rapidly be leached out.

Silica and many **silicates** are relatively insoluble in temperate regions. Tropical soils, on the other hand, become de-silicified and so enriched in iron and alumina, whereas, with us, silica is the most stable and humic acids from plentiful vegetation tend to leach out the sesquioxides of iron and alumina, after more soluble basic substances have already been lost. Taking silica as the stable basis of a soil, the silica-sesquioxide ratio is a measure of intensity of humic eluviation.

Alkali-soluble humus

The content of organic matter changes considerably from one horizon to another in some soils (e.g. podsols), but is generally highest near the actual surface on which grows the vegetation from which it is derived. Apart from any other features which we may take to identify a soil forming part of an archaeological section, a concentration of organic matter at any level is prima-facie evidence for the existence of a buried surface. On sites of human settlement a layer with much organic matter may represent, rather, a hearth- or floor-level. In that case it should be traced laterally, for if it is very widespread and does not change notably in humus-concentration it is probably a natural soil.

Buried Soils

Under a barrow or bank, the excavator looks for what he calls the 'turf-line', meaning the buried surface on which the artificial structure was raised—which was not by any means always turf-covered. It should rather be called a buried soil, land-surface, or A-horizon.

Not uncommonly, the immediate ancient surface is not clearly apparent. In this case it may have been deliberately stripped off by man before some structure such as a mound was thrown up; in naturally-buried soils it may have been denuded by some agency before the fresh deposition began. It is also possible that the humic layer of a buried soil may have been changed by oxidation or removed after burial by percolating water or by the mixing action of worms, and so become visually indistinct. Unless stripped, it is unlikely to be completely obliterated and an even slight increase in the humus-content in a particular layer may still show an approximation to its position.

In the case of barrows, the stripped surface-material was often used to form the inner core of the mound and the high humus-concentration in this part, or its visible structure of discrete humic clods, will readily show when this was done. The stripping may have had some ritual significance, as to expose a white ceremonial area for the obsequies of the deceased (Cornwall, 1953, p. 135); on the other hand, it may merely have served the practical purpose of providing turf or sods to cover and protect the newly-made mound.

When present, a buried soil will typify the environmental conditions of the time immediately preceding its burial. In a loess-section, for example, this will be a relatively moist, temperate period of chemical weathering, intervening between the deposition of the loess on which the soil is formed and that of the loess covering it, both of these being suggestive of dry steppe conditions.

Even the much more recent buried soils below barrows, ramparts and other human structures may differ significantly from the present-day climax soil of the area and indicate, for example, the presence of forest where now there is heath, or a warmer, drier summer climate with grassland, where today forest would be re-established but for the plough.

Nitrogen

This is contained to some extent by all living matter, whether vegetable or animal, and is released to air and soil by the eventual decomposition of proteins. Fresh vegetable debris contains a high proportion of carbohydrate substances (cellulose, etc.) which are the first to break down on decomposition. The better the degree of humification, therefore, the higher becomes the proportion of nitrogen in the sample, the nitrogenous decomposition-products, such as humic acids, being more stable than the carbohydrates. Nitrogen-content is thus an indication of the original presence of plant or animal matter.

Now whereas, in acid soils, phosphates tend to be dissolved out and lost, the nitrogenous materials break down less easily in acid conditions. Where bases are plentiful, as when a farmer applies a dressing of lime, it is well known that such treatment in moderation releases plant-nutrients, but that, by overdoing the lime, the humus is quickly 'burnt up', with impoverishment of the soil.

If the absence of phosphate in an acid soil does not disprove the former presence of a body under a barrow, nitrogen estimations showing local concentration of nitrogenous matter, which is *not merely due to humus*, will perhaps afford positive evidence on the question. Here again, it is necessary to show that the nitrogen-concentration is not laterally widespread, to prove that humus alone could not be responsible. As with other tests, a single value tells us nothing. Results from several samples showing the position of the concentration both in the vertical and horizontal planes are alone significant. This is the chief use of nitrogen estimations in our context.

On agricultural land, one must take into account nitrogenous fertilizers of modern introduction—dung, dried blood, bone-meal, ammonium sulphate, nitro-chalk etc. Parallel tests on the plough-soil and intervening layers will show whether the horizon in question could have been contaminated from this source.

Whether the nitrogenous compounds owe their origin to animal or vegetable matter is not readily answered in the present state of our knowledge of the chemistry of soil organic matter. Plants and animals, if not too decayed, contain some respectively distinctive substances, but in the last stages of disintegration the basic unity of all living matter seems to be shown by the production of similar humus-substances, as yet unidentified, though certainly not unidentifiable, could some competent organic chemist be interested to inquire into the matter.

The time-factor in soil-formation

Archaeologists are always on the look-out for yardsticks to measure intervals of past times. A buried soil between two archaeological deposits of different periods suggests a period of abandonment of a site, or at least a local cessation of human activity. The excavator quite legitimately hopes that a soil-consultant will be able to suggest, from an examination of the material, how long it took to form and therefore to give him some indication of the length of time intervening between his periods of occupation. At the moment, such an estimate could be little but a guess, with a probable latitude of error so large as to be of very little value to the inquirer.

The processes of soil-formation have not long enough been under observation for such measurements as have been possible to be extrapolated with any confidence into the relatively distant past.

Many soils today, barring human disturbance, are the products of variable factors acting on them continuously since the beginning of the Postglacial period at least, a stretch of perhaps 10,000 years. Many others have been more or less disturbed by ploughing, deforestation, the ensuing denudation of considerable slopes and so on, frequently at several periods of recent history, not to mention unrecorded disturbances in prehistoric and earlier historic times. Save in areas of poor soil, always remote from human habitation, one can seldom be sure, in these crowded islands at least, that a given soil is truly natural. In more fertile regions, which have been under the plough from time immemorial, the upper 8–9 inches are inevitably artificially made and maintained tilth.

During the postglacial history of our soils, at least some of the factors—climate and vegetation in particular—have varied considerably, as is known to us through pollen-analysis, so that soil-forming processes have doubtless from time to time accelerated and slowed down in accordance with those changes. We have, moreover, no usable absolute measure of maturity, for all the evidence before us points to the conclusion that the factors of soil-formation are still effective and that evolution is continuous, if slow, and is still going on as we observe our soils today.

It is hard to see how changes can ever be *completed* in what we may justifiably term a 'living' soil. A soil ceases to live, as such, only when it is destroyed by denudation or erosion, becomes degraded under conditions widely different from those which accompanied its growth or is buried by fresh deposition and becomes a fossil, i.e., is removed from the further influence of the soil-forming factors. Its age at 'death' can be estimated only by comparison with a similar soil of known age. Since it cannot be shown that final maturity (complete equilibrium with the environment) is ever attained, it is impossible to characterize a soil as 'half mature', for example, but only to describe its development in general terms, as: 'a typically developed braunerde'.

For the present, then, we have still very much to learn about the rate of soil-formation *from* the archaeologist, rather than being in a position to offer dating by soil-evidence *to* the archaeologist.

In the case of a buried soil below a barrow, the excavator probably knows at least within a few centuries the likely date of his monument. This provides a limiting date (*terminus post quem*) for the beginning of soil-formation on the freshly heaped-up mound. Presuming that, in great part, there has been no later interference with the structure, this enables us to conclude that the soil-profiles observed on the mound have been formed between (say) 1600 B.C. (for a Wessex round barrow) and the present day—a matter of 3,600 years, more or less.

Since various parts of the mound and its complex (berm, ditch, counterscarp bank) have different slopes and exposures, detailed measurements of the profiles in different situations will enable these variables to be averaged out and a 'standard' profile for the monument as a whole to be drawn. This will be strictly comparable with others in the same area, on similar parent rocks and similarly sited. Collection of such data will provide in due course a body of information which may enable a numerical estimate of date to be assigned to monuments for which archaeological or other dating evidence is lacking.

Some 'henges', for example, like Thornbrough Rings (Thomas, 1956), are quite undatable by the usual methods and even the most approximate estimate, derived from comparison with datable soil-formations in the same area, would be valuable. The method would likewise be applicable to defensive ramparts if some comparative materials were locally available.

A different approach has recently been suggested by Atkinson (1957) in a paper on phenomena to be ascribed to earthworm-activity and chemical weathering, especially in sites on chalk subsoils. He has observed at Stonehenge and elsewhere that the highest point of the buried surface under a bank or mound stands noticeably higher than the general level of the present-day turf, where not protected by pre-historic structures. He attributes this, very reasonably, to solution by chemical weathering of the chalk subsoil and general lowering of the surrounding land-surface, having taken place since the erection of the bank, which, if thick enough, has preserved the original level intact. A minimum difference of 20 inches, equivalent to 4,000 years of weathering, is indicated at Stonehenge, where the bank was not high enough completely to isolate the buried soil from subsequent weathering influences. Atkinson also shows that, where the artificial cover is less than about 12 inches thick, the nutritious humic layer of the buried soil is obliterated in time by worms, which penetrate the new material, if not too sterile and unattractive to them, and eject their castings at the new surface.

This author has assembled some comparative figures out of his own experience and from published sections of other sites. Such data as these promise eventually to provide at least an approximate dating-instrument for unknowns. The work is, further, a valuable reminder to excavators that buried stratification and its archaeological contents are not by any means necessarily undisturbed by external (weathering) and internal (earthworms) influences since its deposition.

This emphasis on archaeological monuments, and what may be learned from them about the time-factor in soil-formation, is not to say that the pedologists have altogether ignored the time-factor. It does make clear that the traffic in knowledge between soil-science and archaeology is not all one-way and that study of soil-phenomena associated with datable remains of antiquity can afford valuable information to science on rates of soil-formation. With an increasing body of comparative observations, soil-science may be able, in time, to offer reliable estimates of date in the case of sites without archaeological dating-evidence or with only conflicting indications.

Jenny (1941) has assembled some numerical data on rates of soil-formation as follows:

The bed of Lake Ragunda, in northern Sweden, drained in 1796, was found by Tamm to show some podsolization within a century. It was decalcified to a depth of 10 inches under pine-heath and to 25 inches under mixed forest with mosses. He estimated that a bleached A_2-horizon 4 inches in thickness takes 1,000–1,500 years to form. This worker also investigated recently-formed alluvial sand-terraces, whose ages were fairly closely known. He showed that the silica/alumina value of the A_2-horizon falls for the first century, rises steeply with increasing age up to 600 years and finally levels off. In the B-horizon, the ratio Fe_2O_3/SiO_2 falls in the first 100 years, rises steeply in the next 500 and, at a decreasing slope, up to 1,500 years. This is evidently at first in step with the bleaching of the A_2, but the further accumulation of limonite for 900 years shows that, even with a well-developed bleached layer, the profile as a whole is still far from maturity.

Aaltonen (quoted by Jenny, ibid.) shows that the deposition of colloidal sesquioxides in the B-horizon of a podsol grows from the bottom upwards. According to his curves, the A_2-horizon, in Finland, reaches its fullest development at an age of 3,000 years and is later invaded from below by the still-growing B-horizon. The latter may extend to 50 cms in depth, but the zones of maximum leaching and of maximum deposition may be no more than 5 cms apart at an age of 5,000 years.

Salisbury (1925) investigated soil-formation on a series of sand-dunes near Southport, Lancs, of which the ages were approximately known from the dates of their appearance on old maps, up to 280 years ago. Unweathered material containing more than 6% $CaCO_3$ was leached to a fraction over 1% in a century and to 0.22% in two. Thereafter, the pH fell very steeply and is matched by the rise in organic matter from 2.5% to 15% in the last 80 years.

Hissink (Jenny, ibid.) has studied the soils of Dutch polders, reclaimed from the sea at known dates, beginning 300 years ago. Calcium carbonate amounting to 10% of the surface soil has been completely leached out in that time. Unlike Salisbury's curve, the rate of leaching, here, was slow for 100 years, increasing steadily almost up to the end and finally falling off to nil within 50 years. This difference from Salisbury's results lies in the fine clayey material of the polder-sediments and the presence of sodium-ions at first preventing the formation of an open texture, permitting the passage of rain-water.

In connexion with various archaeological sites, Zeuner (1941, 1947, 1952a, 1954) has made some observations of rates of soil-formation as follows:

(1). Bury Hill, an Iron-age fort, showed 1 inch of immature soil on chalk rubble forming the surface of an Iron Age 'A' rampart, covered by a later reconstruction in Iron Age 'B' times. He considered that the soil had required at least a century, and not more than a very few centuries, for its formation. The archaeological dating of cultural stages of the Early Iron Age is still under discussion, but the minimum figure of 100 years for the formation of this soil would not generally be regarded as unreasonable.

(2). Two sections from the Park Street (Herts) Roman villa are cited by Zeuner, in one of which a soil formed during the last 1,600 years on calcareous building-rubble. Though decalcification had not proceeded beyond the uppermost few millimetres, some humus had penetrated to a depth of 20 cms. In the second case, in which the parent material was non-calcareous, an immature brownearth had formed to a depth of 18 cms in the same time.

(3). At Strehlen, Silesia, a blackearth (chernosem) which has probably been undergoing degradation since at least the Sub-boreal period, showed no mature profile after the lapse of 2,000–3,000 years.

(4). A gap in time between the Neolithic and Bronze-Age occupations of the Jericho tell was shown to be marked by an immature soil of the Xerorendsina type. A period of 300±100 years was regarded as likely by comparison of the buried soil with that formed in modern times since the abandonment of the tell in the Byzantine period.

Quantitative data bearing on rates of soil-formation are thus seen to be very scarce and distributed over several quite distinct types of soil, from Finnish podsols to Jordanian xero-rendsinas, formed under very different conditions. If the archaeologists hope for more definite information in the future as to the time-relations of soil phenomena found on their sites they must notice, sample and preserve more examples of buried soils which are reasonably well dated on other evidence, which may serve for comparison with unknowns. Soil-science, on the other hand, must be prepared to show interest in these evidences, to send competent observers to see them and collect samples in the generally only briefly-exposed sections which the archaeologist can offer, and to spend time on their examination in the laboratory.

19

Examples of Soil-Investigations at Three Actual Sites

✦✦✦

THE APPROACH TO soil-investigations and the interpretation of experimental results is best illustrated by actual examples.

The following are brief accounts of three hitherto unpublished inquiries, among many carried out by the writer during the last ten years. They are selected because they pose typical problems and show the sort of considerations taken into account in interpretation. They are not offered as models of their kind—we are learning all the time and today's best efforts will certainly be eclipsed in the future, just as they themselves represent some advance on earlier work. If they do not shed any fundamentally new light on archaeological problems, these examples afford certain concrete conclusions—which not all such investigations do. They at least demonstrate in action some of the devices and notions described above.

The East Mersea Channel

In 1950 the surface of a small gravelly area of beach at East Mersea, Essex (see map, Fig. 17) yielded plentiful remains of an extinct temperate-forest or parkland fauna and fresh-water shells, from between tide-marks. In view of the interest of these and the relative proximity of the well-known Clacton Channel, in which Lower Palaeolithic implements were found with a similar animal assemblage, evidence was sought to date the remains and, if possible, to find the relation of the deposits to those at the name-sites of the Clactonian industry.

A survey of the site, assisted by some shallow excavations (Fig. 18) showed that the fossiliferous gravel emerged in a narrow tongue from below the modern shingle, at an angle of some $45°$ to the present coastline, and was being eroded by waves at high water to a feather-edge on the London Clay, in which its bench was cut. The gravel apparently represented the bed of a buried channel of a considerable stream.

The beach was backed by a low cliff of silt, very similar in character, at least in its upper levels, to that at present being laid down just off shore and exposed at low water. The section in this cliff showed some evidence, in a slightly redder layer, of an old land-surface, buried by the upper part of the silt, which was more clayey in texture and apparently of marine origin. A series of samples was therefore taken and, in the laboratory, gave the following results:

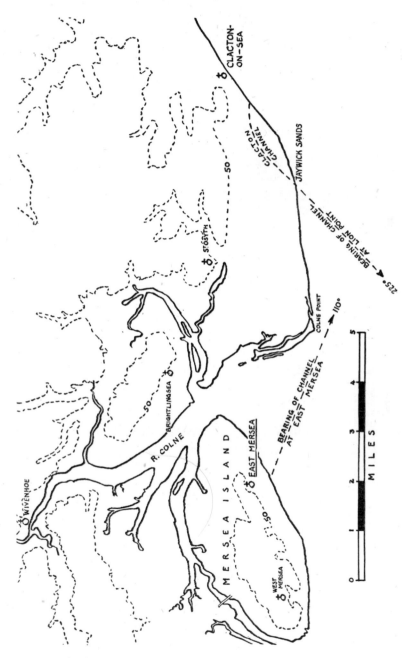

FIG 17.   Map of the Essex coast to show the relation between the East Mersea Channel and that at Jaywick Sands.

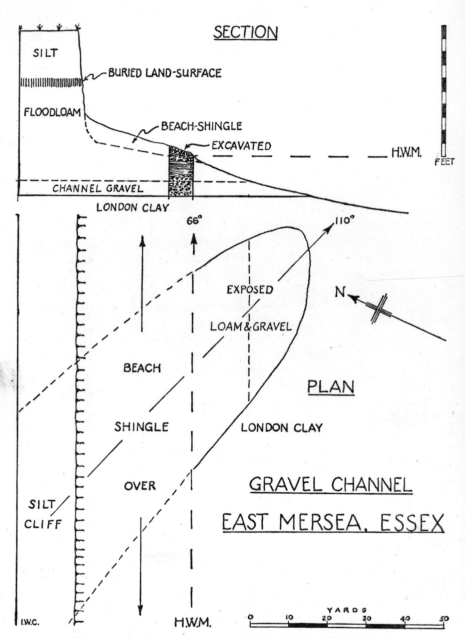

FIG 18. Section and plan of the East Mersea Channel site.

Sample No.	Height above H.W.M.		pH	CaCO₃	Humus (%)
	ft	ins			
Summit	9	6	—	—	—
10	9	5	8.6	+	1.0
9	8	10	6.9	+	0.3
8	8	2	7.1	+	0.2
7	7	2	6.6	—	0.2
6	6	6	6.3	—	0.1
5	5	11	6.1	—	0.1
4	5	4	6.2	—	nil
3	4	8	6.7	—	nil
2	4	5	7.3	+	nil
1	4	2	8.4	+	nil

The interesting feature of these results is the decalcification of samples 3–7 inclusive, shown by the tests for carbonate and borne out by the pH readings. Since both the highest and lowest parts of the section show the presence of calcium carbonate, the decalcification in the middle shows that this must long have been exposed to weathering before the fresh calcareous material above was laid down, i.e. that we have here a buried soil.

Now the position of the ancient surface is not very clear from these figures—it might lie anywhere between 7 feet 2 inches and 4 feet 8 inches, on the evidence of the decalcification, a distance of 2 feet 6 inches. The humus figures do not help us, for they decrease regularly from the summit and appear only to represent organic matter derived from the modern surface. The reddening of the deposits might have been instructive, but neither the Munsell colour-charts nor the thin-sectioning technique were known to us at the time of this discovery. We are left, then, with the pH values. The lowest of these, representing the zone of most intense weathering, is at No. 5 and this level, as it happens, represents the mean height of the whole decalcified zone above H.W.M., our not very exact datum.

This picture, of a gravel-filled river channel with mammalian fossils, followed by finer fluviatile deposits, surmounted by a weathered surface and all covered with a Recent marine silt, is repeated at several places on the Essex coast. A section noted by Zeuner in 1938, at the Lion Point 2, Jaywick sands site, is as follows:

Scrobicularia Clay (marine, with foraminifera)
Peat
Neolithic/Bronze-Age occupation-surface
Brown weathered silt (Lyonesse Surface)
White marl (calcareous clay)
Marine bed, with Ostrea and Cardium shells

Freshwater bed with *Unio*
'Elephant Bed', ferruginous gravel
Weathered London Clay

The 'Elephant Bed' is known to occur at several points, extending from one marked just offshore near East Mersea (i.e. somewhat to the east of the present site) through Jaywick Sands, Clacton and Walton-on-the-Naze (Zeuner 1952a, p.94) to Mill Bay, just south of Harwich (see map, Oakley & Leakey, 1937, p. 252).

The Lyonesse Surface, an ancient land-surface on flood-plain deposits, drowned by the sea since Early Bronze-Age times, is a well-known feature on the east coast. At Jaywick, it lies about 2 feet 6 inches below H.W.M., while at East Mersea our weathering surface is about 5 feet 11 inches above it, a difference of 8 feet 6 inches. Since the direct distance between East Mersea and Jaywick is some 5½ miles, and allowing perhaps 1/3rd more for a meandering stream, the gradient of the surface between the two sites, if belonging to the same stream and period, would work out at just over 1 foot per mile, a reasonable figure for the lower course of a mature river.

The correlation with the channel at Clacton, therefore, seems to be justified under three heads:

1. The fossil fauna (not here considered) points to a similar environment at the two places.

2. The general direction of the East Mersea Channel would lead close to a junction with that at Jaywick Sands (see map, Fig. 17).

3. The level of the presumed floodplain surface of the East Mersea stream would run fittingly into that of the corresponding surface at Jaywick, with an intervening gradient of about 1 foot per mile.

A conclusion of possible environmental interest emerges from the above correlation. While, at Clacton, immense numbers of flint implements of human manufacture have been found in the 'Elephant' gravels, at East Mersea not a single flake has hitherto been recovered despite diligent search, although the remains of the large mammals —the food-animals of Palaeolithic man—were equally plentiful. If we conclude that the latter site represents a higher portion of the course of the same river, the difference in suitability for human occupation in Palaeolithic times must be explained.

The presence of a bed with marine shells at Jaywick, closely succeeding the freshwater phase with *Unio,* shows that a slight sea-level oscillation was sufficient to bring the neck of the estuary above the Jaywick site. At East Mersea there is no break in the fluviatile sequence. This indicates that, while the Clacton sites were close to the sea, that at East Mersea apparently did not suffer any marine incursion during this phase of the Great Interglacial. This fact perhaps illustrates the environmental preferences of the Lower Palaeolithic human inhabitants, for the sea has always afforded a reasonably easy living to the beachcomber.

Flixton, Yorks, Site 1*

The finds of Mesolithic flint implements made in the years 1947–9 in the 'carrs' of the eastern end of the Vale of Pickering, near Flixton, Yorks, by Mr John W. Moore, led to the discovery of the now famous early Maglemosian site of Star Carr, near Seamer, excavated under the direction of Professor J. G. D. Clark (1954).

The carrs are extensive level areas with deep, peaty soil, representing an ancient lake and marsh landscape with low hillocks, now completely levelled by the subsequent growth of the peat. The field-boundaries are deep drainage-ditches, in which the summer water-level is perhaps 4–5 feet below the surface. While, in many places, these ditches do not reach the base of the peat, here and there, where there are hillocks in the underlying drift, the peat is only some 2 feet thick and the ancient land-surface is exposed in section.

In the uppermost 6 inches to 1 foot of the soil underlying the peat, Mr Moore found flints and bones *in situ*, which led him to suppose that, while the peat was forming on the flanks of these hillocks, the summits were occupied by Mesolithic hunter-fishers as settlements. In the summer of 1948 he therefore undertook an excavation on the site of a low, peat-submerged eminence in the neighbourhood of Flixton village and called in the writer to advise on some features of the sections revealed.

A constant feature of the sections was a layer of ferruginous concretion at some depth up to 1 foot below the surface of the archaeological layer. This 'pan' Mr Moore was inclined to regard as the land-surface in existence immediately preceding the occupation. The pan was locally discontinuous, horizontally, for distances of between a few inches and 2 feet, at the edges of which it dipped down into a depression. At the bottom of each depression there seemed, in most cases, to be a sort of 'pipe' penetrating the underlying drift. Mr Moore's own theory about these depressions, at that time, was that they were springs. An explanation of them was sought and also of the processes responsible for the formation of the archaeological layer itself.

It was suspected that the ferruginous concretionary layer would prove to be either a groundwater-hardpan or the B-horizon of a podsol.

Some twenty samples were examined, their positions in the section being shown in Fig. 19, redrawn from the rough sections supplied by the excavator. (It should be noted at this point that, at the time of the inquiry, no reliable method had yet been devised for the quantitative estimation of humus, nor was the value of iron-estimations through such a profile appreciated.) Descriptions of samples were as follows:

1–4. Yellowish-grey sandy clay with chalk pellets, containing only the merest trace of organic matter. pH 8.4.

5. A similar material, less yellow and slightly darker in colour. Free

* Moore, 1950.

o

$CaCO_3$ was visible to the naked eye in distinct particles. There was a small amount of humus. pH 7.2.

6. Iron concretion with very little free carbonate. The acid-insoluble residue was small, coarse-sandy and but slightly humic. pH 6.7.

7. Clayey sand with comparatively little iron. The residue was of coarse sand with markedly increased humus. pH 6.4.

8. As No. 7, but with still less iron. The sandy residue was finer in grade and markedly humic. pH 5.9.

9. Peat with some mineral admixture. Iron not detectable. The mineral residue was fine, clean, silica sand. pH 6.0.

10. Peat. A small residue of fine sand. pH 5.8.

11–16. These samples consisted of almost pure peat, with only a very small mineral content, and that clean sand. pH was 5.3 on the average.

17. Another sample of iron pan from a trodden surface of the excavation. It scarcely differed from No. 6, but contained rather more humus, perhaps due to contamination.

18. Another sample of the ferruginous layer, from a slightly higher level, only 15 inches below the surface, at a distance of 6 feet to one side of the key section. It is more sandy than No. 6.

19. Small blue gravel, from a boring in the bottom of an adjacent drainage-ditch. It was very ferruginous, some of the pebbles consisting of rolled fragments of iron concretion. The finer matrix was mainly sand with small amounts of finer grades. Quartz was the only mineral seen, apart from iron.

20. Brown, stoneless, tenacious clay. On washing, it yielded only a very few particles larger than 0.1 mm, no micro-fossils and only a trace of organic matter.

This examination showed a thick cover of peat on a soil-parent-material rich in iron and calcium carbonate. The pH values as well as the macroscopic appearance showed some leaching, especially of $CaCO_3$, in the upper part of the section and a certain enrichment of iron at a depth of 1 foot or so from the surface. Below this the material was practically unchanged by soil-forming processes.

A soil of the podsolic type was indicated, but not an extreme example with marked bleaching of the A_2-horizon—in Kubiena's terminology, a podsolic braunerde.

Studying the section from the base upwards, the stoneless brown clay is likely to have been deposited from standing water. The geological 'solid' in the Vale of Pickering, below the Pleistocene deposits, is the Kimmeridge Clay, of Jurassic age, lithologically quite different from this brown clay, and full of marine fossils. It may therefore be concluded that the brown clay is of Pleistocene age and either contemporary with, or younger than, the New Drift glaciation, which just reached this area.

Now it is known (Wilson, 1948, p. 12) that in the retreat stage of one of the later glacial phases the Scandinavian ice-front entered the eastern end of the Vale of Pickering and ponded up a great lake between the Chalk Wolds and the Cleveland Hills. This overflowed southwards, cutting a gorge at New Malton, thus reversing the drainage of the Vale, which must, formerly, have reached the North Sea near Filey. The brown clay, therefore, possibly represents part of the deposits of glacial Lake Pickering.

The fine blue gravel of Sample 19 appears to occur in all nearby sections, capping the brown clay. It seems to be a product of running water, as is evidenced by the rounding and abrasion of the pebbles of iron concretion which it contains. The blue colour of the matrix is certainly a secondary feature, due to waterlogging at the present day, exclusion of oxygen and reduction of the iron salts. In the key section (Fig. 19), the surface of this gravel lies more than 2 feet below the groundwater table observed in the unusually dry summer of 1948.

Following the blue gravel comes some 6 feet of yellow-grey sandy clay with stones and chalk granules. Elsewhere, the blue gravel is succeeded by lacustrine marls, containing a temperate fauna of fresh-water molluscs. These were immediately followed by a very deep peat, up to 13 feet in thickness. In other sections, 6–8 feet of peat lies directly on the blue gravel. Clearly, then, the yellow-grey clay is a discontinuous feature. With its content of stones and lack of stratification, it looks like a boulder-clay or a solifluxion-deposit derived from the adjacent Chalk scarp. It could thus hardly have been laid down simultaneously with lake-marls with temperate shells and, since the latter seem to precede the peat without disconformity, one is inclined to conclude that the yellow-grey clay once covered the blue gravel everywhere but was later locally eroded to expose it once more. The surface thus presented was of some irregularity before the beginning of the formation of the peat-marl series.

Ponds and lakes occupied the deeper depressions in this surface and, while these were being filled with marls and subsequently covered with peat, the eminences of grey stony clay were exposed to weathering. The growth of peat continued until it overflowed the lake banks, covering even the higher areas of bare gravel and threatening to engulf even the low hillocks of stony clay.

It was at this stage that Mesolithic man occupied the summits of the hillocks and that his flints and the bones of his food-animals became incorporated in the uppermost 1 foot of stony clay.

Now, before the occupation-debris began to accumulate, the hillocks had long been subjected to some denudation and weathering. This continued during the occupation, until the growth of peat overwhelmed the particular summit in question. The weathering resulted in the formation of a soil-profile, probably initially of the braunerde type, in view of the calcareous parent material. After some time the surface layers had lost all of their calcium carbonate and the acidity had increased to the point where the iron became mobile also. This resulted in a certain

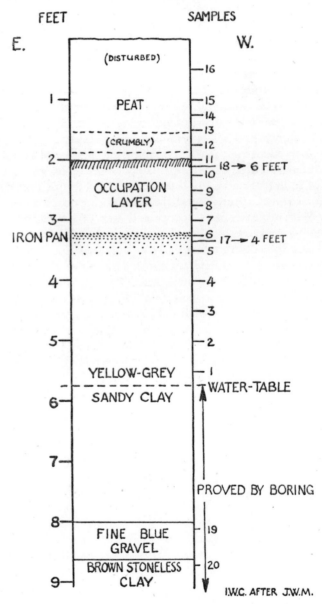

FIG 19.   Flixton, Yorks, Site I. Section after Moore.

degree of podsolization, with formation of iron-pan at the horizon where the decreasing acidity of the unleached calcareous subsoil caused the reprecipitation of the iron compounds.

While this weathering was in progress, it would seem that some trees grew on the hillocks, their spreading roots locally disturbing the iron-pan and their tap-roots penetrating fairly deeply beyond it into the calcareous subsoil. This would probably account for the 'pipes' observed by Mr Moore.

A pollen analysis was carried out by Dr Godwin on a sample of peat from the marrow-cavity of a bone and showed a preponderance of birch-pine, the remainder mainly alder with hazel just over 50% of the total tree-pollen. A single grain of lime pollen was found. This suggests a climate somewhat milder than that of Star Carr, perhaps at a Late Boreal date. The fact that the hillock showed a concentrated occupation suggests that the immediate surroundings were unsuitable for settlement, i.e. that the peat was already advancing and leaving only islands, like this site, of dry ground. The Late Boreal date of the peat on its flanks was confirmed by pollen-analysis. (See Godwin, H., in Clark, 1954, pp. 51–6.)

No tree-stools or roots survived to be found by the excavators on the summit of the hillock, but this would be expected if the level at which they were rooted was above the permanent water-table and so sufficiently aerated to favour ordinary decay. This, of course, excludes groundwater as the cause of the pan-formation. At the northern extremity of the section supplied by Mr Moore, however, there was a preserved tree-stool in the peat, at or about the level of the summer water-table. This proves that an environment suitable for trees existed *at that place* (the pollen is wind-drifted and does not prove that there were trees on the site) so that tree-roots as an explanation for the 'pipes' become highly likely.

The stratification and the samples themselves thus showed some interesting details about the history of the site and the environment of its Mesolithic inhabitants.

'Caesar's Camp', Keston, Kent*

The site is an Iron-Age fort with multiple defences and the soil-problem presented was that of determining the existence or otherwise of reconstructions of the ramparts. Sections were seen in Site 2, the innermost rampart, and in the Middle Bank, separated from this by a deep ditch.

Twelve samples were taken—eight from Site 2 and four from the Middle Bank. No. 1 of the former series was lost through bursting of the bag and contamination of the contents, but this was of no great importance since the material was almost certainly identical with No. 1

* Mrs Piercy Fox, 1956, unpublished at time of writing.

o*

of the Middle bank series, being upcast geological 'solid', forming the unweathered core of the rampart.

The material was very pebbly coarse sand, derived from the Black-heath Pebble-Beds on which the site rests. Minerals present were silica (quartz and flint), ferric oxide and hydroxide (limonite) and little else. All the samples were completely non-calcareous, as might have been expected.

The pH-values and the concentrations of humus and of iron oxides were determined for each sample, as follows:

Site 2.

Sample No.	pH	Alkali-soluble humus (%)	Iron, as Fe_2O_3 (mgs./100 gms. dry soil)
8	5.4	1.8	235
7	5.5	0.3	90
6	4.5	2.2	875
5	4.7	0.25	300
4	4.1	2.8	435
3	5.1	0.17	455
2	4.7	0.5	610

Middle Bank.

Sample No.	pH	Alkali-soluble humus (%)	Iron, as Fe_2O_3 (mgs./100 gms. dry soil)
4	5.7	0.4	90
3	6.2	0.02	90
2	5.2	0.34	90
1	4.4	0.05	475

The figures in the table occupy the positions of the corresponding deposits in the sections, those of the Middle Bank representing the buried soil, the land-surface before any Iron-Age constructions. The lower three samples of Site 2, suspected of being a soil, if proved to be so, must have formed on the surface of an early low bank. The remainder represent the modern soil, formed on the material piled up over this in the completion of the rampart as seen today.

The soil-type throughout was a well-developed podsol, clearly to be seen by the humic and bleached horizons as well as being shown by the experimental results. At the summit we have (No. 8), the modern A_1, dark humus horizon, very acid with accumulated, poorly-humified plant remains (raw humus) amounting to 1.8% and somewhat impoverished in iron. The iron-content of the parent material of this soil is shown by No. 5, a value of 300 mgs/100 gms soil. This is distinctly lower than the 475 mgs of No. 1 from the Middle Bank, which is the presumably unweathered natural subsoil. This suggests that the make-up material of the reconstructed rampart consists, at least in part, of already weathered and leached soil-material, scraped up from the surface nearby.

Sample No. 7 is clearly a bleached A_2-horizon, poor both in humus and in iron. Only the humus actually in transit through it is found and practically all the iron has been dissolved out and carried further down the profile. A marked concentration both of humus and iron is found again in No. 6, the B-horizon. The succeeding decrease in humus and iron in No. 5 shows that we have reached the parent material of this profile, the C-horizon, formed by the upcast material of the bank, already somewhat weathered when so piled up.

Nos 4, 3 and 2 represent what seems to be a second podsol-profile in the body of the innermost rampart (Site 2). The pH and humus figures bear out this conclusion, indicating that they are A_1, A_2 and B-horizons respectively. The iron-concentration in No. 2 supports this also, but the iron figures for Nos 4 and 3 are rather high in comparison with the corresponding values for the modern soil (Nos. 8 and 7, above). This seems to indicate that the second profile is less mature than the modern one and fits admirably with the theory that it was a soil of a few decades, or even a century or so, in age, representing the weathering of an interval between the first construction and a major reconstruction and strengthening of the defences. If so, its parent-material is likely to have been more ferruginous than the make-up of the reconstructed bank, in fact, the unweathered upcast from the digging of a deep ditch into the undisturbed subsoil. This was the sample which was lost, but in the hand closely resembled the subsoil *in situ* (No. 1) of the buried soil below the Middle Bank. It will be seen from the table that this contained 475 mgs of iron against the 300 mgs of No. 5. This has been reduced by the weathering of the interval between constructions to 435 and 455 mgs respectively in the immature A-horizons, with an increase from 475 to 610 mgs in the young B-horizon of this profile. These figures show fairly conclusively an immature buried soil between the constructions. No attempt is made here to estimate from the degree of leaching the age of this soil. Limiting dates will perhaps emerge in the eventual publication of the archaeological material from this section. In the present state of our knowledge any estimate would be pure guesswork, with the added danger of arguing in a circle from preconceived ideas about the durations of stages in Early-Iron-Age culture.

The Middle Bank samples, Nos. 4, 3, 2, 1, represent a third podsol: this time the mature profile of a soil, for the formation of which some 8,000 years of Postglacial time are available, in existence at the site before any Iron-Age disturbance of the natural soil-régime.

The horizons represented are the A_1 (humus), A_2 (bleached), B_1 (humus illuvial) and C, the relatively unweathered Blackheath Pebble Beds (Eocene). The figures in the table are quite typical. In view of the marked bleaching shown by the iron-figures for Nos. 4 and 3 of this group, there is but slight concentration of iron at 2 or 1. It is likely that, in such porous material, much of the dissolved iron has been carried deeper than the layers reached by the sampling, forming an iron-pan at the level of the subsoil water-table (see Cornwall, 1953, and in Ashbee, 1956 refs. below).

The interest of Caesar's Camp, Keston, from the soil viewpoint, is the superposition of three podsols at a site from which we may hope to get limiting dates for the pedological sequence from archaeological evidence. If so, it will provide one more set of facts from which we may be able, one day, to argue in making estimates of time-intervals marked by soils of this type at sites where dating evidence is lacking.

Brief accounts of results obtained at a few British archaeological sites by the examination of soil-samples were assembled by the writer in a paper read to the Prehistoric Society in 1953 (Cornwall, 1953). These are good examples of their kind and demonstrate the sort of information that can be hoped for. For every site which yields concrete results there are many less informative and even some in which the inquiry proves quite inconclusive. It is perhaps our knowledge, as much as the evidence, which is at fault in these cases.

Including some of these mentioned in the above paper, but unpublished at that time, soil-results of some interest have been published more recently as follows:

Lacaille, A. D., & Grimes, W. F. 1955. 'The prehistory of Caldey', *Arch. Cambrensis, 104, 1955.* Appendix, pp. 159-65.

Posnansky, M. 1955. 'The excavation of a Bronze-Age round barrow at Lockington', Appendix II. *Trans. Leics. Arch. & Hist. Soc., 31, 25-7.*

Ashbee, P. 1956. 'The excavation of a round barrow on Canford Heath, Dorset., Appendix I. *Proc. Dorset Nat. Hist. & Arch. Soc.,* 76, 47-50.

Thomas, N., 1956. 'The Thornborough Circles, near Ripon, North Riding', Appendix I *et passim. Yorks. Arch. J., 38,* 425-45.

These may be consulted as further illustrations of approach and interpretation.

It will be evident that we have still far to go before soil-science becomes an exact tool for interpreting phenomena found in association with archaeological sites. A beginning, indeed, has been made, but progress has been slow for lack of time and pairs of hands to do the practical work. To a very limited extent the archaeologist himself could assist in this, but for routine work there is needed a fairly well-equipped laboratory and some scientific training. The author has been at pains to give working details of the methods which he has used in the hope that some few readers with the necessary interest and equipment may be encouraged to try their own hands in the work, and, it may be expected, improve upon our present performance.

APPENDIX

- -

Demonstration and Reproduction of Thin Sections

Two (OR MORE) HEADS are frequently better than one, and, feeling our way, as we still are in thin-section work, it is often helpful to discuss with a colleague or group the interpretation of a specimen.

A difficulty of all ordinary microscopy is that only one person can see the image at a time. This may be overcome by direct projection on to a screen or by photography, to make an enlarged slide which may be shown, even to a large audience, with the ordinary lantern. Obviously, the latter course will only be followed when a permanent record of the image is wanted.

Projection and photography present similar problems, the image in one case being thrown on to a screen, to be directly viewed, in the other on the sensitive material. For micro-projection very intense lighting is essential. Photography is possible, even of a somewhat dim image, by increasing the time of exposure, but too long an exposure may lead to vibration and fuzziness of the negative, so that it is well to use the shortest practicable exposure. The problems are thus seen to be very alike, and it can be said that an image suitable for direct projection will always make a good photograph.

The human eye accommodates itself readily to a great range of lighting intensities, and this is so automatic that we do not often appreciate the true differences. The photographic material does nothing of itself to help eke out insufficient light and often shows defects both of general intensity and evenness of the lighted field which are inappreciable, or at least acceptable, to the eye.

Most microscopes are provided with three or four objectives, of which the lowest power is usually the 1", with a magnification, on its own, of about x 5 (linear). The usual eyepieces range in magnification between x 4 and x 10. The lowest magnification obtainable with this equipment is then about x 20. In a coarse-grained soil, the field of view is not wide enough, even at this low magnification, to embrace more than three or four mineral grains, so that no general idea of the fabric can be conveyed without scanning a larger area of the slide. For still reproduction this is obviously excluded.

For projection or photography, moreover, the magnification obtained with the same objective and eyepiece is increased by the necessary long throw for the image between eyepiece and screen or plate. The most useful for this purpose, therefore, are 2" or even 3" objectives, combined with a low-power eyepiece (x 2) giving a very flat field. With high-power oculars the centre and edges of the field may not be simultaneously in focus. Some microscopes have not a sufficiently long rack on the tube for the long working-distance of low-power objectives.

Having procured suitable optical equipment for the microscope itself (low-power lenses are, happily, the least expensive to buy), we are next in trouble with lighting arrangements. An Abbé substage condenser designed to illuminate the field for a 1″ objective will not fill the bottom lens of the 2″. The function of the substage condenser is to collect all the available light and to concentrate it into a narrow, intense beam only just large enough to fill the front lens of the objective in use. The higher the power of the objective, the narrower is its front lens and the more intense the spot of light produced by the condenser, using the whole of its aperture in collecting light just to fill it. With low powers, the situation is reversed. The condenser makes a spot of light too small to fill the whole field of the low-power objective. If the substage condenser is an ordinary Abbé, the upper lens may be removed to give a wider beam, but some petrological microscopes have special condensers, and if this is the case, the whole condenser will have to be removed and one of longer focal length substituted. A good rule-of-thumb principle is that the condenser should have a focal length of about twice that of the objective to be used, and indeed a spare long-focus objective will serve admirably as a low-power condenser if it can be suitably mounted in the substage—2″ for a 1″-objective, 3″ for a 1½″ and so on. The difficulty here is often a matter of space. With the mirror, polarizer, substage-diaphragm and condenser of a polarizing microscope, substage space is in any case at a premium and it is unlikely that there will be room, or working-distance, for a long-focus condenser to be fitted in.

A solution may be found by substituting a 'Polaroid' filter for the nicol-prism polarizer, removing the mirror, and arranging a separate mounting (a retort-stand and clamp will serve) for the objective-condenser, with the microscope-tube in the horizontal position. Ideally, a proper optical bench would be best for experimenting.

Messrs C. Baker of Holborn, Ltd supply two special low-power substage condensers, of standard diameter, for projection-work. Their 'Projectolux' illuminating base and camera (in one) are admirable, but not inexpensive, pieces of equipment. If funds will not extend to this sort of thing, ingenuity and trial-and-error, unaided, will yield satisfactory results.

The higher powers of the microscope present no great mechanical difficulty for projection, because most instruments are designed to operate in the range x 20 to x 400 as a matter of routine. Above this we are in the range of oil-immersion objectives (1/12th″, x 100) and this has hitherto seldom been found useful in our context. The higher the magnification the harder it becomes to get enough light on the subject—and for projection we need all the light to be had.

For all projection or photography a high-wattage lamp is desirable. A carbon arc is probably the best, but the writer has had no experience of this. The 'Pointolite' tungsten arc-lamp enclosed in a bulb is good, but a multi-filament incandescent lamp, taking 48 watts at 6 volts, as fitted in the 'Projectolux' has been found better still for the lower powers. This is obtainable separately from the same firm ('Lamplux') in a ventilated housing and with transformer and rheostat. Low-power microscope-lamps, suitable for direct observation, are practically useless.

Even using the low powers of magnification, some 9/10ths of the intensity of illumination are lost on crossing the nicols of the polarizing microscope. This fact restricts direct projection to fairly short throws and to audiences of no more than a dozen people. For many more than this it becomes impracticable, even by back-projection on to a ground-glass screen, which gives a more brilliant image. For smaller groups of two or three observers, projection on to the focussing-screen of a plate-camera, set up as if for photography, is very satisfactory.

The problem of lighting-intensity is not so urgent for photographic purposes, but even lighting of the field of view is essential, especially for colour-work, in which the exposure is somewhat critical.

As has been shown, the state of the iron compounds in fabric and plasma of a thin soil-section is distinguished by their colours, so that monochrome reproductions have only very limited usefulness. In fabric-studies, as, for example, when it is desired to show the humus-coatings on quartz-grains in a podsol B-horizon, black-and-white photographs suffice, but for most purposes colour is essential.

Colour-transparencies on 35-mm. film can be made without difficulty, for use as 2″ × 2″ slides to project thin soil-sections for larger audiences. These 'stills', however perfect in other respects, suffer from the drawback that the extinction of the mineral grains and the birefringence of iron-sol flow-structures on revolving the microscope stage cannot be demonstrated. A ciné-film would be required for this!

Even today, no photographic colour-material gives more than a good approximation to true colour-rendering. The writer has experimented only with 'Kodachrome', with fairly encouraging results, but the process at its best leaves still something to be desired, in comparison with the image seen down the microscope-tube.

Micro-cameras are legion, but good work can be done, using due precaution against camera-shake, even with the simplest equipment. A plain cone, fitted at its base with a plate-holder and a translucent screen for focussing, fastened to the tube of the microscope, is sufficient for monochrome photographs or for cut colour-film of appropriate size. For miniature film, any reasonably stable fitment that will firmly hold the body (less the lens) of a miniature 35-mm. roll-film camera at the desired distance of a few inches from the ocular of the microscope will answer the purpose.

The writer has used a home-made vertical camera-mount, which hangs, by a bent metal flange, from the beaded edge of the shutter panel of the Baker quarter-plate micro-camera mounted on the 'Projectolux' base. The microscope stands on the base with the vertical axis centred on its lighting-window. The camera, a Kine-Exakta, without the lens but with a 2"-long bakelite extension-tube, is swung in over the eye-piece until the cross-lines in the eyepiece are central on the focussing-screen. The extension-tube is lowered over the eyepiece and a black cloth sleeve fastened with rubber bands makes the junction light-tight. The Exakta is ideal for the purpose because, with the reflex mirror, the correct lighting and focus of the image can be confirmed up to the last moment before making the exposure. With a non-reflex miniature camera, the focal distance must first be found by experiment with a ground glass and the focal plane of the film adjusted to coincide with the position of the image thus found.

At an absolute magnification of x 10, using the 'Projectolux' equipment, a 2" objective (x 2.5) and a x 4 eyepiece, exposures of $\frac{1}{2}$ sec. by ordinary light and 5 secs. with crossed nicols yielded successful transparencies on Kodachrome colour-film.

In accordance with the Inverse-Square Law, doubling the magni-fication by changing the objective, *with unchanged lighting equipment*, would require four times the exposure used before. However, since a shorter-focus condenser is used at the higher power to pass approxi-mately the *same amount* of light in a more intense pencil, the *same exposures* as before would apply for all objectives using the appropriate substage condensers. If, however, the magnification is doubled by increasing the distance of the focal plane of the camera from the eyepiece, the same light as before is spread over four times the area, so that four times the exposure must be given.

Allowance in exposing must also be made for the relative density of the subject. Under the above conditions, a 'sol lessivé' from St Pierre was taken as the average subject at $\frac{1}{2}$ sec. and 5 secs under crossed nicols. A terra rossa with only small quartzes (and, therefore, passing much less light even in ordinary light) was given 3/4 sec. and 8 secs. A roterde (largely de-silicified and so with hardly any quartzes) was not over-exposed in ordinary light at 1 sec. Under polarized light it was very dark and was slightly under-exposed with 11 secs.

Reproduction of colour-transparencies for publication by process-blocks is still far too expensive for general use. Half-tone plates from monochrome photographs are generally very inadequate illustrations. This difficulty has not yet been overcome, but the recent appearance of opaque colour-prints, though not yet up to the standard of excellence of transparencies, suggests that a way may, before long, be found to distribute at least limited numbers of colour-reproductions of thin sections to fellow-workers, without prohibitive expense.

BIBLIOGRAPHY

Apart from specific references in the text, the works marked with an asterisk, mainly textbooks, will be found to be valuable sources of supporting information.

ADAM, K. D. (1951). 'Der Waldelefant von Lehringen', *Quartär, 5*, 79–92.

ARMSTRONG, A. L. (1931). 'Excavations in the Pin Hole Cave, Creswell Crags, Derbyshire', *Proc. Preh. Soc. E. Anglia, 6* (4), 330–4.

ASHBEE, P. (1956). 'The excavation of a round barrow on Canford Heath, Dorset, 1951', *Proc. Dorset Nat. Hist. & Arch. Soc., 76* (1954), 39–50.

ATKINSON, R. J. C. (1957). 'Worms and Weathering', *Antiquity, 33* (124), 219-33.

BERSU, G. (1940). 'Little Woodbury, Wilts.', *Proc. Prehist. Soc., 6*, 30–111.

BETZ, J. D. and NOLL, C. A. (1950). *J. Amer. Waterworks Assoc., 42*.

BRITISH ASSOCIATION FOR THE ADVANCEMENT OF SCIENCE. (1891). 'Oldbury Rock-shelters', report of Committee. *Rep. Brit. Ass., 1891*, 353–4.

BRITISH STANDARDS INSTITUTION (1948). *Methods of test for soil classification and compaction.* B.S.1377, London. 88 pp.

BULLEID, H., and GRAY, H. ST G. (1911–17). *The Glastonbury Lake Village*, London, 2 vols.

CAILLEUX, A. (1942). 'Les actions éoliennes périglaciaires en Europe', *Mém. Soc. géol. de France, 21*, (146), 176 pp.

(1945). 'Distinction des galets marins et fluviatiles', *Bull. Soc. géol. de France, 15*, 375–404.

(1947). 'Granulométrie des formations à galets', in Rep. of extraord. Session of Socs. belges de Géol., Brussels, 1946: *La géologie des terrains récents dans l'ouest de l'Europe*, 91–114.

CARTER, G. F. (1956). 'On soil-colour and time', *South-western Anthropology* (Albuquerque, New Mexico) *12* (3), 295–327.

*CHARLESWORTH, J. K. (1957). *The Quaternary Era*, 2 vols, London, 1700 pp.

CLARK, J. G. D. (1954). *Excavations at Star Carr*, Cambridge, 200 pp.

*COMBER, N. M. (1936). *The scientific Study of the Soil*, London, 206 pp.

CORNWALL, I. W. (1952). 'Soils and other deposits from archaeological sites in Southern Britain and their use in the reconstruction of environment', Ph.D. Thesis. Univ. of London (unpublished).

(1953). 'Soil-science and archaeology, with illustrations from some British Bronze-Age monuments', *Proc. Prehist. Soc., 19,* 129–47.

*CORRENS, C. W. (1949). *Einführung in die Mineralogie,* Berlin, 414 pp.

CULLINGFORD, C. H. D. (Ed.) (1953). *British Caving,* London, 468 pp.

DALRYMPLE, J. B. (1955). 'Study of ferruginous horizons in archaeological sections', M.Sc. Thesis, Univ. of London (unpublished).

DARBISHIRE, R. D. (1873). 'Notes on discoveries in Ehenside Tarn, Cumberland', *Archaeologia, 44,* 271–92.

DARWIN, C. (1881). *The Formation of Vegetable Mould through the action of Worms,* London, 298 pp.

DIMBLEBY, G. W. (1955). 'The ecological study of buried soils', in 'Techniques in Archaeology', *Advancement of Science 11* (45), 11–16.

DIMBLEBY, G. W., and GILL, J. M. (1955). 'The occurrence of podzols under deciduous woodland in the New Forest', *Forestry, 28* (2), 95–106.

DUNNING, G. C. (1949). 'A summary account of the excavations of 1948–9 on the site of Anglo-Saxon Thetford', *Arch. J., 106,* 72.

ELLIOT SMITH, Sir G. (1927). *The Evolution of Man,* Oxford, 195 pp.

FAIR, M. C. (1932). 'A reconsideration of the lakeside site at Ehenside Tarn, W. Cumberland', *Trans. Cumberland & Westmorland arch. and antiq. Soc., 32,* 57–62.

GLOB, P. V. (1951). 'A "murder-mystery" of Iron-Age Denmark', *Illust. London News,* 24 Nov. 1951, 862–3.

*GROVES, A. W. (1951). *Silicate Analysis,* 2nd ed., London, 336 pp.

GUGGENMOOS, T. (1934). 'Über Korngrössen- und Kornformenverteilung von Sanden von verschiedener geologischen Entstehung', *Neues Jahrb. f. Mineralogie 72,* Abt. B. 429–87.

HELBAEK, H. (1953). 'Archaeology and agricultural botany', *Inst. Arch. Univ. London, 9th Ann. Rep.* (1951–2), 44–59.

*JENNY, H. (1941). *Factors of Soil-Formation,* New York, 281 pp.

KEREKES, J. (1951). 'Zur periglazialen Sedimentbildung in mitteleuropäischen Höhlen', *Quartär, 5,* 41–9.

*KRUMBEIN, W. C., and PETTIJOHN, F. J. (1938). *Manual of Sedimentary Petrography,* New York, 550 pp.

*KUBIENA, W. L. (1938). *Micropedology,* Collegiate Press Inc., Ames, Iowa, U.S.A., 243 pp.

(1953). *The Soils of Europe,* Murby, London, 318 pp.

LACAILLE, A. D. (1936). 'The palaeolithic sequence at Iver, Bucks.', *Antiq. Journal, 16* (4), 420–43.

LACAILLE, A. D., and GRIMES, W. F. (1956), 'The prehistory of Caldey', *Arch. cambrensis, 104* (1955), 159–65.

LAIS, R. (1932). 'Die postglazialen Sedimente einer Höhle am Isteiner Klotz in Baden', *Fortschr. der Geol. und Paläont., 11* (36).

(1941). 'Über Höhlensedimente', *Quartär, 3,* 56–108.

LEAKEY, L. S. B. (1951). 'Preliminary excavations of a Mesolithic site at Abinger Common, Surrey', *Res. Pap. Surrey Arch. Soc.*, No. 3, Guildford, 44 pp.

LORCH, W. (1940). 'Die siedlungsgeographische Phosphatmethode', *Die Naturwissenschaften*, Hft. 40–41, 633–40.

MARTIN, E. A. (1929). 'The Pleistocene cliff-formation of Brighton', *South-eastern Naturalist, 34,* 60–72.

MEATES, G. W. (1955). *Lullingstone Roman Villa,* London, 168 pp.

MODDERMAN, P. J. R. (1954). 'Gravheuvel onderzoek in Midden Nederland', *Berichten van den Rijksdienst voor het Oudheidkundig Bodemonderzoek in Nederland, 5,* 7–44. (52 Pls).

MOORE, J. W. (1950). 'Mesolithic sites in the neighbourhood of Flixton, N.E. Yorks.', *Proc. Prehist. Soc., 16,* 101–8.

MÜLLER, P. E. (1879). (Danish original). 1887. *Studien über die natürlichen Humusformen,* Berlin.

OAKLEY, K. P., and LEAKEY, M. (1937). 'Report on excavations at Jaywick Sands, Essex (1934)', *Proc. Prehist. Soc. 3* (2), 217–60.

*PETTIJOHN, F. J. (1949). *Sedimentary Rocks,* New York, 526 pp.

PITTIONI, R. (1951). 'Prehistoric copper mining in Austria', *Inst. Arch. Univ. London, 7th Ann. Rep.,* 16–43.

PORTNER, C. (1951). *La formation du sédiment calcaire du Lac de Neuchâtel,* Bâle, 94 pp.

POSNANSKY, M. (1955). 'The excavation of a Bronze-Age round barrow at Lockington', *Trans. Leics. Arch. & Hist. Soc., 31,* 25–7.

PYDDOKE, E. (1950). 'An Acheulian implement from Slindon', *Inst. Arch. Univ. London, 6th Ann. Rep.,* 30–3.

REID MOIR, J. (1923). 'An early palaeolith from the glacial till at Sidestrand, Norfolk', *Antiq. J., 3,* 135–7.
   (1927). 'The silted-up lake at Hoxne and its contained flint implements', *Proc. Prehist. Soc. E. Anglia, 5* (2), 137–65.

REID MOIR, J., and BURCHELL, J. P. T. (1930). 'Flint implements of Upper Palaeolithic facies from beneath the uppermost boulder-clay of Norfolk and Yorkshire', *Antiq. J. 10* (4), 371–83.

*ROBINSON, G. W. (1936). *Soils: their Origin, Constitution and Classification,* 2nd ed, London, 442 pp.

RUSSELL, Sir JOHN (1957). *The World of the Soil,* Collins 'New Naturalist' series, London, 239 pp.

SALISBURY, E. J. (1925). 'Note on the edaphic succession in some dune-soils, with special reference to the time-factor', *J. Ecology, 13,* 322–8.

SANDFORD, K. S. (1932). 'Some recent contributions to the Pleistocene succession in England', *Geol. Mag., 69,* 1–18.

SCHWARZENBACH, G., and others. (1946). *F. Helv. Chim. Acta, 29,* 811.

SMITH, W. G. (1894). *Man the Primaeval Savage,* London, 349 pp.

SOLOMON, J. D. (1932). 'The glacial succession on the N. Norfolk Coast', *Proc. Geol. Assoc., 43,* 241–71.

STOKAR, W. von. (1939). 'Über die Untersuchung organischer Reste aus paläolithischen Kulturschichten', *Quartär, 2,* 147–50.

SUTCLIFFE, A. (1957). 'Cave-fauna and cave-sediments', Ph.D. Thesis. Univ. London (unpublished).

THOMAS, N. (1956). 'The Thornborough circles, near Ripon, North Riding', *Yorks. Arch. J., 38,* (1952–5), 425–45.

*VANLANDE, C. (1955). 'Méthodes d'analyses utilisées par la Section de Pédologie de la Direction de l'Hydraulique et de l'Équipement rural', *Travaux des Sections Pédologie et Agrologie, Bull. No. 1.* Gouvernement général de l'Algérie.

WARREN, S. H. (1923). 'The *Elephas antiquus* Bed of Clacton on Sea', *Quart. J. Geol. Soc. London, 79* (4), 606–34.

(1951). 'The Clacton flint industry: a new interpretation', *Proc. Geol Assoc., 62* (2), 107–35.

WASMUND, E. (1935). 'Die Bildung von anabituminösem Leichenwachs unter Wasser', *Erdölmuttersubstanz* (10), Stüttgart, 70 pp.

WEST, R. G., and DONNER, J. J. (1956). 'The glaciations of East Anglia and the East Midlands', *Quart. J. Geol. Soc. Lond., 112* (1), 69–91.

(1957). 'Interglacial deposits at Bobbitshole, Ipswich', *Phil. Trans. Roy. Soc.,* ser. B, *241,* 1-31.

WILLIS, L., and ROGERS, E. H. (1951). 'Dainton earthworks', *Proc. Devon Arch. Explor. Soc., 4* (4), 79–101.

WILSON, V. (1948). *Brit. Reg. Geology: E. Yorkshire & Lincolnshire,* 12, H.M.S.O., 94 pp.

WOOLDRIDGE, S. W. (1927). 'The Pliocene history of the London Basin', *Proc. Geol. Assoc., 38,* 49–132.

(1938). 'The glaciation of the London Basin and the evolution of the Lower Thames drainage system', *Quart. J. Geol. Soc. Lond., 94,* 627–67.

*WRIGHT, C. H. (1939). *Soil Analysis,* 2nd ed., London, 276 pp.

ZEUNER, F. E. (1932). 'Die Schotteranalyse', *Geol. Rundschau, 24,* 66–104.

(1934). 'Eine neue Nashornleiche aus dem polnischen Erdölgebiet', *Aus der Heimat,* 43–53.

(1941). 'Report on soil-samples from the Bury Hill excavations, 1939', *Proc. Hants. Field Club & Arch. Soc., 15* (1), 1941–3, 50–2.

(1945). *The Pleistocene Period,* Ray Soc., London, 322 pp.

(1947). 'Soil-sections at Park Street villa, St. Albans', *Inst. Arch. Univ. London, 3rd. Ann Rep.,* 25–6.

(1948). 'The Exhibition of Stone-Age and Pleistocene Geology', *Univ. London Inst. Arch. Occ. Pap.* No. 9, 63 pp.

(1952a.). *Dating the Past,* 3rd. ed., London, 495 pp.

(1952b.). 'Pleistocene shore-lines', *Geol. Rundschau, 40* (1), 39–50.

1953. 'Notes on the stratigraphy of the Magdalenian', *Univ. London. Inst. Arch. 9th Ann. Rep.,* 22.

(1954). 'The Neolithic Bronze-Age gap on the tell of Jericho', *Palestine Explor. Quarterly,* May–Oct, 64–8.

(1955). 'Notes on the Bronze-Age tombs of Jericho, I', *Palestine Explor. Quarterly,* Oct., 118–28.

INDEX